Scientific Uses of Earth Satellites

EDITED BY JAMES A. VAN ALLEN

The University of Michigan Press · Ann Arbor

Preface

On 26, 27 January 1956, the Upper Atmosphere Rocket Research Panel held its tenth anniversary meeting at The University of Michigan in Ann Arbor. This meeting was devoted exclusively to specific, detailed proposals for the scientific use of small, artificial satellites of the earth. The present volume is a compilation of thirty-three of the papers which were presented there. The authors are, for the most part, seasoned veterans of physical research at high altitudes, using rockets as vehicles. Such work forms the tangible foundation for the competent utilization of satellites for scientific purposes.

The authors, the editor, and the publishers are well aware of the evanescent nature of descriptions of proposed experiments. Yet it has been felt worthwhile to make available in collected form the best early thinking on this subject. Much of the analytical work herein is of durable value. But the principal purpose of the book will have been served if it brings the potential value of artificial satellites to the attention of the scientific community at large and stimulates broad professional participation in the great and continuing undertaking of extending human knowledge of our physical environment by every conceivable means.

The Upper Atmosphere Rocket Research Panel, though an unofficial and informal body, has been the special custodian of the scientific integrity and the spirit of high-altitude research with rockets in the United States since the earliest beginnings of the subject in 1946. The present book is in effect Panel Report No. 43 of a long series of documents which reflect better than any other written record the heart-beat of this field of research. The present membership of the Panel is as follows: Warren W. Berning, Ballistic Research Laboratories; Louis A. Delsasso, Ballistic Research Laboratories; William G. Dow, University of Michigan; Charles F. Green, General Electric Company; Leslie M. Jones, University of Michigan; George K. Megerian, Executive Secretary, General Electric Company; Homer E. Newell, Jr., Naval Research Laboratory; Marcus D. O'Day, Air Force Cambridge Research Center; William H. Pickering, Jet Propulsion Laboratory; William G. Stroud, Signal Corps Engineering Laboratories; John W. Townsend, Naval Research Laboratory; James A. Van Allen, Chairman, State University of Iowa; Fred L. Whipple, Harvard College Observatory; and Peter H. Wyckoff, Air Force Cambridge Research Center.

JAMES A. VAN ALLEN
Editor

Iowa City, Iowa
1 May 1956

Contents

_____

x   *Contents*

The Orbit of a Small Earth Satellite

by R. J. Davis, F. L. Whipple, and J. B. Zirker
HARVARD COLLEGE OBSERVATORY

ABSTRACT

This paper considers the motion of a small artificial satellite of the earth launched into an inclined, moderately eccentric orbit from a point approximately 500 km above sea level. It discusses in detail the effects on the desired initial orbit produced by small deviations from the desired launching conditions, and perturbations produced by the earth's oblateness and atmospheric drag. Additional minor perturbations are discussed qualitatively. These additional perturbations include the action of the sun and moon, variations of the density of the upper atmosphere with time and latitude, Bernoulli forces acting on a spinning object, and the effect of upper-atmospheric winds, including the westerly wind produced by the earth's rotation. The appendix contains an explanation of all symbols used in the paper.

Introduction

This paper represents a revision of a major portion of a much more lengthy report prepared under the U.S. Office of Naval Research, Contract NONR-1641(00), in collaboration with the Varo Manufacturing Company of Garland, Texas. It considered the motion and observability of a satellite moving in an equatorial orbit of low eccentricity. Other portions of the original report will be published as separate papers that will include data on the radar appearance of a rotating corner reflector, the optical appearance of a small satellite, and the accurate measurement of time.

The original report also summarized briefly several additional findings which are listed here for completeness.

1) An observing program proposed for an equatorial satellite is inapplicable to an object in an inclined orbit.

2) Forward scattering by fine wires or by fine strands of dielectric would not appreciably increase the brightness of the object, and would be mechanically objectionable.

3) The use of fluorescent paints to increase the brightness is found to be impracticable.

4) Orientation of a long satellite of small frontal cross section by the use of tail fins is found to be impracticable for a rapidly rotating object. For a nonrotating object, this method may be of value in increasing the brightness without increasing drag.

5) Infrared observing techniques are considered to be impracticable.

6) The use of photoelectric guiding devices for photography and position determination is considered possible, but much developmental work would be necessary.

7) Photographic techniques have been more thoroughly investigated by Hynek and Whipple.[1]

8) Optical corner reflectors have been more thoroughly investigated by O'Keefe.[2]

The present report, in successive sections, will concern:

1) The desired initial orbit.

2) Changes produced in the initial orbit by deviations from the desired initial conditions.

3) Perturbations by other heavenly bodies.

4) Perturbations caused by the oblateness of the earth.

5) Perturbations caused by atmospheric drag.

6) Possible laws of atmospheric resistance.

7) Effect of air drag on the object's spin.

8) Possible interaction between the extreme upper atmosphere and a spinning, rapidly moving object.

9) Problems created by a rotating earth.

10) Possible atmospheric variations with time and with latitude.

The unperturbed orbit of the satellite object is based on the following initial conditions: launching at time t_0 and altitude above sea level h_0, from geocentric latitude ϕ'_0 and longitude λ_0, at angle θ_0 to the geocentric horizontal direction, in a known azimuthal direction β_0, and at a predetermined velocity V_0.*

The following discussion will consider changes in the orbit produced by deviations from the desired initial conditions, and by perturbations produced by departures of the earth from a homogeneous sphere, by the sun and moon, and by the earth's atmosphere.

The Desired Initial Orbit

In the discussion that follows, we shall consider only elliptical nonequatorial orbits. The results will be generally applicable to all such orbits. Explicit initial conditions will be stated merely to give numerical definiteness.

Computations in the original report were based on equatorial orbits with perigee altitude 200 miles above sea level. Both a circular orbit and an orbit of eccentricity $e = 0.04$ were considered. *With the exception of the discussion on air drag*, we have revised these computations to reflect the more recently proposed orbit of inclination to the equator $i = 40°$, launching altitude $h_0 = 300$ miles, eccentricity $e = 0.055$. In the case of air drag, the results are sufficiently general so that the formulae can be used to compute air-drag perturbations in any orbit.

The pertinent parameters for the initial orbit of the first satellite may approximate the following values:

Launching from the third stage of a rocket at a point 1500 miles downrange from Patrick Air Force Base, Florida, at an altitude above sea level of $h_0 = 300$ miles.

Inclination of the orbit to the plane of the equator, $i = 40°$.

Perigee altitude, q, greater than 200 miles; apogee altitude, Q, near 800 miles.

Mass, m, of satellite, $21\frac{1}{2}$ lb.

Shape of satellite, spherical.

Radius, b, of satellite, 15 in.

It is assumed that the ideal initial orbit, with the launching rockets working exactly as desired, will give an orbit of $q = 300$ miles and $Q = 800$ miles.

Basing our computations on the above set of initial conditions, and using equations (1) through (30) below, with the values for the pertinent physical constants taken from Allen,[3] we obtain the following initial orbit:

Semi-major axis, $a = 7.27671 \times 10^8$ cm.

Eccentricity, $e = 0.05497$.

Inclination to the equator, $i = 40°$.

Angular distance from ascending node to perigee, $\omega = 153°.8$.

---

*Explanation of symbols is given in the Appendix.

The two additional elements, right ascension of the ascending node (Ω) and time of perigee passage (T), require a knowledge of the exact moment of launching. For an object launched in a horizontal direction 1500 miles downrange from Patrick Air Force Base, at Greenwich Mean Time t_0 (corresponding to Greenwich Sidereal Time τ_0), we will have:

$$\Omega = \tau_0 - 220°.6 \; [\tau_0 \text{ in angular measure}]$$

$$T = t_0.$$

The supplementary elements of the initial orbit will then be:
Perigee altitude, $q = 5 \times 10^7$ cm.
Apogee altitude, $Q = 13 \times 10^7$ cm.
Period of revolution, $P = 6177.2$ sec $= 1^h\ 42^m\ 57^s.2$.
Mean motion, $n = 1.0171 \times 10^{-3}$ rad/sec.
It will be noted that the values of q and Q were rounded off to the nearest hundred kilometers for convenience.

In order to achieve this initial orbit, the following initial conditions must be satisfied:
Initial space velocity relative to the center of the earth, $V_0 = 7.3976 \times 10^5$ cm/sec $= 4.5966$ miles/sec.
Initial angle to geocentric horizontal, $\theta_0 = 0°.0$.
Initial azimuthal direction, $\beta_0 = 127°.0$.
Initial geocentric latitude, $\phi'_0 =$ initial geocentric declination, $\delta_0 = 16°.4$ N. $= +16°.4$.
Initial geocentric longitude, $\lambda_0 = \tau_0 - \alpha_0 = 61°.0$ W. $= +61°.0 = +4^h\ 04^m\ 00^s$, where α_0 is initial geocentric right ascension.
Initial altitude above sea level, $h_0 = 5 \times 10^7$ cm $= 310.8$ miles.

It should be noted that both V_0 and β_0 are measured relative to the center of the earth, so that they include the effects of the earth's rotation in addition to the effects of the rocket propulsion. The quantities θ_0 and ϕ'_0 are measured relative to the direction to the center of the earth and not relative to the direction of gravity.

Changes Produced in the Initial Orbit by Deviations from the Desired Initial Conditions

The semi-major axis depends only on the initial velocity V_0 and altitude h_0:

$$a = \frac{GM(r + h_0)}{2GM - V_0^2(r + h_0)}. \tag{1}$$

Differentiating this expression and approximating, we obtain

$$\Delta a = 2\,\Delta h_0 + \frac{2a\,\Delta V_0}{V_0}. \tag{2}$$

In the above expressions, G is the constant of gravitation, M is the mass of the earth, and r is the radius of the earth. According to Allen,[3] $GM = 3.9863 \times 10^{20}$ cm³ sec⁻², and

$$r = r_e(0.998320 + 0.001684 \cos 2\phi - 0.000004 \cos 4\phi) \tag{3}$$

r_e being the mean equatorial radius, 6.378388×10^8 cm, and ϕ being the astronomical latitude.

The formula for an ellipse with one focus at the origin is

$$R = \frac{a(1 - e^2)}{1 + e \cos v} \tag{4}$$

where R is the radius vector and v is the true anomaly. Also, we know that

$$\frac{dR}{dt} = V \sin \theta \tag{5}$$

$$\frac{dv}{dt} = \frac{V}{R} \cos \theta \tag{6}$$

where $(\pi/2 - \theta)$ is the angle between V and R. The angle θ is considered positive when R is increasing.

Differentiating equation (4) and performing the substitutions indicated by equations (5) and (6), we obtain

$$\tan \theta_0 = \frac{ae(1 - e^2) \sin v}{(r + h_0)(1 + e \cos v_0)^2}. \tag{7}$$

The approximate solution of equation (7), valid to within 10% when θ_0 is less than three degrees, is

$$\tan v_0 = -\frac{\theta_0 a}{(a - r - h_0)}. \tag{8}$$

The angular distance from the ascending node to the launching position is

$$\omega + v_0 = \sin^{-1}[\sin \delta_0/\sin i] \tag{9}$$

so it is immediately apparent that

$$\Delta\omega = -v_0 + \frac{\cos(\omega + v_0) \cos \delta_0}{\sin i} \Delta\delta_0 - \frac{\sin \delta_0 \cos i}{\sin^2 i} \Delta i. \tag{10}$$

In this expression, the last two terms will usually be negligible in comparison to the first.

An approximate formula for the perigee altitude, valid to within 10% in Δq when θ_0 is less than three degrees, is

$$q = a - r + \frac{\theta_0 a}{\sin v_0} \cong h_0 - \frac{1}{2} \frac{\theta_0^2 a^2}{a - r - h_0}. \tag{11}$$

The change in q is seen to be approximately

$$\Delta q = \Delta h_0 - \frac{1}{2} \frac{\theta_0^2 a^2}{a - r - h_0}. \tag{12}$$

An expression for the eccentricity is

$$e = 1 - \frac{(r + q)}{a}. \tag{13}$$

From this expression, we find that

$$\Delta e \simeq \frac{1}{a} (\Delta a - \Delta q). \tag{14}$$

The inclination of the orbit to the equator is given by

$$\cos i = \sin \beta_0 \cos \delta_0. \tag{15}$$

Thus it is readily seen that

$$\Delta i = \frac{\cos \beta_0 \cos \delta_0}{\sin i} \Delta \beta_0 - \frac{\sin \beta_0 \sin \delta_0}{\sin i} \Delta \delta_0. \tag{16}$$

The position of the node is given by

$$\sin (\alpha_0 - \Omega) = \tan \delta_0 \cot i \tag{17}$$

whence

$$\Delta \Omega = \Delta \alpha_0 - \frac{\sec^2 \delta_0 \cot i}{\cos (\alpha_0 - \Omega)} \Delta \delta_0 + \frac{\csc^2 i \tan \delta_0}{\cos (\alpha_0 - \Omega)} \Delta i. \tag{18}$$

And since

$$\alpha_0 = \tau_0 - \lambda_0 \tag{19}$$

we have

$$\Delta \alpha_0 = \Delta \tau_0 - \Delta \lambda_0. \tag{20}$$

Since the apogee altitude is

$$Q = 2a - q \quad - 2 \checkmark \tag{21}$$

the change in apogee is given by

$$\Delta Q = 2\Delta a - \Delta q. \tag{22}$$

The mean motion, if we neglect the very small perturbation produced by the oblateness of the earth, is

$$n = \sqrt{\frac{GM}{a^3}}. \tag{23}$$

The change produced in the mean motion by a change in semi-major axis will then be

$$\Delta n = - \frac{3n \, \Delta a}{2a}. \tag{24}$$

Since the period of revolution is given by

$$P = \frac{2\pi}{n} \qquad (25)$$

we will have

$$\Delta P = -\frac{2\pi}{n^2} \Delta n. \qquad (26)$$

Finally, we must find an expression for the time of perigee passage According to Moulton,[4]

$$n(t_0 - T) = E_0 - e \sin E_0 \qquad (27)$$

where E_0, the eccentric anomaly at time t_0, is defined by

$$r + h_0 = a(1 - e \cos E_0). \qquad (28)$$

An equivalent definition is

$$\cos E_0 = \frac{e + \cos v_0}{1 + e \cos v_0}. \qquad (29)$$

Thus it is seen that

$$\Delta T = \Delta t_0 + \frac{E_0 - e \sin E_0}{n}. \qquad (30)$$

From the above equations, we can construct Table I.

Perturbations by Other Heavenly Bodies

Spitzer[5] has shown that perturbations by the sun and moon are very small. The maximum deviation from an otherwise circular orbit 500 km above the surface of the earth would be 67 cm. For an inclined elliptical orbit, the period of rotation of the nodes and of the line of apsides would be in excess of 2000 years. The reference plane in this case is the plane of the ecliptic.

Perturbations Caused by the Oblateness of the Earth

Brouwer[6] discussed the motion of an infinitesimal particle about an oblate spheroid. He has considered an orbit which is both inclined and eccentric.

Brouwer's equations for the motion of the line of nodes and line of apsides are as follows:

$$\frac{d\Omega}{dt} = (-3\gamma_2 + \tfrac{27}{2}\gamma_2{}^2 - 10\gamma_4)n' \qquad (31)$$

$$\frac{d\tilde{\omega}}{dt} = (+3\gamma_2 - \tfrac{9}{2}\gamma_2{}^2 + 10\gamma_4)n'. \qquad (32)$$

TABLE I

Changes produced in the orbital elements by the indicated deviations from the desired initial conditions

Orbital Element Change	$\Delta h_0 = \pm 10^5$ cm	$\Delta V_0 = \pm 100$ cm/sec	$\theta_0 = \pm 1°$	$\Delta \beta_0 = \pm 1°$	$\Delta \delta_0 = \pm 0°.1$	$\Delta \lambda_0 = \pm 0°.1$	$\Delta t_0 = \pm 0^s.001$
Δa (km)	± 2.00	± 1.97	0	0	0	0	0
$\Delta \omega$	0	0	$\mp 17°.6$	0	$\mp 0°.113$	$\mp 0°.053$	0
Δq (km)	± 1.00	0	-21.7	0	0	0	0
$\Delta e \times 10^4$	± 1.37	± 2.71	± 29.8	0	0	0	0
Δi	0	0	0	$\mp 0°.90$	$\mp 0°.119$	0	0
$\Delta \Omega$	0	0	0	$\pm 0°.684$	$\pm 0°.228$	$\mp 0°.100$	$\pm 0°.0000417$
ΔQ (km)	± 3.00	± 3.94	$+21.7$	0	0	0	0
$\Delta n \times 10^7$ (rad/sec)	∓ 4.17	∓ 4.10	0	0	0	0	0
ΔP	$\pm 2^s.53$	$\pm 2^s.49$	0	0	0	0	0
ΔT	0	0	$\mp 251^s$	0	0	0	$\pm 0^s.001$

Here, $\tilde{\omega}$ is defined by

$$\tilde{\omega} = \Omega + \omega \qquad (33)$$

so that, in effect, $\tilde{\omega}$ is measured *along the orbit* from a *fixed point*, whereas ω is measured *along the orbit* from a *moving point*. The moments γ_2 and γ_4 are defined as follows:

$$\gamma_2 \equiv \frac{1}{Mr_e^2} \int [\tfrac{1}{4}(x^2 + y^2) - \tfrac{1}{2}z^2] \, dm = \frac{C - A}{2Mr_e^2} \qquad (34)$$

$$\gamma_4 \equiv \frac{1}{Mr_e^4} \int [\tfrac{9}{64}(x^2 + y^2)^2 - \tfrac{9}{8}(x^2 + y^2)z^2 + \tfrac{3}{8}z^4] \, dm \qquad (35)$$

C being the moment of inertia of the earth about the axis of rotation and A being the moment of inertia about an axis in the plane of the equator. According to Allen,[3]

$$\frac{C - A}{2M} = 2.221 \times 10^{14} \text{ cm}^2.$$

Additional quantities are defined as follows:

$$n'^2 \equiv f_0 n^2 \qquad (36)$$
$$f_0 \equiv 1 + 3\gamma_2 + 5\gamma_4. \qquad (37)$$

As Brouwer points out, $d\tilde{\omega}/dt$ and $-d\Omega/dt$ are only approximately equal; the second-order moment γ_2 can be found from the relationship

$$\frac{d\tilde{\omega}}{dt} + \frac{d\Omega}{dt} = 9\gamma_2^2 n'. \qquad (38)$$

In equations (34) and (35) above, x, y, and z are the geocentric coordinates of an element of mass dm, and the integration is to be performed throughout the interior of the earth.

Strictly speaking, the above relations hold only for small inclination and eccentricity, so that $\cos i \cong 1$ and $e^2 \cong 0$. Spitzer[5] has found that

$$\frac{d\Omega}{dt} = \left\{ \frac{d\Omega}{dt} \right\}_{\cos i = 0} (\cos i) \qquad (39)$$

and Moulton[7] has found that

$$\frac{d\tilde{\omega}}{dt} = \left\{ \frac{d\tilde{\omega}}{dt} \right\}_{e^2 = 0} (1 + e^2). \qquad (40)$$

By symmetry, it appears that the complete solution is

$$\frac{d\Omega}{dt} = (-3\gamma_2 + \tfrac{27}{2}\gamma_2^2 - 10\gamma_4)n' \cos i(1 + e^2) \qquad (41)$$

$$\frac{d\tilde{\omega}}{dt} = (+3\gamma_2 - \tfrac{9}{2}\gamma_2^2 + 10\gamma_4)n' \cos i(1 + e^2) \qquad (42)$$

$$f_0 = 1 + 3\gamma_2 \cos 2i + 5\gamma_4 \cos 4i. \qquad (43)$$

We thus arrive at the necessary conclusion that for $i = 90°$ there is no motion either of the line of nodes or of the line of apsides.

We will now consider what effect the oblateness of the earth will have upon the desired satellite orbit. We have

$$\gamma_2 = 5.47 \times 10^{-4}$$

$$\gamma_4: \quad \text{unknown for the earth}$$

$$f_0 = 1.000284$$

$$n' = 1.0173 \times 10^{-3} \text{ rad/sec.}$$

Since γ_2^2 is probably comparable in magnitude to γ_4, which is unknown, we shall neglect both γ_2^2 and γ_4, and find

$$\frac{d\Omega}{dt} = -1.27 \times 10^{-6} \text{ rad/sec}$$

$$\frac{d\tilde{\omega}}{dt} = +1.27 \times 10^{-6} \text{ rad/sec}$$

$$\frac{d\tilde{\omega}}{dt} + \frac{d\Omega}{dt} = 3.05 \times 10^{-10} \text{ rad/sec}$$

so that the regression of the line of nodes and the advance of the line of apsides will occur with approximately equal periods of 4.93×10^6 sec, or 57.2 days. The difference between these periods will be approximately 1180 sec.

Perturbations Caused by Atmospheric Drag

Now assume an atmosphere for the earth. The object will be subjected to atmospheric resistance, the effect of which is to produce a negative tangential disturbing acceleration F (Moulton[4]). This force will increase as the atmospheric density, ρ, increases and as V increases. Since ρ decreases very rapidly as R increases, and V decreases slowly as R increases, the net result for $e \geq 0.025$ is that F will be effective only in the half of the orbit nearest perigee. From Moulton[4] we have the following equations:

$$\frac{da}{dt} = \frac{2\sqrt{1 + e^2 + 2e \cos v}}{n\sqrt{1 - e^2}} F \tag{44}$$

$$\frac{de}{dt} = \frac{2\sqrt{1 - e^2} \, (\cos v + e)}{na\sqrt{1 + e^2 + 2e \cos v}} F \tag{45}$$

$$\frac{dT}{dt} = -\frac{2(1 - e^2)(1 + e^2 + e \cos v) \sin v}{nae(1 + e \cos v)\sqrt{1 + e^2 + 2e \cos v}} F \tag{46}$$

$$\frac{d\tilde{\omega}}{dt} = \frac{2\sqrt{1 - e^2}\, \sin v}{nae\sqrt{1 + e^2 + 2e \cos v}} F. \tag{47}$$

To a first-order approximation, $1 + e = 1$; $e^2 = 0$, and these equations become

$$\frac{da}{dt} = \frac{2F}{n} \tag{44a}$$

$$\frac{de}{dt} = \frac{2F \cos v}{na} = \frac{\cos v}{a}\frac{da}{dt} \tag{45a}$$

$$\frac{dT}{dt} = -\frac{2F \sin v}{nae} = -\frac{\sin v}{nae}\frac{da}{dt} \tag{46a}$$

$$\frac{d\tilde{\omega}}{dt} = -\frac{dT}{dt} = \frac{\sin v}{nae}\frac{da}{dt}. \tag{47a}$$

It is seen that, to a first approximation, T and $\tilde{\omega}$ oscillate but are not secularly affected. We shall therefore concern ourselves only with a and e.

As a zero-order approximation, we shall assume that the density falls off so rapidly that we may set $\cos v = 1$. That is, we shall assume that $F = 0$ for $\cos v < 1$. We then have for the change Δa produced in a and for the change Δe produced in e during one revolution, the following formulae:

$$\Delta a = K\frac{da}{dt}\bigg]_{t=0} = \frac{2KF}{n}\bigg]_{t=0} \tag{48}$$

$$a\,\Delta e = Ka\frac{de}{dt}\bigg]_{t=0} = \frac{2KF}{n}\bigg]_{t=0} \tag{49}$$

where K is a constant which we shall not evaluate. It is evident that

$$\Delta a = a\,\Delta e. \tag{50}$$

From the definition of q we have

$$q = a - ae - r. \tag{51}$$

Differentiating this, we obtain

$$\Delta q = -e\,\Delta a. \tag{52}$$

Thus it is seen that if the air density, ρ, falls off rapidly enough, less than 3% of the change produced in the semi-major axis is effective in reducing the perigee distance. Therefore, for an eccentric orbit, the perigee distance will remain almost fixed, while the apogee distance decreases, until the eccentricity is small enough so that there is appreciable drag on the object in the entire orbit.

We shall now derive the second-order approximation to Δa, Δe, Δq, and ΔQ. For this approximation, we shall assume $e^2 = 0$.

By definition,

$$\Delta a = \int_0^P \frac{da}{dt} dt \tag{53}$$

$$\Delta e = \int_0^P \frac{de}{dt} dt. \tag{54}$$

For the present we shall assume* that

$$F = -\frac{\Gamma \sigma \rho V^2}{m} \tag{55}$$

where Γ is the coefficient of head drag, σ is the cross-sectional area of the object, and m is the mass of the object. For the present, we shall merely define

$$k = \frac{\Gamma \sigma}{m}. \tag{56}$$

From the polar equation of the ellipse, we have

$$\cos v = \frac{a(1 - e^2) - R}{eR}. \tag{57}$$

Substituting $\cos v$ from equation (57) into equations (44) and (45), and setting $e^2 = 0$, we obtain

$$\frac{da}{dt} = \frac{2\sqrt{R(2a - R)}}{nR} F \tag{58}$$

$$\frac{de}{dt} = \frac{2[a(1 - e^2) - R(1 + e^2)]}{nae\sqrt{R(2a - R)}} F. \tag{59}$$

The e^2 is retained in equation (59) because, when we substitute equation (63) into equation (59), we find that

$$2[a(1 - e^2) - R(1 + e^2)] = 2ae (\cos nt - 2e + e^2 \cos nt).$$

The factor e is canceled by an e in the denominator, and the $2e$ term remains as a result of retaining e^2.

From the equations of motion given by Moulton,[4] we obtain

$$R = a(1 - e \cos E) \tag{60}$$

$$nt = E - e \sin E \tag{61}$$

$$E \simeq n(t - T) + e \sin n(t - T) + \frac{e^2}{2} \sin 2n(t - T). \tag{62}$$

Substituting equation (62) into equation (60) and setting $e^2 = 0$, $\cos e = 1$, we have the approximate formula

$$R = a[1 - e \cos n(t - T)]. \tag{63}$$

---

*The validity of this assumption is taken up in the following section.

Substituting equation (63) into equations (58) and (59), we obtain

$$\frac{da}{dt} = \frac{2}{n(1 - e \cos nt)} F \tag{64}$$

$$\frac{de}{dt} = \frac{2 (\cos nt - 2e)}{na} F. \tag{65}$$

We thus obtain

$$\Delta a = - \frac{2k}{n} \int_0^P \frac{\rho V^2}{1 + e \cos nt} dt \tag{66}$$

$$\Delta e = - \frac{2k}{na} \int_0^P \rho V^2 (\cos nt - 2e) \, dt. \tag{67}$$

Again setting $e^2 = 0$, these become

$$\Delta a = - \frac{2k}{n} \int_0^P \rho V^2 \, dt - \frac{2ek}{n} \int_0^P V^2 \rho \cos nt \, dt \tag{68}$$

$$\Delta e = - \frac{2k}{na} \int_0^P \rho V^2 \cos nt \, dt + \frac{4ek}{na} \int_0^P \rho V^2 \, dt. \tag{69}$$

Also,

$$\Delta q = - \frac{2k}{n} (1 + e) \int_0^P \rho V^2 \, dt + \frac{2k}{n} (1 - e) \int_0^P V^2 \rho \cos nt \, dt \tag{70}$$

$$\Delta Q = - \frac{2k}{n} (1 - e) \int_0^P \rho V^2 \, dt - \frac{2k}{n} (1 + e) \int_0^P V^2 \rho \cos nt \, dt \tag{71}$$

Using the tables of atmospheric density given by Grimminger[8] and plotting $V^2 \rho$ as a function of t, we obtain, by graphical integration,

$$\int_0^P V^2 \rho \, dt = 19.8 \text{ gm cm}^{-1} \text{ sec}^{-1}$$

$$\int_0^P V^2 \rho \cos nt \, dt = 17.7 \text{ gm cm}^{-1} \text{ sec}^{-1}$$

$$\int_0^P V^2 \rho_0 \, dt = 84.0 \text{ gm cm}^{-1} \text{ sec}^{-1}$$

where ρ_0 is the atmospheric density at perigee, and the following values for the orbital parameters are assumed:

$$a = 6.85 \times 10^8 \text{ cm}$$

$$e = 0.025$$

$$n = 1.1 \times 10^{-3} \text{ rad/sec.}$$

We obtain the following results, expressed in cgs units:

$$\Delta a]_{e=0} = -1604000 \ k/\text{rev}$$

$$\Delta a]_{e=0.025} = -384900 \ k/\text{rev} = 0.24 \ \Delta a]_{e=0}$$

$$a \ \Delta e]_{e=0.025} = -319400 \ k/\text{rev} = 0.83 \ \Delta a_{\ e=0.025}$$

$$\Delta q]_{e=0} = \Delta a]_{e=0} = -1604000 \ k/\text{rev}$$

$$\Delta q]_{e=0.025} = -56000 \ k/\text{rev} = 0.145 \ \Delta a]_{e=0.025}$$
$$= 0.0348 \ \Delta q]_{e=0}$$

$$\Delta Q]_{e=0.025} = -717600 \ k/\text{rev} = 1.855 \ \Delta a]_{e=0.025}$$
$$= 12.7 \ \Delta q]_{e=0.025}.$$

Thus it is seen that for $e = 0.025$, the perigee distance will decrease only 1/30 as rapidly as for $e = 0$. The object will, therefore, stay up approximately 25 times as long at $e_0 = 0.025$ as at $e_0 = 0$.

Now taking the Kallmann[9] atmosphere, we obtain the following results:

$$\int_0^P V^2 \rho \ dt = 4.28 \ \text{gm cm}^{-1} \ \text{sec}^{-1}$$

$$\int_0^P V^2 \rho \cos nt \ dt = 4.13 \ \text{gm cm}^{-1} \ \text{sec}^{-1}$$

$$\int_0^P V^2 \rho_0 \ dt = 18.7 \ \text{gm cm}^{-1} \ \text{sec}^{-1}.$$

Also,

$$\Delta a]_{e=0} = -35600 \ k/\text{rev}$$

$$\Delta a]_{e=0.025} = -8410 \ k/\text{rev} = 0.24 \ \Delta a]_{e=0}$$

$$a \ \Delta e]_{e=0.025} = -7500 \ k/\text{rev} = 0.89 \ \Delta a]_{e=0.025}$$

$$\Delta q]_{e=0} = -35600 \ k/\text{rev}$$

$$\Delta q]_{e=0.025} = -700 \ k/\text{rev} = 0.083 \ \Delta a]_{e=0.025}$$
$$= 0.0196 \ \Delta q]_{e=0}$$

$$\Delta Q]_{e=0.025} = -16070 \ k/\text{rev} = 1.917 \ \Delta a]_{e=0.025}$$
$$= 23.2 \ \Delta q]_{e=0.025}.$$

Thus it is seen that different atmospheric models give entirely different results, both for the rate at which the object will spiral in and for the ratio $\Delta q/\Delta Q$. The former quantity is dependent mainly on ρ_0 and on k, whereas the latter quantity is dependent on the manner in which density falls off with height.

Possible Laws of Atmospheric Resistance

We will now consider the law of atmospheric resistance that may apply for the object.

It is known that for normal atmospheric densities and normal velocities, the approximate law of wind resistance is of the form

$$F = \frac{\Gamma \sigma \rho V^2}{m} \tag{72}$$

where Γ is a function of the shape of the object, and also depends somewhat on V and on ρ. As V increases and ρ decreases, Γ becomes less and less dependent on density and velocity; under the conditions with which we will concern ourselves here, it may be considered to be a constant. The problem is to evaluate it.

As is shown by Kopal,[10] the limiting value for Γ for infinite Mach number and a conical regime (conical object and conical shock wave) is approximately 0.75. This value occurs for a semi-apex angle of the conical object equal to $57°.6$, for which case the shock wave has a semi-apex angle of $90°$. However, a shock front cannot have a thickness less than the mean free path, which for the densities contemplated is several orders of magnitude greater than the dimensions of the object. It may be assumed, however, that the coefficient of head drag will be a function of shape only for the object we are considering. It may also be expected that Γ will considerably exceed 0.75, since a sphere is not so sharp an object as a cone.

At a speed of 7.9×10^5 cm/sec, the object is traveling more than five times as fast as the mean molecular speed. To a first approximation, therefore, it may be assumed that no molecules will strike the object from behind. Our first assumption for molecules striking the object from in front will be that every impinging molecule sticks to the object. These molecules will initially have very nearly zero velocity. The amount of matter swept up in time dt will therefore be

$$dm = \sigma \rho V \, dt \tag{73}$$

and, by the law of conservation of momentum, the new velocity will be

$$\frac{V + dV}{V} = \frac{m}{m + dm} = \frac{m}{m + \sigma \rho V \, dt} \tag{74}$$

from which we obtain

$$mV + m \, dV + \sigma \rho V^2 \, dt = mV \tag{75}$$

or

$$\frac{dV}{dt} = -\frac{\sigma \rho V^2}{m}. \tag{76}$$

Therefore, since $dV/dt = F$, we have $\Gamma = 1$.

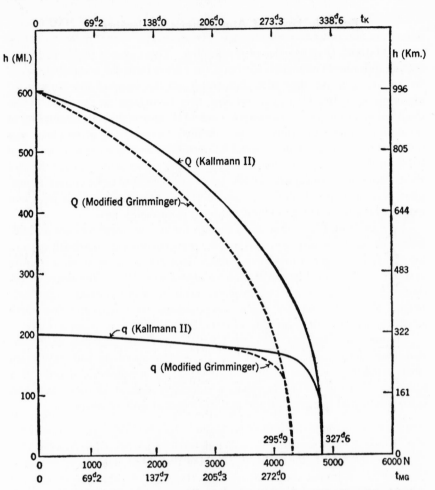

FIGURE 1. Variation of perigee and apogee altitude with number of revolutions and with time.

However, the object cannot continue to accrete mass forever, and the question is what will be the velocity of the molecules that leave the object. If they simply bounce off at double the velocity of the object, Γ will equal 2, as is indicated by Grimminger.[8] If they leave at thermal velocities, Γ will be slightly greater than 1. If the object is spinning, however, and the molecules stick for a length of time comparable to the period of rotation, Γ could be reduced below 1, and nontangential accelerations could develop. This aspect of the problem is quite complex, and will be discussed separate y.

Assuming that $\Gamma = 1.0$, that $\sigma = 5000$ cm^2, and that $m = 10,000$ gm, we have $k = 0.50$ ($\pm 50\%$), which seems to be as logical an assumption as any. In this case, the above values for Δa, $a\,\Delta e$, Δq, and ΔQ, are expressed in units of 0.5 cm, or 0.5×10^{-5} km.

Equations (70) and (71) have been solved at intervals of 1000 revolutions from the initial conditions $q_0 = 200$ miles, $Q_0 = 600$ miles, to obtain curves of q and Q vs number of revolutions. This curve is shown in Fig. 1. Second differences were used to obtain the curves from the computed points. In Fig. 1, t_K is the time after launching, on the basis of the Kallmann[9] atmospheric model II; t_{MG} is the time after launching on the basis of the modified Grimminger[8] atmospheric model III, and N is the total number of revolutions since launching. The modified Grimminger atmosphere was obtained from the published model by multiplication by a constant factor of 0.028 in the density, to bring this model into agreement with the Rocket Panel Standard Atmosphere at 220 km. The modified Grimminger atmosphere approximates Kallmann's model IIIb. These two models represent extremes between which the real atmosphere probably lies.

We see from Fig. 1 that, even though the two atmospheres are normalized to the same density near perigee, the perturbations are markedly greater for the Grimminger atmosphere, which does not have so steep a density gradient. The total lifetime of such an object would be of the order of 300 days. Since the presently contemplated orbit lies approximately eight scale heights above the one on which computations are based, the first earth satellites have a finite possibility of remaining aloft for ten years or more.

Equations (70) and (71) are integral equations in terms of the atmospheric density, ρ. Hence, orbital measurements of Δq and ΔQ for an earth satellite provide a means for determining atmospheric density as a function of altitude. The precision is extremely high at altitudes near and below the initial perigee altitude and decreases at greater altitudes.

Effect of Air Drag on the Object's Spin

As is evident from the preceding section, perturbations of the satellite's orbit due to air resistance do not give an instantaneous value for the density, since ρ can be found only by solving an integral equation. However, if the rate at which the object's spin is slowed down can be measured, and if no other factors tend to affect the rate of spin, the air density at the height of observation can be found easily and directly.

To find out how the air density will slow down the spin, we make the assumption that all molecules striking the object will stick, momentarily at least, and leave in random directions at thermal velocity, which for the expected temperature of the object is negligible. We set up a nonrotating set of coordinates with the z-axis coincident with the spin axis of the object and with the direction of motion of the object lying in the yz-plane. Make the following definitions: ξ is the angle between the positive z-axis and the direction of motion of the object in its orbit; S is the angular velocity of rotation of the object; b is the radius of the object.

Here, we consider the object to be stationary, with a stream of air coming from the left with velocity V. From considerations of symmetry, the only effect that the air can have on the object is to slow down its rate of rotation. Only moments acting parallel to the xy-plane can have this effect. Thus we consider only the velocity parallel to this plane, which is $V \sin \xi$. Since V lies in the yz-plane, $V \sin \xi$ is parallel to the y-axis. Since we are concerned only with the surface of the object, where $x^2 + y^2 + z^2 = b^2$, we have the two linear components of the spin velocity, Sx and Sy. Thus we have an element of the air stream, of cross-sectional area $dx \, dz$, and velocity $V \sin \xi$, striking point (x, y, z) with velocity components $V_y = V \sin \xi + Sx$, and $V_z = Sy$. Thus the velocity of the air-stream element relative to the surface element at the point of contact is

$$V_{xy} = \sqrt{V_z^2 + V_y^2} = \sqrt{V^2 \sin^2 \xi + 2SxV \sin \xi + S^2x^2 + S^2y^2}. \quad (77)$$

The force produced at this point will be $dF = V_{xy}^2 \, dx \, dz$; when $V \sin \xi \gg S\sqrt{b^2 - z^2}$, the radius of action of this force relative to the z-axis will be essentially x, so that the torque produced will be

$$L = \rho \int_{-b}^{b} x \, dx \int_{-(b^2 - x^2)}^{(b^2 - x^2)} [V^2 \sin^2 \xi + 2SxV \sin \xi + S^2b^2 - S^2z^2] \, dz. \quad (78)$$

In this expression, the limits for the integration over dz are obtained by symmetry, a positive contribution beyond the positive z-axis being equivalent to a negative contribution beyond the negative z-axis. $V \sin \xi$ will be $\gg S\sqrt{b^2 - z^2}$ for $\xi > 6°$, so that this expression will lead to a very good approximation to the rate at which the object's spin will be slowed down by air drag. Evaluating this integral, and using the expression $dS/dt = L/I$, where I is the moment of inertia of the object about the z-axis, we find

$$\frac{dS}{dt} = \frac{\pi \rho b^4 SV \sin \xi}{2I} \quad (79)$$

which is accurate to better than 2% when $\xi > 6°$.

Following reasoning similar to the above when $\xi = 0°$, it is a simple matter to derive the formula for small ξ:

$$L' = \rho \int_0^{2\pi} d\theta \int_0^b r'^2 S^2 r'^2 \, dr' \quad (80)$$

from which we find

$$\left. \frac{dS}{dt} \right]_{\text{small } \xi} = \frac{2\pi \rho b^5 S^2}{5I}. \quad (81)$$

We now evaluate dS/dt, using the following values for the parameters:

$$\rho = 5 \times 10^{-15} \text{ gm cm}^{-3}$$
$$S = 1800 \text{ rpm} = 60\pi \text{ rad/sec}$$
$$V = 7.9 \times 10^5 \text{ cm/sec}$$

$$b = 2.54 \times 10^1 \text{ cm}$$

$$I = 10^6 \text{ gm cm}^2$$

to obtain the following results:

$$\left. \frac{dS}{dt} \right]_{\xi=90°} = 5 \times 10^{-7} \text{ rad/sec}^2 = 4 \text{ rev/sec/year}$$

$$\left. \frac{dS}{dt} \right]_{\xi=60°} = 5 \times 10^{-8} \text{ rad/sec}^2 = 0.4 \text{ rev/sec/year}$$

$$\left. \frac{dS}{dt} \right]_{\xi=0°} = 3 \times 10^{-10} \text{ rad/sec}^2 = 0.002 \text{ rev/sec/year}.$$

These rates are several orders of magnitude smaller than the expected damping caused by the earth's magnetic field.

Possible Interaction between the Extreme Upper Atmosphere and a Spinning, Rapidly Moving Object

The exact method of interaction between air molecules and an artificial sattelite is somewhat difficult to determine. In the above discussion, it was assumed that the molecules stick momentarily and leave with thermal velocities; it was further assumed that the object would be very nearly in thermal equilibrium with interplanetary space, since it will lose heat very rapidly by radiation. Thus the thermal velocity will be approximately 1% of the impact velocity. Any effects caused by the molecules' leaving in a different direction from that in which they arrived, due to the spin of the object (Bernoulli forces), will therefore be extremely small, and if the spin axis remains fixed in space or wanders in any manner unrelated to its orbit, the perturbations so caused will be oscillatory, and, thus, probably unobservable. Since this type of perturbation may have an observable effect on the inclination of the orbit,* the constancy of the inclination will be a good indicator as to the justification for neglecting such effects. See also Humphreys.[11]

Other peculiar effects could possibly arise. First, the molecules could be reflected with double the velocity of impact. Since they would then have a kinetic temperature of over 10^5 degrees, such a process would undoubtedly give rise to a luminous train. Another possibility is that the molecules would penetrate the object without appreciably slowing it down. Such a process is also unlikely. It should be borne in mind, however, that air resistance under conditions such as those contemplated is an extreme extrapolation over the experimental data, and that observations on this object may prove of value in theoretical aerodynamics.

---

*The effect of the sun and moon is small and easily and accurately evaluated.

Problems Created by a Rotating Earth

Now let us assume a rotating earth. The atmosphere will be carried around by the rotation at a speed not appreciably different from the earth's velocity of rotation, approximately 0.5 km/sec. Thus a wind is created which tends to decrease *F* due to atmospheric resistance to about 88% of the value it would otherwise have. This decrease is less than the present inaccuracies in ρ at such heights, and it may be neglected for that reason. It should not be neglected in the final reductions.

A second effect of this wind is to "blow" the nodes in an easterly direction. The effect will be small.

The most important effect of the earth's rotation is to carry the launching and observing sites in an easterly direction at from 0.4 to 0.5 km/sec, depending on latitude. Thus the object is given a boost which must be taken into account at the original launching, and the co-ordinate system in which the object's orbit remains invariant (to a first approximation) is different from the co-ordinate system relative to which its position is measured.

Possible Atmospheric Variations with Time and with Latitude

Equations (70) and (71) are sufficiently general to include variations in the atmospheric density with time and latitude in addition to the variation with altitude. However, every additional degree of freedom decreases markedly the accuracy with which the atmospheric density can be determined from a finite number of observations. In general, both the law of variation and the pertinent parameters must be extracted from the observations.

Since the line of apsides advances slowly, and since the density is most accurately determined at perigee, it may be difficult to disentangle variations with time from variations with latitude. In addition, the oblateness of the earth will cause the perigee altitude to be less at the equator than near the northern and southern limits of the orbit, so that variations with height must be disentangled as well.

Part of the interaction between the independent variables may possibly be eliminated by the use of additional satellites in equatorial and polar orbits. For the equatorial orbit, the variation with latitude is eliminated. Nonseasonal time variations could also be best observed for equatorial orbits. The largest expected variations are seasonal, however, so that orbits crossing the temperate zones are indicated. For a polar orbit, there is no advance of the line of apsides, so that the seasonal variation could be studied to best advantage.

APPENDIX
Explanation of Symbols

A = Moment of inertia of the earth about an equatorial axis

a = Semi-major axis of orbit

b = Radius of satellite

C = Moment of inertia of the earth about the axis of rotation

E = Eccentric anomaly at time t, defined by $R = a(1 - e \cos E)$

e = Eccentricity of orbit

F = Tangential disturbing acceleration [produced by atmospheric resistance]

$f_0 = 1 + 3\gamma_2 + 5\gamma_4$

G = Gravitational constant = 6.668×10^{-8} dyn cm^2 gm^{-2}

h = Altitude of object above sea level at time t, $= R - r$

I = Moment of inertia of satellite about spin axis

i = Inclination of orbit to celestial equator

K = Constant of proportionality explained in text

$k = \Gamma\sigma/m$

L = Torque about spin axis of satellite [produced by atmospheric resistance]

M = Mass of the earth = 5.983×10^{27} gm

m = Mass of satellite

N = Number of revolutions of satellite from time t_0 to time t

n = Mean angular velocity of object in orbit of reference

n' = Mean angular velocity of object in orbit, including perturbations caused by the oblateness of the earth

P = Period of revolution of object in orbit

Q = Altitude of object above sea level at apogee

q = Altitude of object above sea level at perigee

R = Distance of object from center of earth at time t

r = Radius of the earth at geocentric latitude ϕ'

r_e = Mean equatorial radius of the earth = 6.378388×10^8 cm

S = Angular velocity of rotation of object

T = Epoch = Greenwich Mean Time of perigee passage

t = Greenwich Mean Time of an observation on the object

t_0 = Greenwich Mean Time of launching the object

V = Linear velocity of the object relative to the center of the earth at time t

v = True anomaly = angular distance of object from perigee measured along the orbit

α = Geocentric right ascension of object at time t

β = Azimuthal direction of motion of object at time t

Γ = Drag coefficient

γ_2 = Second-order moment of the earth = $(C - A)/2Mr_e^2$

γ_4 = Fourth-order moment of the earth
δ = Geocentric declination of object at time t, = ϕ'
Δ = An operator indicating a small change in a quantity
ξ = Angle between spin axis of object and direction of motion of object in its orbit
θ = Deviation of motion of object from horizontal at time t
λ = Geocentric longitude of object at time t measured westward from the Greenwich meridian through 360°, = $\tau - \alpha$
π = 3.1416 . . . , as in mathematics
$\tilde{\omega} = \Omega + \omega$
ρ = Air density at height h, geocentric latitude ϕ', and time t
ρ_0 = Air density at perigee
σ = Cross-sectional area of satellite = πb^2
τ = Greenwich Sidereal Time at time t
ϕ = Astronomical latitude of object or of observing site
ϕ' = Geocentric latitude of object or of observing site
Ω = Right ascension of ascending node
ω = Angular distance from ascending node to perigee
The subscript 0 refers to quantities measured at time t_0

REFERENCES

1. J. A. Hynek and F. L. Whipple, 1956, unpublished.
2. J. A. O'Keefe, "The Geodetic Significance of an Artificial Satellite," a paper presented before the Tenth Anniversary Meeting of the Upper Atmosphere Rocket Research Panel, 1956.
3. C. W. Allen. *Astrophysical Quantities.* London: The Athlone Press, 1955.
4. F. R. Moulton. *An Introduction to Celestial Mechanics.* New York: The Macmillan Co., 1931.
5. L. Spitzer, Jr., "Perturbations of a Satellite Orbit," *J. Brit. Interplan. Soc., 9:*131 (1950).
6. D. Brouwer, "The Motion of a Particle with Negligible Mass Under the Gravitational Attraction of a Spheroid," *Astron. J., 51:*223–231 (1946).
7. F. R. Moulton. *Periodic Orbits.* Washington: The Carnegie Foundation, 1920.
8. G. Grimminger. *Analysis of Temperature, Pressure, and Density of the Atmosphere Extending to Extreme Altitudes.* Rand Report R-105, 1948.
9. H. K. Kallmann. *An Investigation of Atmospheric Properties at Great Altitudes.* Rand Report RM-1047, 1953.
10. Z. Kopal, editor. *Tables of Supersonic Flow Around Cones.* Cambridge, Mass.: Mass. Inst. of Tech., 1947.
11. W. J. Humphreys. *Physics of the Air.* New York: McGraw-Hill Book Co., Inc., 1929.

2

Time Available for the Optical Observation of an Earth Satellite*

by J. B. Zirker, F. L. Whipple, and R. J. Davis
HARVARD COLLEGE OBSERVATORY

ABSTRACT

Light curves during a twilight observation of a satellite are computed for specularly reflecting and for diffusely reflecting spheres of 20-in. diameter. The specular reflector is visible over a larger fraction of its path.

The time available for observation of the specular reflector is computed for several cases. Sky brightness, geometry, and the earth's shadow are factors in the calculation. If the satellite circles 200 miles above the earth's equator, maximum observation time (about 160 sec) is obtained with the observer situated at the equator. The observation time is insensitive to the angle of the sun below the horizon in the range from 5° to 15°. Observers situated at latitudes as high as ±5° would have only 30 sec in which to detect the satellite.

Brightness of Specular and Diffuse Reflectors

This section concerns the brightness of a reflecting sphere in sunlight. We compare the two extreme conditions of purely diffuse and

*The work presented here was supported by the U.S. Office of Naval Research, Contract No. NONR-1641(00), with the Varo Manufacturing Company.

purely specular reflection and show that the specularly reflecting sphere has a larger average brightness under identical observing conditions.

First we consider the diffuse reflector. Lambert's law for a diffusely reflecting surface gives the power radiated (dq) per unit solid angle from a surface element ds, in a direction making an angle ϵ with the surface normal, as

$$dq = \frac{aF_0}{\pi} \cos i \cos \epsilon \, ds \tag{1}$$

where a = albedo
F_0 = incident flux
i = angle of incidence, measured from the surface normal.

The surface element can be expressed in terms of the spherical co-ordinates b, ψ, ω as

$$ds = b^2 \cos \psi \, d\omega \, d\psi. \tag{2}$$

Here the polar axis is taken to be the direction from the center of the sphere (of radius b) to the observer.

The angles of incidence and reflection are determined by

$$\cos i = \cos \psi \cos (\omega - \sigma) \tag{3}$$

$$\cos \epsilon = \cos \psi \cos \omega \tag{4}$$

where σ, the phase angle, is the angle between the directions of the sun and the observer at the center of the sphere. Both sun and observer are assumed to lie at infinity.

Substituting (2), (3), and (4) in (1) and integrating, we obtain

$$q = \frac{aF_0 b^2}{\pi} \int_{-\pi/2}^{\pi/2} \cos^3 \psi \, d\psi \int_{\sigma-(\pi/2)}^{\pi/2} \cos (\omega - \sigma) \cos \omega \, d\omega \tag{5}$$

$$= \frac{2}{3} \frac{aF_0}{\pi} b^2 \left[\sin \sigma + (\pi - \sigma) \cos \sigma\right]. \tag{6}$$

Finally, the observed flux is

$$F = \frac{q}{r^2} \tag{7}$$

where r is the distance between observer and sphere.

We now derive the observed flux for the specular reflector. Let $2\alpha = \sigma$ as previously defined. Consider the radiation incident on a spherical zone of the sphere whose angular diameter is α and whose width is $d\alpha$. The axis of the spherical zone is the direction to the sun.

The power incident on the zone is clearly

$$dE = F_0 2\pi b^2 \sin \alpha \cos \alpha \, d\alpha \tag{8}$$

and falls on an area

$$2\pi D^2 \sin 2\alpha \, (2d\alpha) \tag{9}$$

at the distance D from the sphere. The observed flux is consequently

$$F = \frac{2\pi b^2 F_0 \sin \alpha \cos \alpha \, d\alpha}{2\pi D^2 \sin 2\alpha \, (2d\alpha)} = \frac{b^2 F_0}{4D^2} \tag{10}$$

and is *independent* of α. This property gives the specular reflector an advantage over the diffuse reflector for angles σ close to π, i.e., when the sphere is nearly in the direction of the sun.

A numerical example will demonstrate this point more effectively. We shall compare the variation of apparent magnitude of diffusely and specularly reflecting spheres of the same radius moving in a circular orbit.

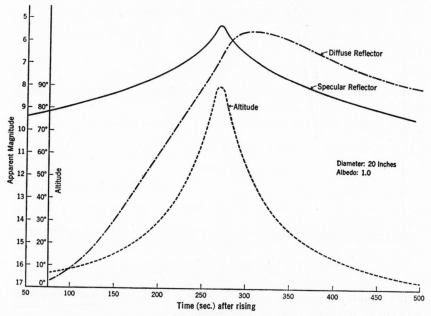

FIGURE 1. Twilight observation.

To simplify the geometry, consider a twilight observation with the sun on the western horizon and with the satellite passing through the zenith. Let the satellite rise in the west, ascend to the zenith, and set in the east. At the assumed height of 200 miles, the satellite will complete this traverse of the sky in about 550 sec. We take

$$b = 20 \text{ in.}$$
$$a = 1$$
$$D = \text{height above earth} = 200 \text{ miles.}$$

To compute the apparent magnitude of the satellite, we compare its flux to that of the sun, using $m_0 = -26.7$ as the apparent magnitude of the sun:

$$m = -26.7 + 2.5 \log \frac{F_0}{F} \cdot \tag{11}$$

Fig. 1 shows the apparent magnitude of the satellite as a function of the time after rising. Note the great superiority of the specular reflector on the rise toward the zenith. The visibility of the satellite depends not only on its intrinsic brightness but also on the background sky brightness. The diffuse reflector suffers from the limitation that it is fainter where the sky brightness is high and near maximum brightness where the sky is dark, but where the

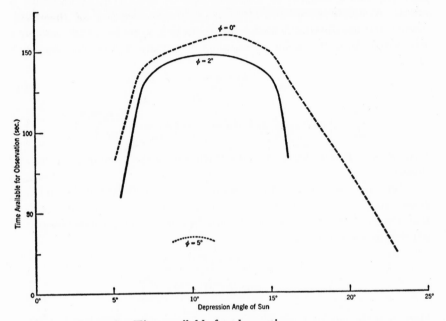

FIGURE 2.   Time available for observation.

earth's shadow may extinguish it. Specular reflection gives a more favorable light curve, relative to the sky brightness.

In the next section we examine the influence of sky brightness and of the earth's shadow on the time available for observation.

Time Available for Observation

In a twilight observation, if we neglect the opacity of the atmosphere for the moment, three major factors limit the visibility of the satellite:

1) Geometry. Obviously, to be visible at all, the satellite must rise above the observer's horizon at some point in its orbit.

2) The earth's shadow. Unless the satellite's brightness is enhanced by the use of fluorescent or phosphorescent paints, the satellite becomes invisible upon entering the earth's shadow.

3) Sky brightness. The satellite must exceed the sky brightness by a certain margin or else, like most stars during the day, it will remain invisible.

We shall examine each of these factors in turn and then give some numerical results for a specularly reflecting satellite. Fig. 2 summarizes these briefly.

Suppose the satellite moves above the earth's equator at a constant altitude of 200 miles. If we ignore refraction, the satellite will rise above the observer's horizon only if the observer's latitude is less than $\cos^{-1} [R_0/(R_0 + 200)] = 17°.8$, where R_0 is the earth's equatorial radius in miles. A simple calculation gives the following formulae for the zenith angle z and the distance D to the satellite as functions of the true anomaly ν (measured from the point of maximum elevation) and the observer's latitude ϕ:

$$\cos z = \frac{R_1 \cos \phi \cos \nu - R_0}{D} \tag{12}$$

$$\frac{D}{R_1} = \left[\cos^2 \nu \sin^2 \phi + \sin^2 \nu + \cos \phi \cos \nu - \frac{R_0}{R_1} \right]^{1/2}. \tag{13}$$

Here R_0 and R_1 are the radii of the earth and of the satellite orbit, respectively.

Ignoring refraction again, assuming the observer's latitude is small and considering only observations near the vernal or autumnal equinox, we see that the position of the earth's shadow becomes a simple function of the depression angle θ of the sun:

$$\tan z_s = \frac{\sin (17°.8 - \theta)}{\cos (17°.8 - \theta) - \dfrac{R_0}{R_1}}.$$

Here z_s is the zenith angle of the last point on the satellite's orbit that is illuminated by the sun.

The geometrical relation of an arbitrarily oriented elliptical orbit to the earth's shadow and to the observer is rather more complicated and will not be presented here.

The effect of sky brightness on the visibility of stars and planets has been investigated by Tousey and Koomen.[1] We have used their charts of threshold magnitude vs position in the sky to compute the available time of observation as a function of observer latitude and solar depression angle.

The calculation is limited in accuracy by the errors in reading the chart and interpolation between charts. We have therefore dispensed with the refinement of refraction effects in calculating the formulae above. We proceed as follows:

1) For a given observer latitude (ϕ), we compute the altitude (H), azimuth (A), and apparent magnitude (m) of the satellite as a function of the true anomaly (ν), using equations (10), (11), (12), (13), and

$$\tan A = \frac{[\cos^2 \nu \sin^2 \phi + \sin^2 \nu]^{1/2}}{\cos \nu \sin \phi}. \tag{14}$$

Here the azimuth is measured from the south if the observer lies north of the equator and vice versa.

2) Next the apparent magnitude at all points in the orbit is corrected for

    a) Extinction.   Tousey and Koomen consider 0.4 magnitude to be conservative for altitudes above 30° and we have adopted this value.

    b) Altitude.   Tousey and Koomen's charts refer to an altitude of 10,000 ft.   The sky brightness at sea level is given as about twice that at 10,000 ft., which makes necessary a correction of 0.6 in the threshold magnitude.

    c) Magnification.   If seven-power binoculars are used, a correction of -4.22 follows.

    d) Albedo.   We adopt a value of 0.6, which gives a correction of 0.55 magnitude.   Total correction is -2.6 magnitudes.

3) Finally, we compute the available time.   A given apparent magnitude of the satellite corresponds to a certain altitude, azimuth, and time. Tousey and Koomen's charts give the depression angle of the sun at which the satellite is first visible at this apparent magnitude.   At this depression angle, the observing interval is (usually) terminated by the earth's shadow whose zenith angle is then determined.   The time of entering the shadow minus the time corresponding to the chosen apparent magnitude is the time available for observation.   By choosing successive values of the apparent magnitude, we have constructed Fig. 2.

We note that under the conditions assumed, the maximum time for observation is about 160 sec.   For observer latitudes near the equator (orbital plane), the available time is fairly insensitive to the depression angle within the limits of about 7° and 15°.   However, the available time is a very rapid function of the observer latitude, dropping to less than 40 sec at $\phi = 5°$. Seasonal effects will not change our results appreciably.

We conclude with some comments on the observation of a satellite whose orbit is inclined to the earth's equator.   If the satellite passes through the observer's zenith, the predictions of Fig. 2 for $\phi = 0°$ are minimal values, regardless of inclination, latitude, or season.   Except for seasonal effects, Fig. 2 gives fairly reliable values (with orbital inclination less than 40°) if ϕ is interpreted as the angle at the earth's center between the observer and the orbital plane.

REFERENCE

1. R. Tousey and M. J. Koomen, "The Visibility of Stars and Planets During Twilight," *J. Opt. Soc. Am., 43:*177–183 (1953).

3

Satellite Tracking by Electronic Optical Instrumentation

by Harrison J. Merrill
SIGNAL CORPS ENGINEERING LABORATORIES,
FT. MONMOUTH, NEW JERSEY

ABSTRACT

Certain characteristics which warrant consideration in the passive detection and tracking of the satellite emphasize the usefulness of optical techniques. In planning for the use of existing equipment, it becomes apparent that there are essential differences between satellite tracking and astronomical observations or missile tracking. The problems associated with the satellite are due principally to the diminished contrast against the sun-illuminated sky and to the tracking acceleration component and the concomitant instrumentation jitter. Improvements in the optical compatibilities of the tracking and location instrumentation can be developed if combinations of electronic techniques are utilized which have characteristics more suitable than photographic film or the eye. These improvements are associated with superior time constants, background elimination, utilization of the optimum spectral region, and the superior characteristics of the electronics in the servo tracking loop.

The experience gained through the developments of astronomy and through the much more recent guided-missile test-range instrumentation indicates that optical location of a satellite during the day will be very difficult even under the most favorable optical environment which exists at White Sands Proving Ground. The difficulties are operational and increase with the need for obtaining location data quickly for further position information. Optical location during twilight or dawn is considerably more favorable. Although under such conditions the object can be seen and photographed, the problems introduced by the rapid change of the sky brightness and the angular velocity and acceleration of the object provide serious operational difficulties.

In considering the instrumentation which might be used for the optical location of an artificial satellite, one immediately is attracted by the similarity of the artificial satellite with natural stars, satellites, or meteors. The analogy with astronomy denotes the possibility of using astronomical-type instruments for the precise location and especially for the first requirement to determine that a satellite exists. There are, however, some striking differences in the analogy which create difficulties in the location system.

First and foremost, the artificial satellite is eclipsed from the end of dusk until the beginning of dawn and there is never a time when the sun-illuminated satellite can be viewed against a night background.

The apparent motion through the sky is rapid and becomes analogous to the motion of meteors. Like meteor motion, the motion has an acceleration component which limits any exposure in an image-forming tracking system to a matter of seconds. For example, the image formed by a 25-in.-focal-length lens moves with a linear velocity which varies from 0.16 in./sec to more than 0.7 in./sec. If the correct velocity has been chosen and velocity tracking is used, the acceleration is such that the image will move 50 μ, a practical image size, in the range from 3 to 21 sec.

While the artificial satellite is resolvable with large astronomical-type lenses and has a unit brightness some 12 times greater than the moon, the total illumination is comparable to those stars which vary between the third and tenth magnitudes. Or, carrying the analogy further, it is very similar to the larger moons of Jupiter in angular size and brightness.

Once an orbit can be predicted so that the location of the satellite can be predicted to approximately 1° of arc and 15 sec of time, special narrow-angle optical trackers will be able to track the satellite. With accurate determination of location, high resolving power and special-purpose astronomical instrumentation will be able to recognize and study the satellite in its orbit.

The background conditions of illumination can be illustrated by

Fig. 1, which shows the illumination on the earth's surface as a function of time. The figure shows illumination due to the direct light from the sun as well as the diffuse skylight, which during the day accounts for a fifth of the total illumination. The time of the setting of the sun and the time of the eclipse of the satellite have been indicated.

The luminous intensity of the satellite against the sky background is calculated on the initial assumptions that the satellite is illuminated only by a combination of direct sunlight, moonlight, and earthlight; that the

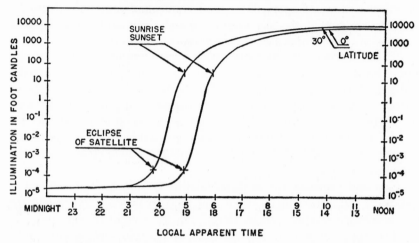

FIGURE 1. Illumination on the earth at summer solstice. From Dept. of Navy Buships.

satellite is a perfect diffuse reflector of unity reflectance and $\frac{1}{2}$-meter diameter; and that the orbit of the satellite is 200 miles above the earth's sea-level surface. When the satellite is not eclipsed, the major contributions to its brightness are due to the illumination from the sun; $E_s = 14.5$ lumens/cm². Under certain conditions, the contribution of illumination reflected from the earth may be appreciable. Considering the moon's albedo to be 0.07, the maximum possible illumination due to reflected light from the moon may be $E_m = 4 \times 10^{-5}$ lumens/cm², a negligibly small value. On the other hand, calculating the illumination from the light reflected from the earth, using an albedo of 0.20, the value may be as great as $E_e = 2$ lumens/cm².

The illumination on the earth due to the satellite depends on the distance, phase, and atmospheric conditions, which will not be discussed in detail. For preliminary engineering purposes a range of values has been calculated and is shown in Table I, reduced to equivalent stellar magnitudes. The table is constructed considering the satellite to be either a $\frac{1}{2}$-meter, 1-meter, or 10-meter object at conditions which have been termed "best case" and "worst case." The "best case" and the "worst case" have been determined by calculating the illumination of the object by direct sunlight and earthlight, the phase change of the satellite, and its distance from the observer. The difference in the table between daylight and twilight is due largely to the phase changes of the earthlight and sunlight.

TABLE I

Approximate satellite magnitudes

Satellite	Magnitudes	
Diameter	Best	Worst
(meters)	Case	Case
Daylight ½	3	10
1	2	8
10	−3	3
Twilight ½	5	10
1	3	8
10	−2	3

The above magnitudes are a function of phase, distance, and earthshine.

A convenient representative magnitude for discussion purposes might be considered as the 8.5 magnitude, which is said to be the absolute magnitude that can be detected by the unaided human eye. Although such detectability is not approached in the satellite conditions, for the visual limit is approached only under "perfect" conditions, 8.5 magnitude does fall within the values of the table. The irradiancy of this magnitude with the spectral quality of the sun is then:

Visual 8×10^{-12} watts/meter^2
Near Infrared 4×10^{-12} watts/meter^2
Intermediate Infrared 8×10^{-13} watts/meter^2.

The visibility of the satellite will be affected by the region of the infrared or optical spectrum in which the satellite is viewed. The effect of scattering by dust particles, water vapor, and air molecules can be reduced by using only the infrared region. This reduces the background illumination and improves the detection inasmuch as the visibility of the satellite depends on the contrast between its brightness and the sky brightness. However, 45% of the natural sunlight lies in the visible region, 25% lies in what might be called the near-infrared region, and only 5% in the intermediate infrared. The lack of radiation in the intermediate infrared region, in addition to the diminishing sensitivity of infrared detectors, tends to reduce the gain derived from the improved scattering conditions. There is evidence that under most conditions of slight haze, photography in the near infrared region to 0.86 micron reduces background illumination and therefore makes it possible to improve daytime minimum photographability by 1 stellar magnitude. Extending further to 1.0 micron in the infrared has produced extraordinary photographs, but such photographs in the satellite case are considered impractical because of the low sensitivity and the difficulty of handling the film. There are possibilities that infrared-detection systems such as image tubes or mosaic assemblies would increase the detectability to an extent not fully evaluated at the present time.

In the optical detection of the satellite the background illumination by the sun and sky exerts a great influence. The illumination changes by a factor of 8 orders of magnitude from daylight condition to nighttime. This corresponds to a change of 20 stellar magnitudes. The daytime sky background is caused either by scatter of visible light by air molecules, which gives the blue sky, or by the scatter of larger particles such as haze particles, water drops, or clouds, which gives the characteristic white or grey color. These scatter effects are rapidly minimized as one views the increasingly longer infrared wavelengths. Beyond about 3.5 microns the daytime sky is practically as dark as the nighttime sky is in the visible region. The change in this illumination during the summer solstice at the equator and north 30th latitude is shown in Fig. 1. The time of the setting of the sun is indicated by arrows in the figure. From the time of the setting of the sun until the nighttime condition the sky brightness drops rapidly as indicated and presents an increasingly favorable seeing condition. During this time the background decreases. However, the luminosity of the satellite diminishes to some extent due to attenuation of an increasingly greater atmospheric path through which the sun rays must travel.

The visibility of the satellite in the sky can be increased by a filter. The effect of short-wave scattering can be reduced either by photographing through a red filter against a blue sky or by using a polarized filter oriented in such a manner as to suppress the polarized components of the scattered background. It is also possible to reduce the background effects by treating the background and the desired target signal by differential detection.

In view of the astronomical background[1,2,3,4] associated with the detection of the satellite, the stellar magnitude of the object can be easily determined and compared with other backgrounds reduced to equivalent stellar magnitudes. In Tables II and III this is performed visually and photographically. Further extension of the tables to other pickup devices such as photoelectric cells can be accomplished by considering the visual case as also the limit to photoelectric detection. The location of the satellite is complicated by the orbit, which has such a high velocity that it takes only 10.7 min for the satellite to go from horizon to horizon,

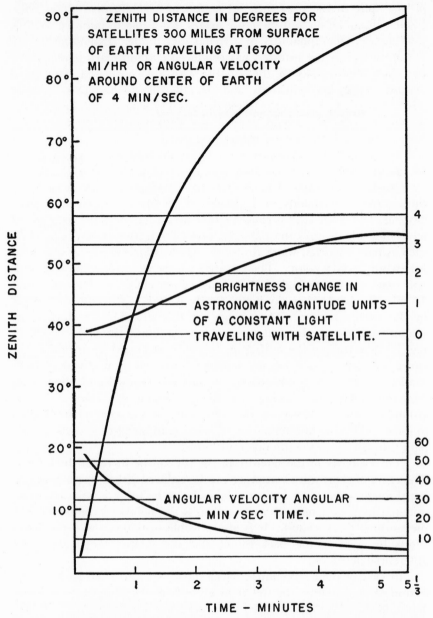

FIGURE 2. Plot of I. Zenith distance. II. Angular velocity. III. Change of brightness vs time.

as indicated in Fig. 2. Much of this time the satellite is at low elevation and as it rises in elevation the angular acceleration becomes large, which complicates the tracking problem. To complicate further the location and tracking, the velocity is smallest at low elevations where the brightness is low. When the brightness is high and the object is most visible, it has risen in elevation and the angular velocity and acceleration become large.

TABLE II

Limiting photographable magnitudes

		During Daylight		
Focal Length (inches)	*Focal Ratio*	*Image Size 20μ*	*Image Size 50μ*	*Maximum Exposure* Time (seconds) 50μ*
10	.85	−2	−4	3/1000
25	4.5	0	−2	1/500
50	12	2	0	1/200
160	14	4	2	1/100
320	28	6	4	1/16

Sun on Horizon, Satellite in Opposite Hemisphere		
Focal Length (inches)	*Limiting Magnitude*	*Maximum Exposure Time (seconds)*
10	3	1/50
25	4	1/12
50	6	1
121	8	1/8
160	9	6
320	(9)	(6)

Sun 15° Below Horizon, Satellite in Opposite Hemisphere		
Focal Length (inches)	*Limiting Magnitude*	*Exposure Time (seconds)*
10	10	10
25	3	10
50	8	10
121	13	10
160	10	10
320	10	10

* Exposure calculated for ASA-200 film speed, to give exposure density 0.6 above fog density. A 50-micron-diameter spot was assumed to receive all the light reaching the lens.

The computation of the visual and photographic detectability of the object is complicated by the assessment of the "jitter" of the tracking over a short period of time. As the angular acceleration of the object at

TABLE III

Limiting visual magnitudes during twilight and daylight hours

Three telescopic powers are considered. A polarizer set to maximum darkening is used. Data are determined for an observational elevation of 10,000 ft above sea level. To make correction to sea level, subtract 0.5 magnitude.

Daylight

Satellite 30° above horizon, looking away from sun.

10×—0 mag.;   20×—1 mag.;   40×—2 mag.

Pre-twilight

Satellite 30° above horizon, sun within 5° of horizon.

10×—2.5 mag.;   20×—4 mag.;   40×—5.5 mag.

Twilight

Satellite 15° above, sun 15° below horizon.

10×—10 mag.;   20×—11 mag.;   40×—13 mag.

a ground station is appreciable, tracking cannot be done for any extended time by clockwork. The tracking will have to be controlled by a servo or computer, which definitely limits the ability to track.

When the background illumination is appreciable, as it usually will be in the satellite case, the limit of detection is imposed by the contrast against the background. The limiting magnitude can be calculated by assuming that the illumination due to the sky imaged by a lens

$$E = \pi B_{sky}/4(f/no.)^2$$

is equal to the illumination E_{star} from a distant source imaged into an area A_{image}

$$E = E_{star}A_{lens}/A_{image} = E_{star}D^2_{lens}/D^2_{image}$$

where A is the area and D the corresponding diameter. It is further assumed that the area of the image is larger than the limit imposed by diffraction considerations. Then the minimum illumination from a star easily detectable against a background brightness B_{sky} is

$$E_{star} = \pi B_{sky}D^2_{image}/4L^2_{lens}$$

where L_{lens} is the focal length of the lens. The units must be consistent, that is D and L must be in the same units and B_{sky} is given in candles/unit^2 and E_{star} in lumens/unit^2. Results for various lenses where E_{star} is converted to stellar magnitude are shown in Table II. It is noted that, contrary to the usual nighttime astronomical conditions, the diameter of the lens only becomes important in a secondary sense. In photography, a large light-gathering power is useful so that an exposure may be made in a shortened time, thus reducing the tracking effects on the image size, the atmospheric shimmer effects and the tracking jitter. The effect of the lens speed on the exposure is indicated in Table II by listing typical maximum allowable exposure times.

It is noted that the photographic technique is not ideally suitable for detecting a satellite. An improvement in detectability may be instituted immediately by choosing an instrument with a short time constant, such as a photocell, and by choosing a differential-type circuit for detection. Immediately the sky background signal is diminished to that of the fluctuations in the sky or to the induced or shot noise, or to fundamental thermal noise. Although during the day this noise may be considerable, the wanted signal due to the presence of a satellite may be enhanced in the differential circuit by chopping the signal in some favorable way. For instance, a simple method would be to form the image of the chosen section of the sky on a line grid having a line width and spacing of .002 in. equivalent to the image. The passage of the satellite would produce a rather pure sine wave which could be detected by a photocell having a narrow-bandwidth amplifier with a chosen frequency and bandwidth to fit the expected range of angular velocity.

Optical instrumentation systems are important in the detection and location of the satellite. They serve as a standard of performance, prove that a satellite exists, and provide information of sufficient precision to accomplish scientific measurements. The successful installation of optical devices may be simple and of prime responsibility in early phases of the satellite instrumentation in which studies can be made independent of the loading of the satellite and the data may be important in the reentry problem.

An electronically controlled optical instrumentation has certain advantages over photographic or visual equipment. The tracking function may be compatible with radio location equipment and the techniques may supplement each other during conditions of interference, instrumentation failure, and atmospheric disturbances. Two varieties of optical equipment are required to fulfill location and tracking functions.

The search-location function requires wide-angle intercept equipment which will form a "picket" image of the sky capable of detecting the satellite image as it passes over the detector. The advantage of a photoelectric or photoconductive detector as the sensitive element resides in its time constant, spectral sensitivity, field of view, and readiness. These characteristics may be chosen in such a variety as to fit engineering requirements. The presence of a satellite may be determined by measuring the velocity and acceleration parameters over a short interval of time. The time of passage through the "picket" may be measured with a high precision, for the equipment has the capability of being calibrated at about the same time by measuring the transit of a star.

The tracking and precise location function may be performed by a servo-aided tracking system. The system will consist of a precision mount compatible in its guidance through electrical servo input and output with radar or real-time computed data. The instrument is so designed in order to permit a maximum flexibility for the installation of optically sensitive devices such as photoelectric, photoconductive, mosaic, and photographic detectors. The mount has a precision bearing assembly operating in azimuth and elevation coupled to two external surface plates suitable for holding the objective and the detection device. The displacement and velocity will be controlled by aided tracking from external sources, automatic sensing, or a visual operator. Although jet planes have been tracked with a probable deviation of 18 sec of arc, the tracking of a satellite, which is much slower, may be improved by adding an automatic acceleration drive which can control in accordance with an expected program. Three types of output data are available. They are, in order of precision: first, a fine servo control accurate to 1.5 min of arc; second, a real-time digital take-off accurate to 0.3 min of arc; and third, a divided circle photographed on film accurate to 5 sec of arc. The precision of location of the satellite will depend on the care with which the instrument is operated, for it is a dynamic system subject to many errors of misalignment. In special cases, the instrument is capable of photographing stars simultaneously with the location of the satellite. The photograph could then be used as a standard to calibrate the position and improve the position.

REFERENCES

1. R. Tousey and E. O. Hulburt, "The Visibility of Stars in the Daylight Sky," *J. Opt. Soc. Am., 38:* 886–896 (1948).
2. R. Tousey and M. J. Koomen, "The Visibility of Stars and Planets During Twilight," *J. Opt. Soc. Am., 43:* 177–183 (1953).
3. J. A. Hynek, "Photographing Stars in the Daytime," *Sky and Telescope,* January, 1951.
4. M. J. Koomen *et al.,* "Measurements of the Brightness of the Twilight Sky," *J. Opt. Soc. Am., 42:* 353–356 (1952).

4

Possibility of Visual Tracking of a Satellite

by Donald E. Hudson
INSTITUTE FOR ATOMIC RESEARCH AND DEPARTMENT OF PHYSICS,
IOWA STATE COLLEGE, AMES, IOWA

ABSTRACT

It is suggested that visual tracking of the satellite at night may be feasible by means of short flashes of light. A point source having an intensity of about 400 candle-sec would give a flash barely visible to the naked eye under good viewing conditions. Energy for 10,000 such flashes from a xenon discharge tube can be supplied by about 8 lb of commercially available batteries and condensers in a total volume of less than 100 in.^{3} A weaker source suitable for telescopic tracking could weigh of the order of 1 lb. In addition to supplementing the local oscillator, a flasher could provide a valuable beacon in case of transmitter failure.

Sensitivity of the Eye

The fact that the human eye is an extremely sensitive detector has suggested the possibility that a visible light source might be carried practicably on a satellite for viewing at night. Under ideal conditions and with proper light shields, a dark-adapted person[1] can see an 8.5-magnitude star, corresponding to a flux on the cornea of 8.3×10^{-10} lumens/ m^2. Laboratory experiments give results in good agreement with this figure.[2a,2b]   Under normally good conditions, a sixth-magnitude star may be seen at ten times the minimal illumination. We shall adopt the visibility of a sixth-magnitude star as a standard practical lower limit for the unaided eye in this report. A standard source distance of 500 km will also be used to approximate a minimum reasonable satellite distance. At 500 km a 2000-candle point source corresponds to the indicated minimum.

In estimating the power for such a source it is necessary to take into account the increased efficiency of scotopic vision over the photopic vision characteristic of normal stimulus levels.[3] For photopic vision the monochromatic conversion from radiation flux to lumens at 555 mμ is 680 lumens/watt, whereas for scotopic vision the ratio is 1746 lumens/watt at 510 mμ. A black body dissipating one watt at 6500°K radiates about 93 lumens for normal vision but may be considered to radiate about 240 lumens if it is to be observed under scotopic conditions. An efficient green fluorescent lamp would require about 130 watts of electrical power on the satellite to be seen. Such a lamp would have a limited life on a satellite without a severe reduction in average power. However, by proper temporal cycling a steady light could be used for tracking. An alternate procedure is to effect the reduction in mean power by using spaced millisecond flashes.

The sensitivity of the eye to square pulses of light t seconds long is given by the equation $I = I_0 (t + t_o)/t$, where I_0 is the threshold source intensity for steady light, I is the threshold intensity for the pulse under the same conditions, and t_o is a short time called the critical duration or retinal action time.[4] Various authors give values of t_o from 0.1 to 0.2 sec, and to be conservative we shall use 0.2 sec. On this basis the satellite needs a source of 400 candle-sec for a short flash lasting the order of milliseconds. (This value also checks reasonably well with laboratory experiments done independently with millisecond flashes.[2a]) About 5000 lumen-sec of light is emitted by a 400-candle-sec point source.

A Possible Source

A direct way to produce millisecond flashes is with a xenon-filled gas discharge tube such as is currently used in portable photographic "speedlights." A typical source consists of a battery (about 500 volts), a condenser to store about 50 joules (400 μf), and a triggering device.[5] The problem of component selection to squeeze out the last flash per pound in a satellite not only involves engineering complications but also cannot be solved properly without detailed knowledge of many boundary conditions. However, a practical solution will be given which shows about what can be done with *available* components under reasonable operating conditions. The energy storage per pound in both the battery and the condenser is approximately independent of the operating voltage; it is convenient to consider a 500-volt unit.

Xenon flash tubes have efficiency averaging about 40 lumens per electrical watt on a photopic basis, or about 100 lumens/watt for scotopic adaptation. Hence, about 5000/100 or 50 joules of electrical energy is required per flash. (Although a "color temperature" of around 6500°K is stated for such tubes, a true black body at that temperature would require only 20 joules.) Fortuitously, the energy requirement is met by a standard 50-watt-sec flash tube.

Both the Mallory "Mercury cell" and the Yardney "Silvercel" have outstanding energy yields of 40–50 watt-hours/lb. We have used the former in this illustration because they stack to high voltage more conveniently in small sizes. A 500-volt stack of 430 Mallory 1R cells occupies about 75 in.^{3}, weighs 7.5 lb, will deliver 1.2×10^6 joules, and has an internal impedance of 1300 ohms. The condenser problem is difficult for large energy storage because weight limitations strongly favor electrolytic condensers. Usual 500-volt, 400-μf electrolytics may drain more than 100 joules from a battery in leakage during a short 2-sec charging period. However, an outstanding recent type soon to appear on the market stores 50 joules in 9 oz (12 in.^{3}) and is claimed to have remarkably low leakage.[6] An estimate of 20 joules loss per charge has been made for this unit. (These computations have allowed for the fact that the leakage is especially bad immediately after the voltage is applied. The usual quoted leakage figures apply after longer times.) More rapid charging than about 2 sec places an excessive drain on the batteries. Unfortunately, whenever a condenser is charged in an RC circuit, the energy loss exactly equals the energy stored. Hence, each flash takes 120 joules and the unit gives 10^4 flashes, or enough for about 2.3 days if the flasher goes every 10 sec during dark hours only.

Periodic triggering may be reliably done by a tiny auxiliary relaxation oscillator employing a W.E. 395A trigger tube driving a small relay. When the trigger tube fires, one relay contact connects the condenser to the battery. The relay coil is arranged to be in series with the charging current. The relay holds until the current is very small (and the condenser is nearly charged). At this time the relay releases and another set of contacts triggers the flash. The flash trigger is accomplished by means of a small passive circuit consisting of a resistor, a condenser, and a model-airplane ignition coil. Losses in the oscillator and trigger circuits are negligible.

The proposed flasher design represents a realistic solution in terms of existing technology. The components are not sensitive to acceleration and should work satisfactorily between 0°C and 80°C.

General Comments

The criterion of a flash barely visible to the unaided eye is arbitrary. A unit with 100 times less output would have its weight limited more by the flash-tube and auxiliary components than by the theoretically very small weights of batteries and condensers; if a suitable battery could be built, such a unit would weigh in the order of 1 lb and still be visible with a modest telescope on a good night. On the other hand, it is easy to get considerably more light in fewer flashes. An optical system with a gain of 50 (or common 7×50 binoculars) would permit excellent vision of the 400-candle-sec unit on a clear night and vision on a hazy night when a second-magnitude star (Polaris) was barely visible.

Temporal cycling of the flasher could be flexible within wide limits. It would, of course, be turned off while the satellite was in sunlight. Flash patterns more complicated than uniformly periodic could be arranged and it is possible to alternate flashes of different intensities. The latter pattern might be suited to possible photographic applications where an occasional brighter flash may be desirable. Or, the unit might be used only at the beginning and end of the satellite life. Various prospects are available for improving the efficiency of a flasher. Batteries and condensers are improving rapidly. Charging the condenser through an inductance would reduce the charging loss, provided that a sufficiently low-impedance battery were available. The procurement of more lumens per watt in special flash tubes is unlikely to be spectacular but is a possibility. Judicious use of reflectors on the satellite would help, provided tumbling were not excessive. More fanciful is the prospect of using "solar batteries" to replenish a rechargeable type of battery during illuminated periods.

Specific treatment of methods of reducing the visual flashes to tracking data is appropriately left for specialists in this field. However, the flashes themselves provide natural time markers for the various observers engaged in a triangulation. The use of the flasher as an auxiliary beacon in case of local oscillator failure is an attractive possibility. Although an independent unit has been assumed in this paper, it is clear that the instrumentation must be correlated with other installations. Finally, the possibilities of a visible flasher could have interesting implications in terms of bringing the satellite program somewhat closer to the average man.

REFERENCES

1. H. N. Russell, "The Minimum Radiation Visually Perceptible," *Astrophys. J., 45:* 60–64 (1917).

2. (a) See M. H. L. Pirenne, *Vision and the Eye* (London: Chapman and Hall, Ltd., 1948). (b) A. C. Hardy and F. H. Perrin. *Principles of Optics*. New York: McGraw-Hill Book Co., 1932, Chapter X.
3. *The Science of Color,* published by the O.S.A. Committee on Colorimetry, Crowell Co., New York, 1953.
4. A. R. E. Chapanis *et al. Applied Experimental Psychology.* New York: Wiley and Sons, 1949.
5. A good introductory description is found in "Eveready Battery Engineering Bulletin No. 6, Electronic Flash," National Carbon Co., 30 E. 42 St., New York, N. Y., 1954.
6. Private communication from A. Kariotis, Sprague Electric Co., North Adams, Mass., January 23, 1956.

5

Interpretations of Observed Perturbations on a Minimal Earth Satellite

by Jackson L. Sedwick, Jr.
BALLISTIC RESEARCH LABORATORIES,
ABERDEEN PROVING GROUND, MARYLAND

It has been shown in the case of a small satellite revolving about the earth that the perturbations produced by the sun and the moon are negligible when compared to the effects due to the oblateness of the earth.[1] Satisfactory methods are available for computing the oblateness by observing the perturbations it produces in the orbit of such a satellite.

A further important perturbation of the orbit of a satellite is caused by the resistance of the atmosphere. A minimal satellite will be an invaluable aid to investigating atmospheric drag by supplying the magnitude of this drag for a variety of satellite velocities and altitudes. It is the purpose of this discussion to give a method for calculating the perturbing forces from observations of the orbit. Only air resistance and effects of the earth's oblateness will be considered.

We shall assume the drag force to be tangent to the satellite trajectory and shall further assume that the earth is an oblate, homogeneous spheroid. In connection with this problem the following quantities will be of importance:[2]

n = Mean angular motion
Ω = Angle to the line of nodes
i = Inclination of the orbit referred to the equator
π = Angle from the line of nodes to the pericenter
a = Major semi-axis of the orbit

e = Eccentricity of the orbit

σ = Mean angular motion times the time at perigee

r = Distance from center of the earth to the satellite

ν = True anomaly

u = Longitude of satellite from node

p = Semi-parameter of orbit

x, y, z = Rectangular co-ordinates of the satellite in an inertial frame of reference

W = Component of perturbing acceleration normal to the plane of the orbit with the positive direction toward the north pole

S = Component of perturbing acceleration in the plane of the orbit perpendicular to the radius vector and making an angle of less than 90° with the direction of motion

R = Component of perturbing acceleration along the radius vector with positive direction away from the earth

T = Component of perturbing acceleration tangent to the orbit and positive in the direction of motion

N = Component of perturbing acceleration in plane of orbit perpendicular to the tangent and positive when directed to the interior of the orbit.

It can be shown by the method of perturbations[3] that the following equations describe the motion of the system:

$$
\left.
\begin{aligned}
\frac{d\Omega}{dt} &= \frac{r \sin u}{na^2\sqrt{1 - e^2} \sin i}\, W \\[2mm]
\frac{d\pi}{dt} &= 2 \sin^2 \frac{i}{2}\frac{d\Omega}{dt} + \frac{\sqrt{1 - e^2}}{nae}\left\{ -R \cos \nu + S\left(1 + \frac{r}{p}\right)\sin \nu\right\} \\[2mm]
\frac{da}{dt} &= \frac{2}{n\sqrt{1 - e^2}}\left(Re \sin \nu + S\frac{p}{r}\right) \\[2mm]
\frac{di}{dt} &= \frac{r \cos u}{na^2\sqrt{1 - e^2}}\, W \\[2mm]
\frac{de}{dt} &= \frac{\sqrt{1 - e^2}}{na}\left\{ R \sin \nu + S\left(\frac{e + \cos \nu}{1 + e \cos \nu} + \cos \nu\right)\right\} \\[2mm]
\frac{d\sigma}{dt} &= -\frac{1}{na}\left[\frac{2r}{a} - \frac{1 - e^2}{e}\cos \nu\right] R - \frac{(re^2)}{nae}\left[1 + \frac{r}{p}\right] S \sin \nu
\end{aligned}
\right\} \tag{1}
$$

where it is assumed that the orbit is noncircular and is inclined to the plane of the equator. These elements were chosen because of the particularly simple form the equations take when the components of the perturbing acceleration are taken as R, S, and W or as T, N, and W, as is necessary for use in the development.

The values of the co-ordinates and their derivatives can be measured in an earth-fixed co-ordinate system. All the quantities save R, S, and W used in the right-hand members of equations (1) can then be calculated for a great many values of time by means of digital computers. If the intervals between these times are small enough, the derivatives appearing on the left can be computed to a fairly high approximation. The equations can then be solved for R, S, and W.

It is seen that only three of the equations are needed. The first three would be a good choice for most of our applications since, as can be seen by examining the equations, the derivatives of Ω, π, and a are usually large quantities in comparison with the others.

Let F_x, F_y, and F_z be components of the disturbing acceleration along the x-, y-, and z-axes, respectively. Then,

$$\begin{pmatrix} F_x \\ F_y \\ F_z \end{pmatrix} = \begin{pmatrix} \cos\Omega & -\sin\Omega & 0 \\ \sin\Omega & \cos\Omega & 0 \\ 0 & 0 & 1 \end{pmatrix} \begin{pmatrix} 1 & 0 & 0 \\ 0 & \cos i & -\sin i \\ 0 & \sin i & \cos i \end{pmatrix}$$

$$\begin{pmatrix} \cos u & -\sin u & 0 \\ \sin u & \cos u & 0 \\ 0 & 0 & 1 \end{pmatrix} \begin{pmatrix} R \\ S \\ W \end{pmatrix}. \quad (2)$$

If we denote disturbances due to the oblateness of the earth by the subscript "o" and those due to the drag by the subscript "d," then

$$R = R_o + R_d$$
$$S = S_o + S_d \quad (3)$$
$$W = W_o, \quad \text{since } W_d = 0.$$

Rotating the x, y, z co-ordinate system about the z-axis until the y,z-plane contains the satellite and calling the new co-ordinate system the x', y', z'-system, we find that

$$\begin{pmatrix} F_{x'} \\ F_{y'} \\ F_{z'} \end{pmatrix} = \begin{pmatrix} \dfrac{x}{r} & \dfrac{y}{r} & 0 \\ -\dfrac{y}{r} & \dfrac{x}{r} & 0 \\ 0 & 0 & 1 \end{pmatrix} \begin{pmatrix} F_x \\ F_y \\ F_z \end{pmatrix}. \quad (4)$$

It is obvious that the acceleration due to the oblateness of the earth lies in the y', z'-plane so that $F_{y'_o} = 0$. We therefore have

$$F_{y'_o} = \left[-\frac{y}{r}(\cos u \cos \Omega - \sin u \sin \Omega \cos i) + \frac{y}{r}(\cos u \sin \Omega + \sin u \cos \Omega \cos i) \right] R_o$$

$$+ \left[+\frac{y}{r}(\sin u \cos \Omega + \cos u \sin \Omega \cos i) - \frac{x}{r}(\sin u \sin \Omega - \cos u \cos \Omega \cos i) \right] S_o$$

$$+ \left[-\frac{y}{r}\sin \Omega \sin i - \frac{x}{r}\cos \Omega \sin i \right] W_o = 0. \tag{5}$$

T, N, and W and R, S, and W are related by

$$\begin{pmatrix} R \\ S \\ W \end{pmatrix} = \begin{pmatrix} \dfrac{e \sin v}{\sqrt{1 + e^2 + 2e \cos v}} & -\dfrac{1 + e \cos v}{\sqrt{1 + e^2 + 2e \cos v}} & 0 \\[2ex] \dfrac{1 + e \cos v}{\sqrt{1 + e^2 + 2e \cos v}} & \dfrac{e \sin v}{\sqrt{1 + e^2 + 2e \cos v}} & 0 \\[2ex] 0 & 0 & 1 \end{pmatrix} \begin{pmatrix} T \\ N \\ W \end{pmatrix}. \tag{6}$$

Since $N_d = 0$ we have,

$$N_d = -\frac{1 + e \cos v}{\sqrt{1 + e^2 + 2e \cos v}} R_d + \frac{e \sin v}{\sqrt{1 + e^2 + 2e \cos v}} S_d = 0. \tag{7}$$

Letting

$$\alpha \equiv -\frac{y}{r}(\cos u \cos \Omega - \sin u \sin \Omega \cos i) + \frac{x}{r}(\cos u \sin \Omega + \sin u \cos \Omega \cos i)$$

$$\beta \equiv \frac{y}{r}(\sin u \cos \Omega + \cos u \sin \Omega \cos i) - \frac{x}{r}(\sin u \sin \Omega - \cos u \cos \Omega \cos i)$$

$$\gamma \equiv \frac{y}{r}\sin \Omega \sin i + \frac{x}{r}\cos \Omega \sin i$$

$$\xi \equiv -\frac{1 + e \cos v}{\sqrt{1 + e^2 + 2e \cos v}}$$

$$\eta \equiv \frac{e \sin v}{\sqrt{1 + e^2 + 2e \cos v}},$$

we see from equations (3), (5), and (7) that

$$\xi R_o + \eta S_o = \xi R + \eta S$$

$$\alpha R_o + \beta S_o = \gamma W.$$

Solving,

$$R_o = \frac{\begin{vmatrix} R + \eta S & \eta \\ \gamma W & \beta \end{vmatrix}}{D}$$

$$S_o = \frac{\begin{vmatrix} \xi & R + \eta S \\ \alpha & \gamma W \end{vmatrix}}{D}$$

where

$$D = \begin{vmatrix} \xi & \eta \\ \alpha & \beta \end{vmatrix}.$$

R_d and S_d can now be found from equations (3) and the drag, T_d, is given by equations (6).

An approximate expression for the potential of the earth can now be found from $F_{z'_o}$ which is now known from equations (2) and (4). Writing the potential as

$$U = \frac{\mu}{r}\left\{1 + k\left(\frac{1}{r^2} - \frac{3z^2}{r^4}\right) + \cdots\right\}$$

where $\mu \equiv GM$ and $k \equiv \frac{3}{10}b^2\epsilon^2$, and observing that

$$F_{z'_o} = \frac{\partial U}{\partial x'} - \frac{\mu z'}{r},$$

we have

$$F_{z'_o} = -\frac{\mu z'}{r^3}\left\{\frac{9}{r^2} - \frac{15z'^2}{r^4}\right\}k; \tag{8}$$

and since the expression

$$M = \frac{4}{3}\pi\sigma\frac{b^3}{1 - \epsilon^2}$$

can be used to eliminate b from (8), the eccentricity, ϵ, of a meridian section of the earth can be found. Actually higher-order terms in the potential could be retained and the values of the constants involved could be obtained since the value of $F_{z'_o}$ would be known for a large number of positions of the satellite.

REFERENCES

1. L. Spitzer, Jr., "Perturbations of a Satellite Orbit," *J. Brit. Interplan. Soc., 9:*131 (1950).
2. The notation is the same as used in F. R. Moulton's *Introduction to Celestial Mechanics* (New York: The Macmillan Co., 1931).
3. *Ibid.*, Chapter X.

6

Systems Design Considerations for Satellite Instrumentation

by L. G. deBey
BALLISTIC RESEARCH LABORATORIES,
ABERDEEN PROVING GROUND, MARYLAND

ABSTRACT

The Military Services have proposed a number of satellite programs. Each has objectives tailored to the interests of the sponsoring agency. The magnitude of any satellite program warrants careful consideration of the program output in terms of the number of scientifically useful data obtained. To achieve maximum output, compatible with the missile-system limitations, in turn requires a careful choice of observing methods.

The types of observations required for different programs are discussed, as are factors affecting choice of observing systems, their locations, and technical specifications. The importance of adhering to the philosophy of redundancy in observing methods is stressed. An array of instrumentation systems is proposed as being the minimum that could be expected to yield successful results in the first satellite firings.

Within the last year a number of programs for launching an artificial satellite have been proposed by organizations within the Department of Defense. The speculation and conjecture of a few years ago have given way to specific proposals for achieving successful establishment of small vehicles in earth-circling orbits. The technical achievements of the last few years leave little doubt that a satellite can be successfully launched within the next few years. Financial backing for such a project has been assured through the public announcement that the United States will launch a satellite during the forthcoming International Geophysical Year. There remains, however, another issue which is worthy of discussion: of what scientific value will the satellite be to the country which finances the effort?

Sufficient experience has been gained to establish the fact that the program will be costly. It is recognized that a number of complete satellite systems must be prepared for firing and perhaps expended before a successful orbiting satellite is achieved. Considering the magnitude of the effort, it is wise to insure that the program will yield a large useful output of scientific data.

It is admittedly difficult to specify the quantity of data that would justify the total effort. It is obvious that the program output will depend to a large extent on the physical limitations imposed by the particular satellite system employed. To an equal, if not greater, extent the output will depend on the foresight exhibited in planning the scientific objectives and providing appropriate observing methods for achieving these objectives. It is the purpose of this paper to discuss some of the factors which must be considered in establishing sound objectives and adequate observing methods.

It is expected that there will be as many proposed objectives as there are proposing agencies; more, if a poll were to be taken of the suggestions of nongovernment scientists. Of the two system proposals which appear to be feasible for accomplishment during the International Geophysical Year program, each stresses quite different objectives; each is tailored to the interests of the sponsoring agency. One such proposal, for a minimum satellite, recommended concentration of effort on what might be called external measurements. The minimum satellite, because of weight and space limitations, offers little hope of making any but the most rudimentary measurements of phenomena taking place within the vehicle during flight. Thus the scientific program was based on objectives dependent primarily on the measurement of trajectory parameters. Through such measurements data may be obtained on the shape of the earth, on the variation of ionization in the high atmosphere, and on the effective high-altitude atmospheric density. In addition, provided data of sufficiently high accuracy and quantity are obtained, preliminary geodetic measurements may be made.

The second of the two proposals recommended the use of a somewhat larger satellite with an allowable weight several times that of the minimum satellite. Under these less restrictive conditions it is natural that the program objectives should be based on the capabilities of the larger vehicle to carry a significantly greater amount of on-board instrumentation. The payload can easily accommodate a number of telemetry transducers and an appropriate telemetering transmitter. Internal measurements thus become quite practical. It is highly probable that proposals for internal measurements will far exceed those for external measurements. This should not be construed to mean that external measurements are less important. The final scientific program should be carefully examined to insure that each of these types of measurement is given proper emphasis.

In spite of the apparent difference between the stated objectives of the two programs there appears to be no valid reason why both sets of objectives cannot be achieved with the larger satellite if the instrumentation systems are carefully selected and properly designed.

Systems design must include consideration of appropriate location of observing stations, effects of geometry on system accuracies, numbers of observing sites required to yield sufficient data, as well as careful choice of system characteristics. It is important, particularly for geodetic measurements, that more than the minimum number of observing sites be provided. If only the minimum number are employed, measurement errors will deteriorate the quality of data. Since it will be necessary to determine the effects of the oblate earth and its irregularities before precise measurements of intercontinental distances can be determined, a large number of observing sites would be desirable. Logistic considerations will undoubtedly preclude the use of as many stations as might be desired; however, it is essential that at least five sites, more or less uniformly distributed around the earth, be provided.

The dual objectives of making both internal and external measurements will require a different approach to the instrumentation problem than if only one or the other is to be attempted. Each objective requires quite different placement of design emphasis. The prime requisite for internal measurements is a telemetering system, since internal data storage, and later recovery, is hardly feasible. Missile-borne equipment will be relatively complex and, from the standpoint of weight, will require much larger and heavier power sources than would be necessary if only external measurements were to be made. Ground-station equipment can be fairly simple and of conventional design. It is unfortunate that the complex equipment must be carried by the satellite at the expense of either greater required propulsion power, less margin of excess energy, or relatively short equipment operating life. The utmost care should be taken in the design of the data-transmission system to conserve intelligence bandwidth to the full extent consistent with the data to be transmitted, even at the expense of added complexity in the ground-station equipment. The application of information-theory concepts to the design will permit significant reduction in telemetering power requirements aboard the satellite.

External measurements require not only the most simple and reliable type of missile-borne electronic equipment, but an extensive and moderately complex array of ground-based tracking instrumentation of both optical and electronic types. Electronic systems, if selected properly, may be of the omnidirectional type, thus giving much greater angular coverage than applicable optical systems and accommodating much greater deviations of the missile trajectory from the intended orbital plane. Thus, in spite of the generally lower quality of position data obtained from electronic systems, they serve as a vitally necessary adjunct to the optical systems by providing the latter with acquisition data. Such data offset the disadvantage of the narrow field-of-view of the optical systems. Furthermore, since electronic systems offer the possibility of making a larger number of observations during the satellite lifetime, the quality of the final, statistically improved, electronic data may very nearly equal the quality of the less abundant optical data. Optical systems, on the other hand, do not depend on a beacon in the satellite and thus are not subject to total loss of data, as are electronic systems if their signal source should fail. This remark is not intended as a prediction that the sun will cease to emit light during the International Geophysical Year.

Both internal and external electronic measurements are related by their common requirement of a signal source in the missile. The choice must be made to provide either one common source or two independent sources to meet the somewhat different characteristics desired for telemetering and tracking systems. The telemetering source, by definition, must be modulated, and the modulation sidebands can be detrimental to the operation of the tracking system, especially to those types which are based on phase-difference measurements at the carrier frequency. Power requirements, to achieve adequate signal-to-noise in each system, are considerably different. It will probably be necessary to interrogate the telemetering system at selected intervals to conserve battery drain while a separate tracking beacon could be designed to operate continuously for several months at the required power levels. It would appear that separate sources should be used, but certain compromises may dictate the use of the telemetering transmitter as the sole signal source. Techniques have been developed at the Ballistic Research Laboratories, and perhaps elsewhere, which will permit the accurate measurement of carrier phase differences in the presence of complex modulation sidebands. It becomes important, then, to weigh the disadvantages of such complex ground equipment against the advantages accruing through reduction in missile power consumption if only a single source is used. Insofar as the satellite is concerned, here is an opportunity to "get something for nothing" and perhaps to gain additional operating lifetime.

The choice of carrier frequency for electronic systems must be made primarily on the basis of technical considerations related to the communication problem. The factors of greatest importance combine to limit the choice to a relatively narrow segment of the radio frequency spectrum. The results of at least three independent studies show a frequency in the region near 100 mc/sec to be near the optimum. It is submitted, however, that final choice should take into account the effect of frequency on the ionosphere experiment proposed by the Ballistic Research Laboratories[1] in another paper at this meeting. If the operating frequency is chosen without regard for the critical dependence of this experiment on frequency, there will be little chance that useful data will be obtained. However, by a relatively small shift in frequency to 75 mc/sec, a near optimum frequency is achieved and valuable additional scientific data may be obtained at relatively little additional cost to the program. Sufficient evidence has been accumulated during many years of operation of the DOVAP* system at a frequency of about 75 mc/sec to show that refraction errors are not greater than about 0.05 mil and should not seriously affect operation of such systems as COTAR,† MINITRACK,† or EMA,† which depend only on the difference in signal path lengths and not directly on refraction effects.‡ This is one of the cogent reasons why continuous-wave, phase-difference systems are better suited to the satellite instrumentation problem than radar systems and others which do depend on the direction of arrival of the radio waves.

It is perhaps desirable to turn for a moment to the role instrumentation might play in the launching phase of a satellite firing. It is known that orbit lifetime is critically dependent on the velocity vector of the final propulsion stage; particularly on the vertical velocity component. Depending on the missile system used, it may be necessary to determine the vertical velocity component of the initial stages by direct measurement and provide for firing the final stage when the vertical velocity is within predetermined limits. It is entirely feasible to make such measurements with the required accuracy, provided doppler-type instrumentation is used in conjunction with an angle-measuring system of the MINITRACK or EMA type. An investigation of this instrumentation and

---

* DOppler Velocity And Position Instrumentation. A continuous-wave doppler system developed by Ballistic Research Laboratories for use at White Sands Proving Ground.

† Code names for phase-difference measuring systems being developed by Cubic Corporation, Naval Research Laboratory, and Ballistic Research Laboratories.

‡ Author's note: Theoretical investigations in progress at the time this paper goes to the publisher indicate that under certain conditions the sighting error due to differential refraction may be considerably larger than that experienced in DOVAP field operation.

data-reduction problem indicates that it should be quite practical to determine the velocity vector within 0.1 to 0.4 mil in real time. Serious consideration should perhaps be given to the use of this method of helping to assure successful launching.

The advisability of adhering to the philosophy of redundancy in observing methods and the desirability of relying only on techniques well within the limits of the current art cannot be too strongly emphasized. Systems with 100% reliability are not known today and new systems require months, and sometimes years, to "debug." The fact that several satellite vehicle systems will be readied is in itself recognition that failures will occur. So in the instrumentation system alternate methods of making critical measurements must be provided, wherever feasible, to guard against the possibility that the entire effort may be lost through the failure of relatively inexpensive instrumentation. "For want of a horseshoe nail the battle was lost."

The overall observing system must provide adequate coverage of each important phase of the program. To accomplish this, the following minimum array of systems is proposed. Optical instruments of four types, each carefully designed and engineered in accordance with accepted and proven methods, must be provided at a minimum of five different and widely separated geographical locations. An electronic tracking system of the hyperbolic type and a telemetering system, either combined or independent, must be employed and should be operated at a carrier frequency of 75 mc/sec. An appropriate stage of the mother missile configuration should carry a DOVAP transponder to permit ground-based observing stations to determine velocity vectors in real time through the use of an available special-purpose digital computer. Additional DOVAP receivers should be provided at each observing site to permit determination of ion concentrations as a function of altitude and lateral displacement. This complement of instrumentation systems will insure the best possible chance, consistent with cost, of successfully instrumenting the first satellite and will yield a worthwhile return on the investment.

It has been characteristic in programs of this type for instrumentation to receive insufficient emphasis; it has suffered from "too little, too late." If the satellite program is to measure up to expectations, it is imperative that instrumentation planning, and execution, should in no way be slighted. The types of systems and their characteristics must be selected with due regard for the lessons learned in ten years of test-range instrumentation experience. There is no substitute for such experience.

REFERENCE

1. L. G. deBey *et al. Scientific Objectives and Observing Methods for a Minimum Artificial Earth Satellite.* BRL Report 956, 1955.

7

Components for Instrumentation of Satellites

by H. K. Ziegler
SIGNAL CORPS ENGINEERING LABORATORIES,
FT. MONMOUTH, NEW JERSEY

ABSTRACT

The environmental conditions of satellite instrumentations
are reviewed. Present and predictable availability of suitable
chemical batteries, solar batteries, electron tubes, transistors,
and frequency-control devices is discussed. Special attention
is given to the comparison of power sources.

In the area of components for the instrumentation to be
carried by a satellite, the experience obtained from upper-atmosphere
rocketry will provide an extremely valuable design basis. The major
difference will be in the considerably prolonged period of operation of
the equipment. Numerous environmental factors which could be
neglected for the short time exposure of rocket flights require, therefore,
consideration for the design of satellite equipment; and, of course, power
requirements increase in proportion to operating time. It seems, however, that the majority of the new requirements can be satisfied by
additional protective measures and engineering techniques rather than
by the development of radically new components.

The environmental conditions during the satellite launching, very similar to those of high-altitude rocket launchings and the corresponding protective measures, are shown in Table I. As far as mechanical and

TABLE I

Instrumentation of satellites

Environmental Condition during Launching (Similar to Rocketry)	Protective Measures

Mechanical
  Acceleration
  Shock
  Vibration
  Spin
  Gravity Change
	Components Design (Mounting and Assembly Design)

Thermal
  Preflight Temperature
  Ambient Temperature
  Aerodynamic Heating
  Thermal Shock
	Components Design and Thermal Engineering of Assembly

Atmospheric Pressure Composition of Atmosphere (Humidity)	Components Design
Radiation Cosmic Rays through Infrared	Unnecessary for Short Time Exposures
Longer Electromagnetic Waves Magnetic Fields Electrostatic Fields	Shielding
Electrostatic Charge (Ionization, Charged Particles)	Usually Unnecessary (Compensable by Radio-active Means)

thermal conditions and changes in pressure and composition of the atmosphere are concerned, there is no doubt that inherent components design assisted by engineering methods in assembly and in thermal control will be the answer. It is most fortunate that the development in these areas has been particularly successful in recent years and that components are already at hand which satisfy most of the expected launching requirements. The other listed conditions such as radiation, magnetic and electrostatic fields, and electrostatic charge of the satellite, can be partly neglected or made ineffective by shielding methods. The compensation of the electrostatic charge, if required, by means of nuclear sources inside the satellite would be a rather complex problem.

The conditions for in-orbit operation are shown in Table II. In contrast to rocketry, the entire radiation spectrum from cosmic rays

TABLE II

Instrumentation of satellites

Environmental Conditions in Orbit	Protective Measures
Cosmic Rays Gamma Rays X-Rays	} Shielding
Ultraviolet Visible Spectrum Infrared	} Thermal Engineering of Satellite (Absorbing and Emitting Surfaces, Thermal Insulation of Interior)
Longer Electromagnetic Waves Magnetic { Design to Minimize Fields { Magnetic Braking of Spin Electrostatic Fields Micrometeorites	} Shielding
Meteorites Meteors	} No Protection
Atmospheric Pressure Composition of Atmosphere	} Components and Enclosures Design
Gravity Change or Loss	None (in General, No Problem)
Electrostatic Charge (Photoemission, Ionization of Atmosphere, Collision with Charged Particles)	} Compensable by Radio-active Sources, if Required (Complex)

through infrared and the hazards of the bombardment with particles of meteoric origin must be taken into account. The provision of protective shielding for the entire instrumentation assembly against the higher energy radiation and against meteoric particles appears more advisable than the development of individually protected components. The same philosophy applies to the consideration of the radiation in the thermal range where thermal over-all engineering of the satellite is expected to keep the operating temperature of components within reasonable limits. Although it is generally agreed that such temperature control can be achieved, the final thermal design of satellites will nevertheless represent a formidable engineering task. As far as shielding is concerned, weight limitations will determine the obtainable degree of protection or, in other words, the life expectancy of the instrumentation. With presently available satellite payloads, protection against cosmic rays and meteoric particles above the size of micrometeorites can hardly be provided. Fortunately, the probabilities of serious damage by these hazards are low. The remainder of the conditions listed in Table II are not much different from those discussed for the launching. The very low atmospheric pressure deserves increased consideration in components selection or design or in provision of suitable enclosures. The braking effect caused by the geomagnetic field upon the rotational motion of a metallic, enclosed, spinning satellite may require designs which avoid closed electrically conductive loops.

The status of availability of suitable components, as we see it within the Signal Corps Engineering Laboratories, is illustrated in Table III.

TABLE III

Instrumentation of satellites
Availability status of components

	Production Quantities Available	Laboratory Quantities Available	Development Required	Basic R&D Required
Power Sources				
Primary Batteries	X			
Storage Batteries	X			
Solar Devices		X	X	X
Nuclear Devices			X	X
Electronic Parts				
Capacitive Elements	X			
Inductive Elements (Coils, Trafos, Chockes)	X			
Resistive Elements	X			
Frequency Control Elements up to 125 mc/sec	X			
up to 200 mc/sec		X	X	
Electromechanical Elements	X			
Electron Devices				
Subminiature Tubes and Germanium Transistors up to 150 mc/sec		X	X	
Subminiature Tubes up to 300 mc/sec			X	
Germanium and Silicon Transistors up to 300 mc/sec			X	X
Shielding Material	X			
Thermal Engineering Material	X		X	X

In the power-sources field, production is available in primary and storage batteries. Laboratory quantities of solar devices are available, but further development of known systems and basic research and development to uncover possibly superior systems seem advisable. Nuclear power devices require further investigation.

The situation in the electronic-parts area is very gratifying. Production is available in all major parts. If frequency-control elements above 125 mc/sec should be required, some development work would be desirable, although laboratory quantities are available up to 200 mc/sec.

In the area of electron devices, low-filament-drain subminiature tubes as well as a transistor up to 150 mc/sec are available in laboratory quantities. Further development would be desirable for both devices. For frequencies up to 300 mc/sec, subminiature tubes would require further development and transistors call for further development as well as basic research.

Shielding materials are available. Thermal-engineering materials are available but research and development efforts should be directed toward suitable surfaces and coatings for thermal-radiation control in various parts of the spectrum.

So far this is the roughly outlined over-all picture regarding components for satellite instrumentation.

Some specific areas such as power sources, tubes, transistors, and frequency-control devices may deserve a more detailed discussion.

The success of the entire scientific satellite program will, to a large extent, depend on the selection of the most suitable power source for the operation of the instrumentation. One of the most crucial questions is whether performance-proven primary batteries are the only reliable source at present or whether the utilization of the so conveniently available solar energy is already above the status of a risky venture. There is no conclusive answer available, but it might be interesting to look at and compare the presently known facts.

The capacity in watt-hours/lb vs operating temperature is illustrated in Fig. 1 for several primary battery systems based on 350-hour discharge rates for 80% cut-off voltage. The zinc silver oxide alkaline system appears slightly superior in capacity per weight and in lower temperature operation than the mercury alkaline system (RM system). For temperatures above 70°F, both systems start to overlap and one can assume rather safely that in this range, with either battery type, at least 45 watt-hours/lb can be obtained. The decision on which of the two systems should be preferred may be influenced by other factors besides temperature. Zinc silver batteries can be activated immediately prior to operation; their volume-to-weight ratio is approximately 18 in.^{3}/lb. RM batteries are activated in production, and their volume-to-weight ratio is approximately 10 in.^{3}/lb. Neither system is yet designed for operation in extreme vacuum, but necessary modifications can be made.

For comparison, the Leclanche battery system of normal and special low-temperature design is included in the graph, illustrating that this system, with its lower capacity per weight, is not attractive for satellite applications.

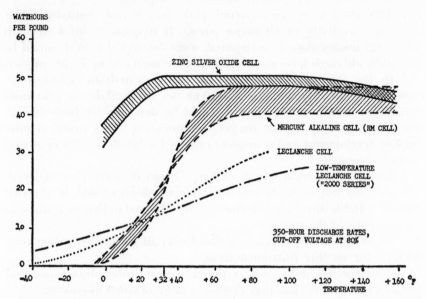

FIGURE 1.   Battery capacity per unit weight vs temperature.

The conditions which could be expected from solar power devices, based on the use of silicon photovoltaic cells as developed by Bell Telephone Laboratories, are briefly outlined in Fig. 2 and Table IV.

Corresponding to a solar constant of 2.0 cal/cm² min, the solar radiation in the satellite orbit will amount to 140 milliwatts/cm². Regarding the utilization of this energy offering, two different cases must be considered. Case A concerns a stabilized satellite on which the solar device is always oriented toward the sun, and Case B concerns an uncontrollably tumbling satellite which requires provision of additional solar devices to provide sufficient receiving area for any satellite position. The lowest-order polyhedron which offers low variation between maximum and minimum projection area is the equilateral tetrahedron. Four solar devices arranged at the corners of such a tetrahedron appear therefore to be a recommendable design and are used as a basis for the following computations. It is assumed that each of the four devices in Case B is equal in area to the one in Case A. For the most unfavorable orientation of the tetrahedron, the effective area would then be less than in Case A, but it can be assumed that some of the four cells receive also albedo-reflected energy in an amount to at least compensate for that deficiency. With a conversion efficiency of 8% for the silicon cells, which the Bell Telephone Laboratories believe can be guaranteed

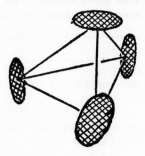

FIGURE 2. Instrumentation of Satellites.

Solar Power Devices:
1. *Solar-Radiation Density in Orbit:*
140 milliwatts/cm^2

Case A:
Stabilized satellite, solar device always oriented perpendicular to sun rays.

Case B:
Unstabilized, tumbling satellite, requires several solar devices. Figures below based on 4 devices arranged on an equilateral tetrahedron.

BTL silicon photovoltaic cell, 8% efficiency (below +80°C)
Power Output:

11.2 milliwatts/cm^2	> 2.8 milliwatts/cm^2
or	> 1 watt/360 cm^2
1 watt/90 cm^2	(total area of devices)

Estimated minimum weight: Existing laboratory model of BTL cell with 5–cm^2 effective area weighs approx. 10 grams.

180 grams/watt	720 grams/watt
or	
2.5 watts/lb	0.63 watt/lb

Load voltage per cell: approx. 0.33 v
Lowest current capacity per cell due to mechanical limitations: approx. 7 ma (0.2 cm^2)

Possible change in power output due to abrasive effects of micrometeorites on surface of solar device taken as 15%:

207 grams/watt	828 grams/watt
or	
2.19 watts/lb	0.55 watt/lb

already, these power-output figures would result: 11.2 milliwatts/cm^2 or 1 watt/90 cm^2 in Case A, and at least 2.8 milliwatts/cm^2 of total devices area or 1 watt/360 cm^2 in Case B.

TABLE IV

Instrumentation of satellites
Solar power devices (refer to Fig. 2)
Provision for power storage

	Case A	Case B
Estimated weight of systems adapted to energy storage (exclusive of weight of storage battery)	352 gm/watt or 1.3 watt/lb	1408 gm/watt or 0.32 watt/lb
Estimated total weight including solar device and NI-CAD storage battery	0.65 watt/lb	0.26 watt/lb

Notes: (a) A 70% increase in rating of solar device is provided due to the approximately 40-min of eclipsed orbit per revolution.

(b) 95% efficiency assumed for NI-CAD battery.

(c) Average weight of sealed NI-CAD battery for approximately 60-min charge and 40-min discharge is 1.3 watt/lb.

(d) Voltage per NI-CAD cell is 1.33 $V \pm 5\%$.

(e) Estimated battery life is 2000 charge-discharge cycles.

Laboratory models of solar devices, completely embedded in plastic material, are of a design which may be suitable for satellite applications. These units have a weight of approximately 10 gm/5 cm² effective area. Therefore, the weight relations can be estimated for Case A as 180 gm/watt or 2.5 watts/lb and for Case B as 720 gm/watt or 0.63 watt/lb.

The load voltage of these silicon devices is approximately 0.33 volt per cell. Due to mechanical and economical limitations, there seems to be no advantage in making the cell area smaller than approximately 0.2 cm², which corresponds to a lowest current rating of approximately 7 ma.

Great concern has been expressed regarding the possible loss of power of solar devices due to the expected sand-blasting effects on optical surfaces by micrometeorites. Although no valid simulation of actual operational conditions can be made at present, some crude experiments with frosted and sand-blasted plastic surfaces of solar devices might be of interest. Two representative tests of such surfaces resulted in power-output reductions of 11% and 25%. Based on micrometeorite data given several years ago by Dr. Whipple, one could expect that the complete frosting of a surface could take several thousand days. An estimate of 15% loss of power during the expected, much shorter satellite life appears reasonable and results in these figures: Case A, 207 gm/watt or 2.19 watts/lb, and Case B, 828 gm/watt or 0.55 watt/lb.

If power should be stored for the approximately 40 min of the eclipsed portion of a 100-min orbit, approximately 70% increase in power rating of the solar devices is necessary. This figure is based on 95% storage efficiency of available, sealed-type, nickel-cadmium batteries when utilized with only 10% of their storage capacity and charged during the approximately 60 min of the illuminated portion of the orbit. With this increase in rating, the figures change to: 352 gm/watt or 1.3 watts/lb in Case A, and 1408 gm/watt or 0.32 watt/lb in Case B. The weight of the storage battery for these conditions would be 1.3 watts/lb at a voltage of 1.33 v ± 5% per cell. A battery life of from 1500 to 2000 cycles is expected, after which the storage would cease but the solar device would continue to operate during the illuminated portions of the satellite orbit.

The capacity per unit weight of solar devices including storage batteries would then be 0.65 watt/lb in Case A and 0.26 watt/lb in Case B, with an operational life expectancy of at least 100 days.

The results of the preceding computations in comparison to primary battery data are more clearly illustrated in Fig. 3. The weight-vs-power drain is shown for 45-watt-hours/lb-type primary batteries for 100, 200, 300, and 500 hours of operation. The dash-dot line corresponds to the solar device exclusive of storage battery, and the heavy line includes the storage battery, both based on Case B. The position of the heavy line between the lines for 200 hours and 100 hours primary-battery operation would indicate that the discussed solar power sources will always be lower in weight than primary batteries, if the operational period exceeds approximately 180 hours. This is, however, not entirely correct since the previously mentioned minimum current rating limitation of 7 ma, resulting in approximately 3.6-ma load current limitation for a solar cell, causes deviations from the straight-line weight relation, depending on voltage and power requirements. (Considering a constant voltage of the solar cells, a 15% power reduction due to sand-blasting effects and the 70% power increase for energy storage reduces the 7-ma current rating limitation to 3.6 ma, as far as the actual equipment load current is concerned.) If we assume, for instance, 140 volts, the lowest rating for which a solar device can reasonably be designed will be 140 v × 3.6 ma or 0.5 watt. For any lower power requirement, the weight of the solar cells will not decrease further, although the weight of the associated storage battery, which has a lower minimum rating, will. This is indicated in Fig. 3 by the uppermost triangle. Similarly, the deviations from the straight-line relation are shown for 70 and 28 volts. It is evident that with higher voltages and lower power requirements, the region where the solar power source weighs less than the primary battery moves more and more toward longer periods of operation. (For very small power drains the minimum current limitations of primary and storage batteries would have to be considered too.) Since the power drain of the entire satellite instrumentation may be expected to be in the order of at least ½ watt and voltages will hardly be above 80 volts, solar power sources will in general weigh less than primary batteries for operational periods of more than 200 hours. For an oriented satellite (Case A), this figure would drop to approximately 75 hours.

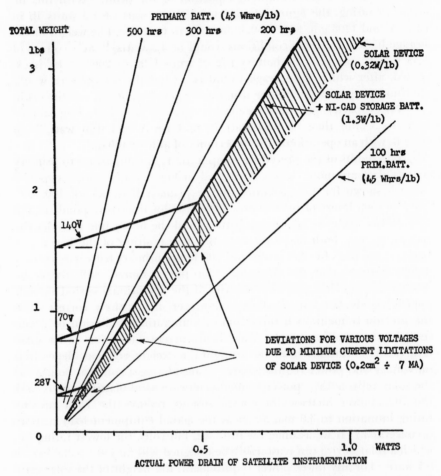

FIGURE 3. Weight relations between primary-battery power and solar power.

The weight conditions for solar power sources therefore would seem quite favorable, even for present-day satellite planning, if the other factors of uncertainty, such as influence of high-energy radiation, micro-meteorites, and temperature extremes of satellite surfaces upon the solar cells, could be finally clarified. There is little doubt that future highly instrumented and long-life satellites will have to rely on solar- or nuclear-type power sources. Serious work in this field therefore should be started as soon as possible.

Electron devices for telemetering transmitters of satellite instrumentation are another area of special interest. Table V lists the devices

TABLE V

Electron devices
(Up to 150 mc/sec)

Subminiature Tubes			
Tube No.	5971	5677	6611
Filament Voltage (v)	1.3–1.2	1.3–1.2	1.25
Filament Current (ma)	80	60	20
Plate Voltage (v)	70	80	70
Plate Current (ma)	1.3	1.9	1.3
Power Output (mw)	47	43	33
Plate Circuit Efficiency (%)	52	28	36.3
Over-all Efficiency (%)	24.6	19	28.4

Transistor PNP Type 2039 (Temperature Range: Below $+ 65°C$)	
Collector Voltage (v)	40–50
α	≈ 0.95
Cut-Off Frequency (mc/sec)	500
Efficiency (%)	25
Power Output (mw)	150

which are available in laboratory quantities within SCEL for operation up to 150 mc/sec.   There are three low-filament-drain subminiature tubes, 5971, 5677, and 6611, which were originally developed for other applications but have proven very satisfactory as high-frequency oscillators.   They are also mechanically extremely rigid, withstanding accelerations of 1000 g, especially if launched with cold filaments.   The minimum life expectancy has cautiously been quoted as 500 hours, but similar tungsten-filament tubes have exceeded 3000 hours in other modes of operation.   The pertinent operational data are listed in the table.

Also, one transistor of the PNP diffused-base type, No. 2039, is already available in laboratory quantities, and its further development is expected to proceed rapidly.   The mechanical rigidity, the lower operating voltage, the higher power rating, and the expected long life will render it eventually the preferred choice for satellite applications.

The most significant data of frequency-control elements as developed or under development at SCEL are listed in Table VI.   As mentioned, production is available up to 125 mc/sec and laboratory quantities are at hand up to 150 mc/sec.   These mechanical overtone devices are designed for a stability of 5 parts in 10^7 per week, if temperature is controlled to 0.01°C.   Stabilities for other temperature conditions are quoted in Column 3.   Frequency-control devices are expected to play an important part in present and future satellite instrumentation.

TABLE VI

Frequency-control devices

Type	Frequency Range	Stability over Temperature Range	Stability with Time (Constant Temperature within .01°C)	Space Required	Weight	Remarks
CR-54/U	50–100 mc/sec (up to 121.5)	±.005%–55°C to +90°C (±.0001% with 1° oven control)	0.5 ppm/week or 1 in 10^5/yr (ext. average)	2.7 cc	3.5 grams	Presently in production. Commercial equivalent in production at 121.5 mc.
CR-(Y)	100–150	±.005%–55°C to +90°C (±.0001% with 1° oven control)	0.5 ppm/week or 1 in 10^5/yr (ext. average)	2.7 cc	3.5 grams	In development—available within 2 years.
CR-(Y)	150–250	±.005%–55°C to +90°C (±.0001% with 1° oven control)	0.5 ppm/week or 1 in 10^5/yr (ext. average)	2.7 cc	3.5 grams	In development—available within 5 years.

In conclusion, it can be stated that the area of components for instrumentation of satellites is well advanced. Basically new components design will hardly be required. Further development, especially in the power-sources and electron-devices field, can be expected soon to clear the way for long-time operation of instrumentation in future long-life satellites.

8

Experiments for Measuring Temperature, Meteor Penetration, and Surface Erosion of a Satellite Vehicle

by Herman E. LaGow
U.S. NAVAL RESEARCH LABORATORY, WASHINGTON, D.C.

ABSTRACT

Satellite experimentation represents a tremendous step from rocket instrumentation. It offers obvious advantages in studying variations in physical quantities in time and latitude and perhaps even altitude. However, there are several evident disadvantages. The chief disadvantage is the limited payload. Not only does the instrumentation have to be two orders of magnitude lighter than rocket instruments, but it must last for from one to five orders of magnitude longer. This means that the instrumentation must be miniaturized to the limit. To do this reliably, one must know the environment in which the instrumentation is required to operate. Some of the environmental conditions can be estimated from theory and rocket soundings, but others must be evaluated from measurements on the satellite. Plans are described for measuring temperature extremes, surface erosion, and surface penetration.

A Satellite's Temperature

A satellite's temperature will be determined almost completely by radiations absorbed and reradiated because heat transfer at the low air densities, even at the high velocities, will be negligible and because internal power dissipation must be negligible due to payload restrictions. For example, a black body at 300°K radiates 40 milliwatts/cm²; while if all of the kinetic energy of the colliding molecules at 300 km was absorbed, the energy input averaged over the surface area would be only 0.01 milliwatt/cm². Internal power dissipation would be equivalent to

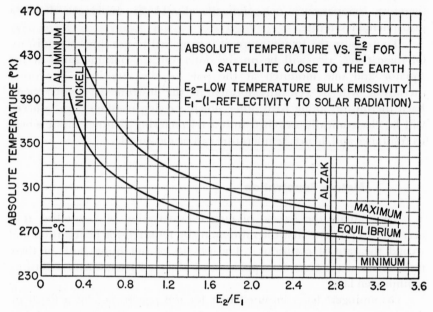

FIGURE 1.

0.08 milliwatt/cm², assuming that 4 lb of batteries would be used in 14 days in a 30-in. sphere. Radiant-energy sources are direct sunlight, reflected sunlight, and infrared radiations from the earth. By selecting a material with the proper emissivities in the infrared and the visible, it is possible, in theory, to adjust the temperature of the satellite. Fig. 1, due to Easton and LaGow, shows the temperatures to be expected for various emissivity ratios. The nighttime equilibrium temperature will be about −35°C, independent of the emissivity of the satellite. This results from the fact that it will be losing energy from approximately twice the area (assume spherical shape) on which it will be receiving energy. The daytime equilibrium temperature will depend rather sharply on the ratio of the emissivity in the infrared to that in the visible. If this ratio is 2, the equilibrium temperature will be 30°C, while if it is 1, the temperature will be 70°C. For most polished metals this ratio is one-half or less and the equilibrium daytime temperature will be 115°C or greater. However, the heat capacity of the body will prevent the satellite from reaching these extremes. If one assumes that the heat capacity is great enough to make the temperature change from darkness to daylight negligible, the average temperature can be readily computed. An emissivity ratio of 2 gives an average temperature of 10°C. A point that should be considered in connection with the temperature is the possibility that the surface emissivities will change due to the bombardment of photons, ions, molecules, atoms, and micrometeorites. Neither theory nor empirical results are available for estimating this effect; therefore, temperature measurements should be made on the first instrumented satellite.

To measure the temperature, it is proposed to use three thermistors. Of these three, two will be on the outer surface, one mounted at the equator and one mounted at the pole of the satellite. The other thermistor will be centrally located in the instrument compartment. Each thermistor, along with other slowly varying resistance transducers, will be electronically switched into a telemetering channel input where its resistance and, hence, temperature can be measured.

Meteor Penetration

To evaluate the hazard of meteor penetration of a satellite, it is necessary to estimate first the minimum size required for penetration and second the rate of collisions. The physics of obtaining both of these numbers involves gross extrapolation of observed phenomena according to unproven laws.

Grimminger[1] has computed that for the penetration of a 0.020 in. dural plate, a meteorite of magnitude 14, diameter 75 microns, and density 3.4 gm/cm^3 would be required. He derives a formula predicting that a meteorite will penetrate 6.5 to 7.0 of its diameters in dural for a velocity of 45 km/sec by assuming that the body penetrates as though the metal plate were perfectly deformable, like a fluid with a drag coefficient of 1 for high velocities. For velocities less than 5000 ft/sec he uses, with a slight extrapolation, an empirical formula for armor penetration. The number of meteorites entering the atmosphere per day has been estimated by a number of workers.[1,2,3,4] Visual observations for meteors of magnitude −3 down to 5 and radar observation down to 8th magnitude were used. The computed meteor rates vs magnitude for these observations are in agreement with each other. However, their extrapolation to the rate for magnitude 14 meteors gives about 1/1000 of the rate estimated by Van de Hulst as necessary to account for zodiacal light as being due to dust particles. Van de Hulst's rates are within an order of magnitude of Öpik's analysis of Petersson's work on the nickel content of sedimentation from the bottom of the ocean. Using the rates corresponding to visual observations, Grimminger computed the probability of meteorite hits on a satellite. According to his calculations, the time interval between hits on a 5-ft² surface (approximately 30-in.-diameter sphere) with meteorites large enough to penetrate would be 4300 days. Other ways to state these results are: (a) in 43 days the satellite would have a 100-to-1 chance of not being hit and (b) in 3000 days the satellite would have a chance of 0.5 of being penetrated. Using the flux predicted by zodiacal dust, one would estimate that penetration is likely within two weeks.

Because of the numerous uncertainties in arriving at the above figure, it appears worthwhile to measure the occurrence of punctures by measuring the leak rate of the sphere with a pressure gage (aneroid or switches). The more interesting geophysical experiment of counting the smaller micrometeorites with a microphone is being studied, but with probable payload limitations for the first satellite the opportunity to do this does not look favorable. Grimminger estimates that 1 to 2 collisions per second would result if particles of limiting magnitude 30 (diameter 0.5 micron with kinetic energy 2 ergs) were detected.

Surface Erosion

Bombardment of the surface of the satellite with photons, ions, molecules, atoms, and dust particles is a cause of erosion of the surface coating and windows of detectors. For example, ultraviolet radiation is known to deteriorate organic materials in paints, and ions are known to sputter metal surfaces. The erosion hazard cannot be evaluated because neither laboratory data for calculating collision effects at velocities of 8 km/sec nor geophysical data for estimating collision rates are available. Therefore, it is proposed to make direct erosion measurements by forming two resistive elements on the outside surface of the satellite. A circuit similar to that used for the thermistors will be used for observing the resistance as a function of time.

A combination of all of the above detectors will weigh one-fourth of a pound, exclusive of the telemetering.

REFERENCES

1. G. Grimminger, "Probability That a Meteorite Will Hit or Penetrate a Body Situated in the Vicinity of the Earth," *J. Ap. Phys., 19*: 947–956 (1948).

2. F. G. Watson. *Between the Planets.* Philadelphia: The Blakiston Co., 1941.
3. E. J. Öpik, "Astronomy and the Bottom of the Sea," *Irish Astron. J.,* April, 1955.
4. H. K. Kallmann, "Quantitative Estimate of Frequency and Mass Distribution of Dust Particles Causing the Zodiacal Light Effect," *Mém. Soc. Roy. Sci. Liège, 15:* 100–113 (1955).

9

Insolation of the Upper Atmosphere and of a Satellite

---

by P. R. Gast
GEOPHYSICS RESEARCH DIRECTORATE,
AIR FORCE CAMBRIDGE RESEARCH CENTER

ABSTRACT

The temperature of a satellite will be the resultant of the sum of radiations from three sources: directly from the sun, solar radiation returned from the atmosphere and the earth (both 6000°K radiation), and low-temperature (250°K) radiation from the earth. Assuming various characteristics for the model of the satellite (absorptivity of the surface, shape, mass, specific heat) and orbit trajectories (distance of perigee and apogee, duration of insolation, and duration in shadow of the earth), the ranges of maximum and minimum temperatures may be calculated. For one possible elliptical trajectory the mean temperatures for an 0.8-meter, 100-kg spherical satellite are not far from 0°C; as the satellite in its orbit passes from sunlight into the shadow of the earth, the temporary maximum temperatures in the sunlight range from 13° to 3°C and the temporary minimum temperatures in the shadow from −3° to 5°C. The highest maximum temperature is with the sun in line with the projected major axis and the illuminated satellite at a perigee of 300 miles, and the lowest minimum temperature with the sun in the same position and the satellite at an apogee of 1000 miles. Measurements of insolation freed from difficulties of atmospheric attenuation and measurements of the albedo of the earth will be possible from a satellite vehicle. But to achieve the required accuracy, rather precise knowledge of the orientation of detectors is essential. Hazards which are unique to the environment may be encountered in attempting measurements from a satellite—the effects of the vacuum ultraviolet irradiation and of accumulation of micrometeorites on surfaces of detectors or on the surfaces of windows, and on surfaces of the skin of the satellite.

For the measurement of several aspects of the insolation of the upper atmosphere—for instance, the probable variation in ultraviolet emitted by the sun—the satellite will have several advantages over rockets.

Possibly, however, it has not been noted that the temperature of the satellite, *per se*, will give approximate confirmation of current estimates of the intensities of insolation and low-temperature emission by the earth. The satellite would be heated by radiation received directly from the sun and also indirectly by reflection and scattering from atmosphere and terrestrial surface. To these is to be added the low-temperature energy emitted by the earth and the atmosphere together. All these data are important to geophysics. Deserving more detailed consideration, the low-temperature emission is discussed by Dr. King in another paper in this volume.

Should estimates of the intensities of these three sorts of radiation be seriously in error, the satellite may become too hot or too cold for the installed equipment to remain functional. Clearly, there is a reciprocal interest between more exact determination of insolation and the engineering design of the vehicle.

Some seem to expect that the satellite may become too hot if the absorptivity of the surface for radiant energy is "gray." The results of the following calculations indicate that it may become colder than desirable; to conserve the heat liberated by the electronic devices, it may be mandatory to insulate their enclosures and conduct some of the heat to the battery compartments.

Certainly some heating of the satellite will result from collision with whatever particles may be encountered in the orbit, even at the anticipated low densities of 10^{-7} to 10^{-10} mm Hg. It seems, however, that such heating is relatively small compared with the heating effect of the solar and earth irradiations. In the discussion to follow, aerodynamic heating by friction with low-density atmosphere has been neglected.

For a better understanding of the temperatures which may be expected, temperature calculations were completed for a variety of shapes, absorptivities, and conditions of irradiation. The shape of the satellite is important; so first a plate—an improbable shape, used for discussion only—was compared with a sphere. In the comparison of a plate with a sphere, the input (the total of the various irradiation intensities) and the

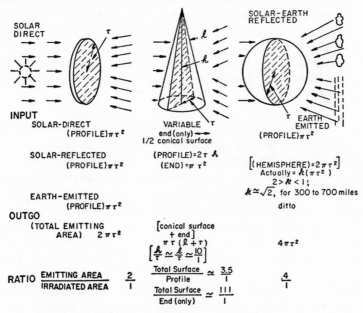

FIGURE 1. Vehicle geometry.

outgo (the emission) can be evaluated without using the absolute dimensions of the two kinds of objects.

Another likely shape for the satellite might be a cone. But in the absence of information on its orientation, including tumbling—which will determine the surface presented to radiant energy—it will only be mentioned. The plate and the sphere may be taken as the extremes in their ratios of the areas for radiation input and outgo. A cone might, on the average, present a ratio of areas for outgo and for input intermediate between plate and sphere. But the probabilities of changing aspect are too complex for succinct discussion. For convenience, the term "profile" —"irradiated profile" being understood—is used for "irradiated area," or "projected area." (See Fig. 1.)

In considering the plate (radius τ) the flat surface is taken as always normal to the line from sun to earth. Its profile is $\pi\tau^2$, its emissive area is $2\pi\tau^2$. For a sphere (radius τ) irradiated by the distant sun, the profile will again be $\pi\tau^2$, but the emissive area will be $4\pi\tau^2$. For the other two sorts of irradiation—the solar reflected and earth emitted—the system, earth-plus-atmosphere, is the virtual source for both. It is therefore necessary to consider the curved surface of a sphere as receiving radiation from an extensive diffusing plane.

Some altitude must be assumed as the mean height from which the reflected solar radiation and the low-temperature radiation are emitted. Probably no serious error would be made in preliminary calculations of the irradiation of the satellite by taking the altitude of these virtual sources as zero. But, so that the discussion may be meticulous, the effective altitude for the reflected radiation is taken as 5 miles above the earth, and the effective altitude for the low-temperature emission as 20 miles above the earth. These values would not be adamantly defended against opinions that they are too high. If they are too large, the heating effect of the irradiation from the earth is overestimated.

The solar constant has been taken as 2.00 gm cal cm^{-2} min^{-1} (1.396 $\times$ 10^6 ergs cm^{-2} sec^{-1}), recognizing that it may be in error by 2%, but reasonably closer to 2.00 than to the Smithsonian value of 1.94, which is 3% lower. The solar temperature approximates 6000°K; this is important because it establishes the spectral distribution of the insolation. The solar constant is by definition the radiation incident on the upper atmosphere at mean earth-sun distance; actually, the intensity will vary $\pm$3.4% through the year, increasing in December at perihelion to about 2.07 gm cal cm^{-2} min^{-1}, and decreasing in June at aphelion to about 1.93.

Another value which is used with some misgiving is the estimate of the albedo of the earth. For preliminary calculations a single value will be used. For more accurate appraisal of the temperature of the satellite, the dynamically varying reflection and emission beneath the satellite must be deduced from climatological information. To repeat, the data required for an accurate engineering design will result from observations best made from the satellite. An albedo of 36% has been used; others may rationalize a somewhat different value.

The apparent brightness (B_r) of radiation (high temperature, 6000°K) reflected and scattered from the insolated hemisphere of the earth will be

$$\pi B_r \times 2\pi R_r^2 = SC \times A \times \pi R_r^2 \tag{1}$$

where R_r is the radius of the effective reflecting hemisphere, equal to 3960 miles plus 5 miles; SC is E_d, the solar constant, equal to 2.00 gm cal cm^{-2} min^{-1}; A, albedo is 0.36.

Thus,

$$\pi B_r = 0.36 \text{ gm cal cm}^{-2} \text{min}^{-1}. \tag{2}$$

The apparent emission (B_ϵ) by the earth of low-temperature (250°K) radiation diffusely emitted from the entire surface will be

$$\pi B_\epsilon \times 4\pi R_\epsilon^2 = SC \times (1 - A) \times \pi R_\epsilon^2 \tag{3}$$

where R_ϵ is the radius of the emitting sphere, equal to 3960 plus 20 miles; SC is the solar constant; $(1 - A)$ is used because all energy not reflected must ultimately be emitted as infrared radiation by the system, earth-atmosphere—this follows since the average temperature of the system apparently has not changed over the last several millenniums.

Thus,

$$\pi B_\epsilon = 0.32 \text{ gm cal cm}^{-2} \text{ min}^{-1}. \tag{4}$$

To calculate the heating effect on a plate, the values of B_r and B_ϵ are used. The irradiation on a plate by reflection (E_r) or by earth emission (E_ϵ) when the object is at height (h) will be

$$E_r = \pi B_r \frac{R_r^2}{(h+r)^2} \pi \tau^2 \tag{5}$$

$$E_\epsilon = \pi B_\epsilon \frac{R_\epsilon^2}{(h+r)^2} \pi \tau^2 \tag{6}$$

where r is the radius of the earth and τ the radius of the plate.

In the case of the sphere, at heights less than several thousands of miles from the earth,

$$E_r = \pi B_r \, 2 \left(1 - \frac{[(h+r)^2 - R_r^2]^{1/2}}{(h+r)} \right) \pi \tau^2 \tag{7}$$

$$E_\epsilon = \pi B_\epsilon \, 2 \left(1 - \frac{[(h+r)^2 - R_\epsilon^2]^{1/2}}{(h+r)} \right) \pi \tau^2 \tag{8}$$

where τ is the radius of the sphere.

From these are calculated the inputs shown in Table I for several different heights above the earth from 200 to 2000 miles and respectively appropriate for a plate and for a sphere—both with a "profile" equal to $\pi \tau^2$.

It is noted that the "totals" are the inputs while in sunlight, but when the sun is eclipsed by the earth the irradiation by earth emission will be the only input.

After indefinitely long exposures, the plate or the sphere will reach an equilibrium temperature $T°K$ (Kelvin) at which input and outgo are equal. That is,

$$g T^4 = \frac{E_d + E_r + E_\epsilon}{81.35 \times 10^{-12}}, \, g = \begin{cases} 2 \text{ for plate} \\ 4 \text{ for sphere} \end{cases} \tag{9}$$

where E_d, E_r, and E_ϵ are, as above, solar direct, solar reflected, and earth emitted, respectively, and the values both for the power per unit area and the Stefan-Boltzmann constant are in gm cal cm^{-2} min^{-1}.

But another factor must be considered: that of the absorptivity of the surface of the satellite. For example, contrast a gray surface with a

TABLE I

Input energies on plate or sphere at different heights above earth

Input Sources	200 Plate	200 Sphere	300 Plate	300 Sphere	350 Plate	350 Sphere	700 Plate	700 Sphere	1000 Plate	1000 Sphere	2000 Plate	2000 Sphere
	Input divided by πr^2, gm cal cm^{-2} min^{-1}											
Solar Direct	2.00	2.00	2.00	2.00	2.00	2.00	2.00	2.00	2.00	2.00	2.00	2.00
Solar Reflected	0.32_7	0.50_2	0.31_2	0.45_6	0.30_5	0.43_8	0.26_1	0.34_2	0.23_0	0.28_7	0.15_9	0.18_2
Earth Emitted*	0.29_3	0.45_4	0.27_9	0.41_2	0.27_3	0.39_4	0.23_3	0.30_7	0.20_6	0.25_8	0.14_3	0.16_4
Total	2.62_0	2.95_6	2.59_1	2.86_8	2.57_8	2.83_2	2.49_4	2.64_9	2.43_6	2.54_5	2.30_2	2.34_6

Header: Height, miles

* While satellite is in eclipse shadow, the earth-emitted energy will be only input.

selectively absorbing surface such as magnesium oxide. The gray surface would be uniformly absorbing (= emitting) from wavelengths $0.2\,\mu$ to $25\,\mu$. The MgO surface would be reflecting in the visible and near infrared but absorb the far infrared; the coefficient of absorptivity for 6000°K radiation would be 0.08, but 0.8 for 250°K radiation.[*] This latter would be the temperature of the system earth-atmosphere emitting $\pi R_e^2(1 - 0.36) \times 2.00$ gm cal cm^{-2} min^{-1}.

In Table II are the equilibrium temperatures, under continuous irradiation, of the several cases: (1) various altitudes, $h = 300$, 350, and

TABLE II

Equilibrium temperatures for *constantly* *irradiated* satellites

At different altitudes; either irradiated by sunlight, or in earth's shadow; gray surface vs magnesium oxide surface; plate vs sphere.

	Altitude, Miles					
	300		350		700	
	Plate	Sphere	Plate	Sphere	Plate	Sphere
			Degrees Centigrade			
Fully Illuminated						
Solar direct plus solar reflected plus earth emission						
Gray Surface	82	33	82	33	79	27
MgO Surface	−36	−61	−37	−63	−42	−71
In Earth's Shadow						
Receives earth emission only						
Gray Surface	−69	−84	−71	−86	−78	−98
MgO Surface	−69	−84	−71	−86	−78	−98

700 miles, (2) plate and sphere contrasted, (3) gray or MgO surface compared, and (4) with the objects either continuously irradiated by direct and reflected solar energy together with the radiation emitted by the earth or by the latter only. The last case represents the equilibrium temperature when the object remains indefinitely in the eclipse shadow of the earth.

Inspection of Table II shows that the absorptivity of the surface of the satellite is more important than shape in determining the balance between heat income and outgo. The sphere and the plate have the

---

[*] It should be remarked that for refined engineering calculations it probably will be necessary to use for the absorptivity of the skin of the vehicle and for the irradiance intensities the summation of values for relatively narrow bandwidths, rather than the gross values for 0.2 to 25 microns as taken here.

same irradiated profile, the sphere has twice as much emitting surface as
the plate, yet the contrasts between effects of different surface absorptivities is greater than the contrasts between effects of different shapes.

We may assume that the absorptivity of the surface of the satellite
will be carefully studied. Other chapters of this book consider the effects

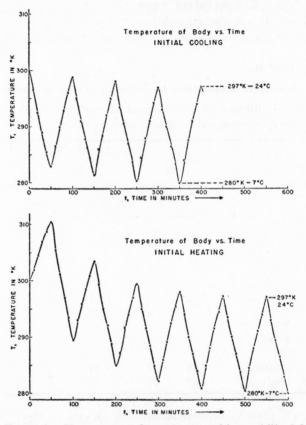

FIGURE 2.   Temperature changes approaching stabilized fluctuations.

of vacuum ultraviolet and of the impact of micrometeorites on materials.
Can we assume that the initial surface will remain constant in its
spectral absorptivity?

In the preceding I have used calculations by Mr. Marden H. Seavey;
some of the following I owe to Mr. Robert M. Slavin and Lt. C. Nealon
Stark of this Directorate.

The satellite in orbit will not be continuously illuminated by the
sun nor continuously shaded. Its temperature will vary cyclically as in
Fig. 2, which was derived by plotting the increase or decrease in temperature of a special object in a special orbit during 10-min intervals.

In thinking about the temperature of a satellite some definite orbit must be used. One possible orbit would be an ellipse with perigee 300 miles, apogee 1000 miles, period 106 min. The relative lengths of time while illuminated and while shaded are as in Table III. In Table IV,

TABLE III

Time spent by a satellite in sun and in eclipse shadow in elliptical orbit; compared with circular orbit

Condition	Illuminated Minutes	Shaded Minutes		Total Period Minutes
Case I				
Illuminated at perigee, 300 miles; shaded at apogee, 1000 miles.	73.2	32.8	31%	106.0
Case III				
Illuminated at apogee, 1000 miles; shaded at perigee, 300 miles.	69.0	37.0	35%	106.0
Cases II and IV				
Illuminated at right angles to axis: perigee-apogee (300–1000 miles).	70.8	35.2	33%	106.0
Circular orbit, constant 300 miles.	58.4	35.8	38%	94.2
Circular orbit, constant 400 miles.	62.4	35.1	36%	97.5

three cases are distinguished: Case I, the satellite is in the sun at perigee and in the shade at apogee; Case III, the satellite is in the sun at apogee and in the shade at perigee; Cases II and IV, the irradiation by the sun is at right angles to the major axis from perigee to apogee. (See Fig. 3, which shows the relative illuminated or shaded conditions for the three cases.)

To arrive at estimates of the likely temperatures of a spherical satellite, values for the dimensions of the input and outgo areas, the weight, and the thermal capacity must be used. The heat flow through the mass of the vehicle is supposed to be unimpeded; the heat conductivity approximates that of copper or silver.

Assume a sphere of 80-cm (31.5 in.) diameter; average specific gravity 0.38 (23.5 lb/ft³) for a mass of 100 kg (220 lb). (The equivalent "cross-sectional loading" is about ten times that proposed for the Vanguard satellite; it is in the lower range of the volume loading of the instrument nose of rockets, 20 to 40 lb/ft³.)   For thermal capacity (or "specific heat") we use 0.1 gm cal gm⁻¹/°C.   The absorptivity (= emissivity) is gray, 0.25, that is, uniform at 25% throughout the spectrum from $0.2\,\mu$ to $25\,\mu$.

The dynamic change in irradiation as the distance between satellite and earth varies is ignored in the calculations.   Instead, it is assumed that the value of the irradiation at perigee or apogee may be taken from Table I as appropriate to the altitude of the satellite for the illuminated

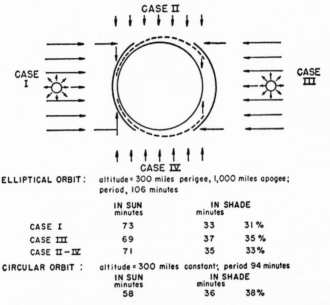

ELLIPTICAL ORBIT:	altitude = 300 miles perigee, 1,000 miles apogee; period, 106 minutes		
	IN SUN minutes	IN SHADE minutes	
CASE I	73	33	31%
CASE III	69	37	35%
CASE II–IV	71	35	33%
CIRCULAR ORBIT :	altitude = 300 miles constant; period 94 minutes		
	IN SUN minutes	IN SHADE minutes	
	58	36	38%

FIGURE 3.   Periods in sun and in shadow in orbit (see Table III).

or shaded periods shown in Table III.   The flux is taken as constant for that part of the whole period while the object is either in sunlight or in eclipse.

From Table IV and Fig. 4 it is seen that, according to the complementary lengths of time that the object is in sunlight or in eclipse, the mean temperatures and the amplitudes of the rise and fall of temperatures between the maxima and minima differ.   In Table IV are given the data for a perigee of 300 miles.   With due regard for all the indeterminate estimates it was necessary to use, it would appear that in the absence of an internal source of heat approximating 10 watts or more, in a satellite with the size and other characteristics as assumed, there would be the danger of critically low temperatures.   This will appear from the sections of Table IV in which the temperatures are shown with inputs of internal heat of 1 watt, 10 watts, and 100 watts.

TABLE IV

Temperatures of a satellite for various periods of irradiation (in sun and in eclipse) in an orbit of 300 miles at perigee and 1000 miles at apogee

Sphere, diameter 80 cm; mass 100 kilograms; thermal capacity 0.1 cal gm^{-1} per °C.   Absorptivity (gray) = 0.25.   Period 106.04 minutes.

Condition	Time in Shade	Mean Temperature	Amplitude	Minimum Temperature	Maximum Temperature
		No Internal Heat			
Case I					
Perigee in sun	31%	282°K	7.4°K	13°C	5°C
Case III					
Apogee in sun	35%	273°K	6.4°K	3°C	−3°C
Cases II and IV Illuminated at right angles to major axis	33%	280°K	7.7°K	11°C	3°C
		1 Watt Internal Heat			
Case I		Same as *no* internal heat			
Case III		Same as *no* internal heat			
Cases II and IV		Same as *no* internal heat			
		10 Watts Internal Heat			
Case I		286°K	7.4°K	17°C	9°C
Case III		277°K	6.4°K	7°C	1°C
Cases II and IV		284°K	7.7°K	15°C	7°C
		100 Watts Internal Heat			
Case I		315°K	7.4°K	46°C	38°C
Case III		308°K	6.5°K	38°C	37°C
Cases II and IV		314°K	7.6°K	45°C	37°C

If current estimates of the insolation of the upper atmosphere are to be improved, the measurements of the solar constant must be accurate to at least 1.5%, and preferably 0.7% or better. It is obvious that a very high standard of radiation measurements is required. The angle between sun and surface of thermal detector, the calibration of its sensitivity, and especially the correction for its temperature coefficient must be known quite accurately; the requirements for accuracy of these last two items approach the limits possible under the best laboratory conditions. Clearly, a "stabilized" platform for orientation of detector toward the

sun is necessary.   Looking earthward, the instrumental accuracy required
is less stringent.   But the knowledge of cloud cover and the terrain will
be important for discriminating interpretation of the synoptic albedo
and the radiation balance in the atmosphere.

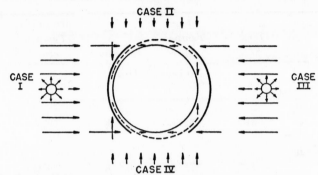

ELLIPTICAL ORBIT :
    altitude = 300 mi. perigee, 1,000 mi. apogee; period, 106 minutes
VEHICLE : sphere, diameter 0.8 meter
    <u>no</u> internal heat ; absorptivity (gray) 0.25; mass 100 kg. spec. heat
    0.1 cal gm⁻¹ per 1°C

	MEAN	RANGE amplitude	MAXIMUM	MINIMUM
		TEMPERATURES		
CASE I	9°C	7.4°C	13°C	5°C
CASE III	0°C	6.4°C	3°C	-3°C
CASE II – IV	7°C	7.7°C	11°C	3°C

FIGURE 4.   Temperature data in orbit.

As indicated at the beginning, the average temperature and the
fluctuations of temperature of the shell of the satellite and of various
points in the interior will in themselves be informative.   But should the
signals from the satellite eventually be lost, one possible cause might be
the influence of unfavorable temperature effects on the equipment.   In
such an event, the values used for insolation, for albedo, and for the
absorptivity of the skin might well be re-examined with the help of
information obtained while signals were still being received from the
devices installed for measuring radiative flux.

Satellite Drag and Air-Density Measurements

by L. M. Jones and F. L. Bartman
ENGINEERING RESEARCH INSTITUTE AND
DEPARTMENT OF AERONAUTICAL ENGINEERING,
UNIVERSITY OF MICHIGAN, ANN ARBOR

ABSTRACT

The problems of obtaining density values at satellite altitudes from drag measurements on the satellite are discussed. Tracking measurements alone will yield only average densities over many orbits. In the final high-drag phase, the distance over which the density average is taken will be somewhat less but will be at lower altitudes. Instantaneous measurements of drag with an accelerometer will permit synoptic measurements of density or improve the precision of average density measurements. Results early in the life of the satellite will be possible, thus increasing the probability of obtaining results.

A 5-lb, 5-ft-diameter inflated sphere is proposed. It would carry an improved version of the transit-time accelerometer used in Michigan sphere-drop density experiments. The required improvement in accelerometer performance and such problems as inflation, active satellite life, and ground stations are discussed.

Introduction

The calculation of air density from the measured drag of a satellite is one of the more frequently suggested uses of the vehicle. Inasmuch as we at Michigan have been engaged in obtaining upper-air-density values from sphere drag measurements, it is of quite some interest to us to consider whether or not the techniques developed can be applied to the satellite.

Rocket Experiments for Drag and Density

In our first experiments, inflated nylon spheres 4 ft in diameter and weighing 20 lb were dropped from Aerobees and tracked by DOVAP (doppler velocity and position). Velocity and acceleration were obtained from the DOVAP position data by differentiation and used in the equation of motion of the falling sphere to obtain air density. The equation can be written as

$$\vec{F_D} = m\left(\vec{g} - \frac{\vec{dv}}{dt}\right) = \frac{\rho A C_D}{2}|\vec{V}|\vec{V}$$

where $\vec{F_D}$ = drag force

m = sphere mass

$\vec{g}$ = acceleration of gravity

$\dfrac{\vec{dv}}{dt}$ = total sphere acceleration

ρ = density

$\vec{V}$ = velocity

C_D = coefficient of drag

A = sphere cross-sectional area.

In a later experiment a transit-time accelerometer was placed in a rigid 7-in. sphere so that drag acceleration might be measured directly. Velocity was obtained by integrating the resultant acceleration of drag and gravity, with a correction for horizontal velocity as measured by radar.

The features of these experiments which are of significance to the satellite are: (1) the use of inflated spheres to obtain a large drag-to-weight ratio and (2) the use of an accelerometer (as against tracking) to obtain drag acceleration.

The value of inflated spheres is apparent. With very little increase in weight, the drag force on a given piece of instrumentation can be increased a hundred times with consequent increase in the range of density which can be measured. The engineering problems of an inflated-sphere satellite will be discussed later.

The value of using an accelerometer for measuring drag may be seen by comparing the probable errors in the measurement of acceleration in the sphere experiment. In the case of the big spheres with DOVAP, the statistical probable error of the average acceleration over a half-second interval under nearly free fall conditions was ± 1.7 ft/sec^2. In the case of the accelerometer, it was $\pm 32 \times 10^{-4}$ ft/sec^2, a factor of improvement of about 500. The increased precision of the accelerometer enabled us to use the much smaller spheres as well as to extend the altitude range of density measurements.

Satellite Drag from Tracking

In a recent Ballistics Research Laboratories report[1] a phase system for satellite tracking is proposed. Following the BRL method it can be shown that the probable error in measuring the total energy of a 5-lb, 5-ft-diameter sphere in a circular orbit of 220 miles altitude is 1.4×10^4 ft-lb. Thus, 14×10^4 ft-lb of energy change can be measured with a probable error of 10%. At 220 miles altitude, with the densities of Fig. 1, such an energy change would be experienced in 15.5 orbits. See Figs. 2 and 3. Considering the effect of the oblateness of the earth, orbital eccentricity, and the latitude variation of vehicles launched at points not lying on the equator, it can be seen that a density derived from tracking during the period of stable orbiting will be a one-day average over enormous orbital distances and appreciable vertical distances. If the orbit is quite elliptical, the region of drag will be concentrated around the perigee. However, the number of orbits required to make a measurement will be about the same and the perigee drag regions will move about geographically in the same manner as circular orbits. In order to reduce the averaging to one orbit (circular), the satellite must be orbiting at about 146 miles, and in order to reduce the averaging to one horizon-to-horizon traverse, it must be orbiting at 112 miles. Below this region the drag acceleration will come within the "instantaneous" measuring capabilities of a tracking system and increase to the point of destroying the vehicle. If this phase occurs beyond the range of a tracking station, densities will not be obtained.

Fig. 4 shows the probable errors in densities calculated from tracking measurements, based on the errors in the proposed BRL system.

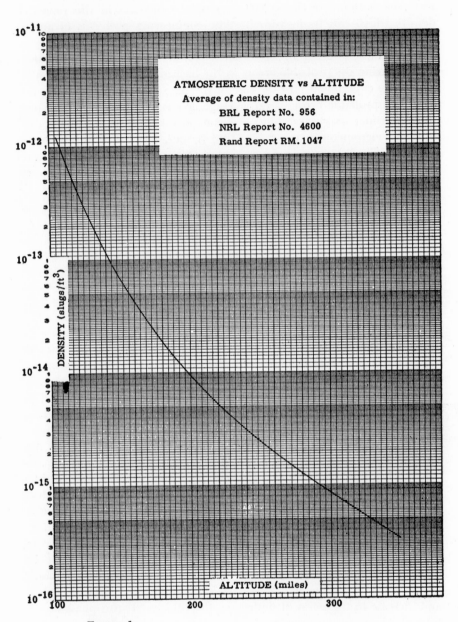

ATMOSPHERIC DENSITY vs ALTITUDE
Average of density data contained in:
BRL Report No. 956
NRL Report No. 4600
Rand Report RM. 1047

DENSITY (slugs/ft³)

ALTITUDE (miles)

FIGURE 1.

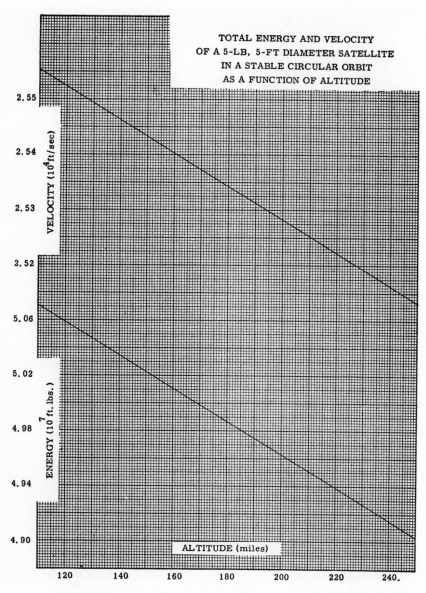

FIGURE 2.

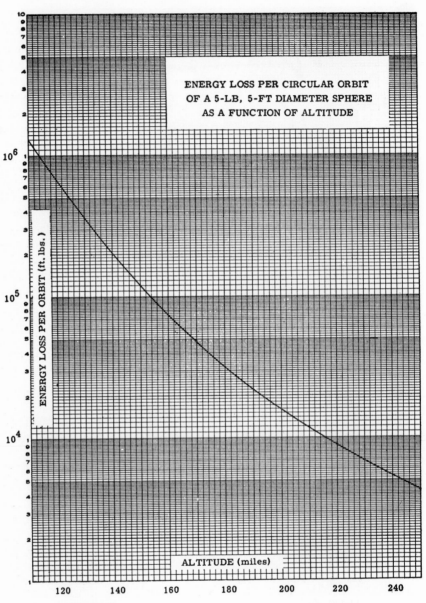

Figure 3.

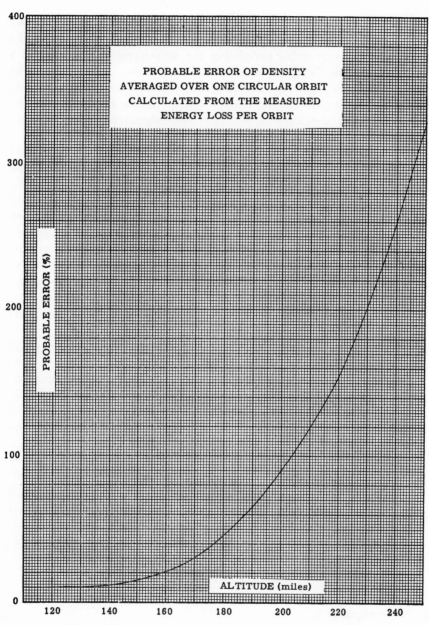

PROBABLE ERROR OF DENSITY
AVERAGED OVER ONE CIRCULAR ORBIT
CALCULATED FROM THE MEASURED
ENERGY LOSS PER ORBIT

FIGURE 4.

A Satellite for Direct Measurement of Drag

It follows that the instantaneous measurement of drag acceleration added to the velocity and position data from tracking would have the tremendous advantage of permitting the measurement of density as a function of time, latitude, longitude, and altitude. Lesser advantages would be the improvement in the accuracy of average density measurements and the measurement of densities early in the life of the satellite before batteries or equipment failed or before the satellite was shot down by a meteor.

The satellite we propose for making such measurements has the same specifications used in the discussion above: 5 lb and 5 ft in diameter. It is a combination of the two kinds of spheres used in our work heretofore; that is, we propose to use a 7-in.-diameter rigid sphere as the instrumentation center containing accelerometer, intervalometer, batteries, antenna, inflation gas, etc. The inner sphere is carefully balanced to put the center of the accelerometer mass on the center of rotation (CG). The outer sphere is of lightweight construction. It is centered with respect to the inner sphere by strings and is inherently balanced and light enough so as not to disturb the over-all CG. In the final high-drag part of the flight the outer sphere will burn off but the inner sphere might permit further density measurements to lower altitudes.

A successful flight for density measurements might be one which orbited for a day, during which time it would be acquired and tracked for position and velocity. Thus precise instantaneous density measurements would be obtained in a situation in which they could not be obtained by optical and/or electronic tracking methods alone. If orbital-position predictions were quickly available, the simple telemeter ground station could be flown to various places for synoptic measurements.

Inasmuch as the velocity and position data from tracking are required in addition to acceleration data, provision will have to be made to carry a tracking beacon, unless a purely optical tracking system is devised. This tracking beacon would also serve as the telemeter transmitter.

Problems of Design and Operation

The Accelerometer

Figs. 5 and 6 illustrate the accelerometer. A mechanical caging arrangement periodically centers the bobbin within a cavity which is the same distance from the bobbin in any direction. The transit time of the

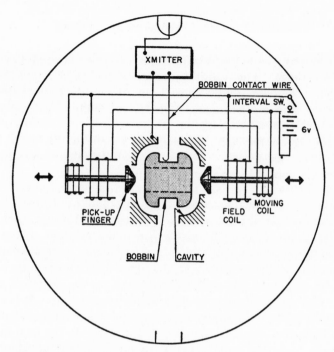

FIGURE 5. Accelerometer schematic.

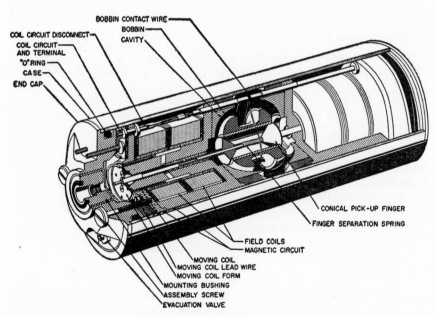

FIGURE 6. Transit-time accelerometer.

bobbin from the instant of release to the instant of contact with the cavity is a function of the drag acceleration. There is no theoretical limit to the magnitude of accelerations which may be measured under ideal conditions. However, several factors must be considered in extending the low range. The transit distance and time must be made reasonably short. The bobbin must be well centered on the CG of the satellite to minimize spin accelerations. Finally, the bobbin must be released with negligible initial velocity.

The drag on the 5-lb, 5-ft-diameter sphere at 230 miles is 32×10^{-5} ft/sec^2. See Fig. 7. To make acceleration measurements at a point with a probable error of 10%, the accelerometer must measure $(32 \pm 3.2) \times 10^{-5}$ ft/sec^2. See Fig. 8. Since it is now capable of measuring $(32 \pm .32) \times 10^{-2}$ ft/sec^2, the sensitivity and accuracy must be improved by 10^3 and 10^2, respectively. There is no inherent limit to the sensitivity, so the problem is that of reducing errors by a factor of 100. The error figure given is based on actual calibrations at 32×10^{-2} ft/sec^2. However, in a flight test accelerations of 15×10^{-2} ft/sec^2 were measured with no increase in scatter. It is also interesting to note that in laboratory calibrations the probable error was $\pm 1\%$ at both 32 ft/sec^2 and 32×10^{-2} ft/sec^2. Thus the accelerometer as now built may be capable of making the desired measurement. However, we do not know this to be the case and, consequently, have calculated the upper limits of the improvements required in the various factors which contribute errors in order to reduce each by a factor of 100.

TABLE I

Design changes to extend accelerometer range

From $(32 \pm .32) \times 10^{-2}$ ft/sec^2 to $(32 \pm 3.2) \times 10^{-5}$ ft/sec^2

	$(32 \pm .32) \times 10^{-2}$ ft/sec^2	$(32 \pm 3.2) \times 10^{-5}$ ft/sec^2
Transit distance, in.	$.188 \pm .002$	$.050 \pm .005$
Transit time, sec	$.312 \pm .002$	$5.09 \pm .26$
Initial velocity of bobbin on release, in./sec	.006	.001
Bobbin centering, in. (for 10-sec spin period)	.1	.001
Bobbin centering, in. (for 1-sec spin period)	.001	.00001

The errors shown in transit distances and times, the initial velocities, and the tolerances in bobbin centering are those which would alone cause all the errors in acceleration shown. The design limits for the improved performance are not excessive, except in the case of centering for a 1-sec spin period. A 1-sec spin period is quite short, however, and a longer one may be hoped for. Also, since vector spin accelerations add

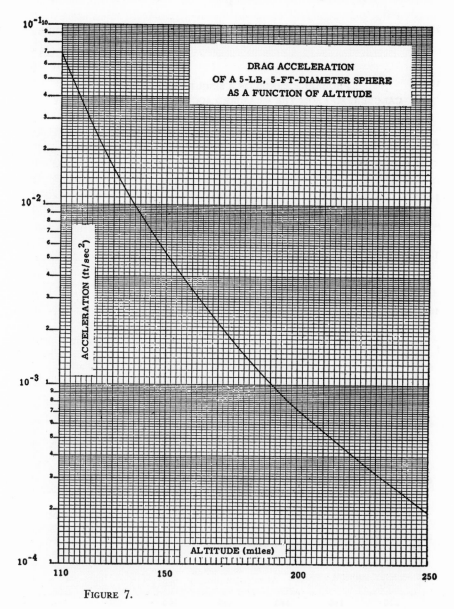

FIGURE 7.

more or less randomly to the drag accelerations, an average of several measurements will reduce the probable error. There will be problems in checking the accelerometer at the low accelerations, and these techniques have not been worked out. It appears that an over-all check at

3.2×10^{-4} ft/sec² will be difficult, but that it may be possible to check initial velocity and errors in time and distance separately.

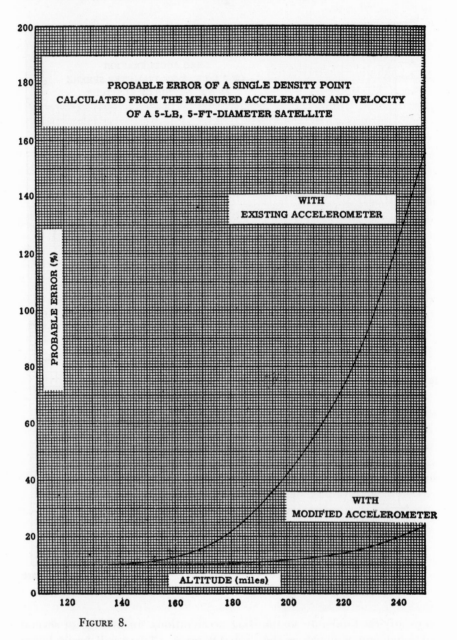

FIGURE 8.

The above discussion concerns the performance required to make instantaneous measurements of drag on a 5-lb, 5-ft sphere orbiting at

230 miles. It is interesting to note that the present accelerometer in the same sphere is now capable of measuring drag to $\pm 10\%$ at 135 miles and to $\pm 1\%$ at 95 miles.

Operating Life, Batteries

Undoubtedly, transistorized components will be developed for satellite use and the electronics of the sphere experiment is capable of being developed in this direction. A first step in transistorization would be a command receiver capable of turning on and off battery-operated equipment. Such a receiver, which would certainly have application to other satellite experiments, would extend the life of the sphere experiment about 18 times. Without such command operation and with the components and batteries we are now using, we can get about 500 individual density measurements. If we take 5 points at a time for a statistical average, we will have 100 such groups. If the groups are spaced 5 min apart to insure getting at least one set per orbit at one ground station, we will get data for nearly 5 orbits. The number of data received would in this case be increased by increasing the number of ground stations. On the other hand, with a command receiver the entire 100 groups of data points could be received and spread over a considerable time, during which time the ground station could be moved.

Radiated Power

The first small-sphere experiment was operated c-w at 0.6-watt output from the antenna. Since the information is basically pulse position, the experiment is suitable for pulse-position modulation and the development of a pulse-position transmitter putting out 50-watt pulses is well along. This should be adequate for horizon reception. Pulse operation also solves the B-battery problem to the extent that the A-batteries determine the life of the experiment. Most of the A-battery load is now the accelerometer caging mechanism which is designed to operate up to 162 ft/sec^2. Since no such accelerations will be encountered in the satellite, the load on the A-batteries could be reduced.

The Inflated Sphere

The inflated sphere might be constructed of polyethylene. It is desirable that it be as light and simple as possible so as not to affect seriously the CG of the combination and to make easier the achievement of a leak-proof envelope. A 5-ft sphere of 1-mil polyethylene would weigh 0.4 lb. The inner sphere, which contains all the operating apparatus, would be placed inside through a slit and attached to the centering strings. The outer sphere would then be heat sealed tight. No access ports would be required. The inflation air would be contained in the inner sphere. A pressure of 1 atm in the inner sphere would inflate the outer sphere to a pressure of about ½ mm Hg. Since the outer pressure and drag forces are practically zero, only enough pressure is required to overcome the stiffness of the material. Various techniques for preventing collapse of a punctured outer envelope can be imagined:

    1) Many inflated inner cells
    2) Umbrella-type frame
    3) Self-sealing envelope
    4) Foamed-plastic interior.

Three methods of ejecting spheres from rockets have been tried, two of which were completely successful. The ejection of the proposed satellite poses no special problem. In the recent small-sphere flights, the entire metal protective nose cone, ejection mechanism, and sphere weighed 30 lb and was 8 in. in diameter. Similar weight and size are certainly possible for the satellite device.

Coefficient of Drag

The aerodynamic characteristics of spheres in the molecular-flow region are not completely known. The coefficient of drag is usually given as 2 and the error is in percent rather than order of magnitude.[2] Outgassing of the sphere envelope may affect the C_D and this will be investigated. A leak-free envelope will shortly become degassed since the pumping conditions are ideal. Whatever uncertainties attach to C_D because of outgassing or other cause apply, of course, to any satellite on which drag measurements are tried by any method.

Conclusions

In summary it may be said that density measurements with a satellite will be greatly improved by the addition of nearly instantaneous acceleration data to the tracking data. Although current equipment has not been used in the desired range of measurement, it appears that a simple combination of proven techniques together with a reasonable extension of accelerometer performance will do the job.

REFERENCES

1. L. G. deBey *et al.* *Scientific Objectives and Observing Methods for a Minimum Artificial Earth Satellite.* BRL Report 956, 1955.
2. S. F. Hoerner. *Aerodynamic Drag.* Published by author, 1951.

On the Determination of Air Density from a Satellite

by Lyman Spitzer, Jr.
PRINCETON UNIVERSITY OBSERVATORY

ABSTRACT

Methods are analyzed for determining upper-air densities by means of a satellite, either by measures of the orbit or by measures of the change in orientation of a suitably designed vehicle. The orbital method gives enormous accuracy for the air density at perigee altitude, but fluctuations of perigee density with time may prevent accurate density determinations at heights much above the perigee altitude. If a satellite is designed so that its center of pressure is far from its center of mass, measures of the change in orientation with time can, in principle, determine air densities much less than the probable density of 4×10^{-15} gm/cm^3 at 300-km height. For a spinning satellite of about the weight and size planned for the IGY, a measurement of the precession rate by means of photocells observing the sun and the earth would permit measuring air densities as low as 10^{-16} gm/cm^3, after eddy currents produced by the earth's magnetic field increased the spin period to about 100 sec.

A primary purpose of the IGY satellite is the determination of the air density, ρ, at great heights. Observational evidence on ρ, summarized by the Rocket Panel,[1] is reliable up to about 100 km ($\rho \approx 10^{-9}$ gm cm^{-3}) and becomes increasingly uncertain up to about 200 km ($\rho \approx 2 \times 10^{-13}$ gm cm^{-3}). Above about 200 km there are no direct determinations of air density or pressure, and ρ must be computed from an assumed temperature and molecular weight. Extensive computations of this type have been carried through by Kallmann[2] and others, but lack of definite information concerning the temperature makes the results uncertain.

Evidence on the temperature of the outer atmosphere has been summarized by Bates[3,4] and Spitzer.[5] There is some indirect observational evidence for a temperature of some 1500°K at about 700 km and above. However, so high a temperature is difficult to account for theoretically—see Bates[4]—and the mean temperature at these great heights may be more nearly 500°, with much higher temperatures perhaps occurring in occasional bursts. The corresponding scale height is thus uncertain over the range from 18 to 95 km, if uncertainty concerning dissociation of N_2 is added to the uncertainty concerning the temperature. With the lowest scale height, ρ is about 7×10^{-16} gm/cm^3 at 300 km, and 3×10^{-18} gm/cm^3 at 400 km (if ρ at 200 km is set equal to 2×10^{-13} gm/cm^3). With the highest scale height, ρ is 6×10^{-14} and 2×10^{-14} gm/cm^3 at these two levels. Thus at 300 km, the projected perigee altitude of the IGY satellite, the air density is clearly uncertain by a factor of one hundred, and perhaps by an even greater factor.

These results are admittedly extreme. On the one hand, the temperature is not likely to rise abruptly to 1500°K, and all the N_2 to dissociate, at about 200 km. On the other hand, the lower value for ρ at 300 km corresponds to a particle density of about 2×10^7 cm^{-3}, only twenty times the electron density observed at this height; it seems unlikely that the fractional ionization in the F2-layer is as great as 5%, although even a higher fractional ionization cannot be entirely excluded at present. We shall adopt here as the "probable" density at 300 km the value 4×10^{-15} gm/cm^3, which is intermediate between the two determinations above, and about the value found by Kallmann.[2] We see that this estimate might be in error by about an order of magnitude either way. Since the lifetime of a satellite is inversely proportional to the atmospheric density, it is evident that these uncertainties are of great practical importance in the satellite program.

The present paper discusses various possible methods of evaluating the atmospheric density. Section I considers the determination of density by observations of the satellite's orbit. Section II proposes a different method for determining the air density, by measuring the change of spatial orientation of a suitably designed satellite vehicle, with the center of pressure far from the center of mass.

I. Density from Satellite Orbit

The retarding force, F, on a satellite, moving with velocity v through a gas of density ρ is readily shown to be

$$F = \rho A v^2 \tag{1}$$

where A is the projected area of the satellite on a plane perpendicular to the direction of motion; we use cgs units throughout. Equation (1) is based on the following assumptions: (a) that v is large compared to the random molecular speeds; (b) that the mean free path is large compared to the satellite dimensions; and (c) that the molecules, after striking the solid surface, do not carry away any net momentum relative to the satellite. Assumption (a) is clearly satisfied, since v is about 8 km/sec, while the root mean square random thermal velocity of a nitrogen atom, in one dimension, at 1000°K is 0.8 km/sec. Assumption (b) is fully satisfied, since according to the Rocket Panel[1] the mean free path even at 200 km is 0.3 km. Assumption (c) is valid in a wide variety of situations.

The general problem to be considered is the accuracy with which ρ can be determined from orbital observations. We treat first a circular orbit, postponing until later the effect of ellipticity.

For a body in a circular orbit, a retarding force produces, as is well known, a spiraling of the body in toward the central mass. The change of energy during one revolution is given by

$$\Delta W = -2\pi r F = -2\pi r A \rho v^2 \tag{2}$$

provided ΔW is sufficiently small so that the orbital radius, r, and the velocity, v, do not change appreciably during one revolution. For a satellite of mass M, the total energy, W, equals $-\tfrac{1}{2}Mv^2$, and $\Delta P/P$, the relative change in period in one revolution, is given by

$$\frac{\Delta P}{P} = \frac{3}{2}\frac{\Delta W}{|W|} = \frac{6\pi r A \rho}{M}. \tag{3}$$

For a satellite with M equal to 10^4 gm, and A equal to 3×10^3 cm^2, and at a height of 300 km, r is 6.8×10^8 cm; $\Delta P/P$ ranges from 2.7×10^{-6} for the lowest density to 2.3×10^{-4} at the highest density. The lifetime of the satellite is about the time required for r to decrease about a scale height, or about 40 km, corresponding to a relative change of about 6×10^{-3} in r, or about 10^{-2} in P. Thus the lifetime of such a satellite at 300 km may be expected to range from about 40 revolutions to as much as 4000 revolutions, or from about 3 days to a year. Corresponding to the "probable" value of 4×10^{-15} gm/cm^3 adopted above for ρ, $\Delta P/P$ in a single revolution is 1.7×10^{-5}, and the life is 800 revolutions, or about 50 days.

Let us suppose that the time of meridian passage of a satellite may be measured with a probable error t_1. If p such observations are made during an interval of n revolutions, the mean period during this interval is known with a probable error equal very roughly to $t_1/np^{1/2}$. For radio observations, p may be set equal to n, since one observation every revolution may be anticipated. If t_1 is 0.1 sec, then in 10 revolutions, P is known to about 0.003 sec, or an accuracy of about one part in 10^6. Since P will change by one part in 10^2 during the satellite lifetime, such measures could yield the mean density, during the satellite lifetime, with an accuracy of one part in 10^4. This accuracy is much greater than is needed, and in any case for such a precise determination the effects neglected in equation (1) would have to be taken into account.

High accuracy is required, however, for determination of density fluctuations in the upper atmosphere. Over an interval of 10 revolutions the probable relative change of period is 1.7×10^{-4}, and a measurement of P with a relative accuracy of 10^{-6} will determine the mean density during a period of 10 revolutions with an accuracy of a few percent. Density fluctuations between one such interval and a subsequent one can readily be measured. However, fluctuations from one period to the next cannot be measured if the time error t_1 is as great as 0.1 sec and if ρ is no greater than 4×10^{-15} gm cm^{-3}.

For optical observations t_1 is presumably much less than for radio measures. With t_1 equal to 0.01 sec, in one revolution the relative accuracy in P is about 2×10^{-6}. Since we have already seen that the probable relative change in P per revolution is about 2×10^{-5}, density fluctuations of more than 10% from one revolution to the next can be measured in this way. Slower density fluctuations can be measured even more precisely. Evidently, such measures would provide vastly more accurate information on the variability of atmospheric density than has been obtained hitherto at rocket altitudes.

Turning next to elliptical orbits, we see that these provide, in principle, the possibility of measuring atmospheric densities at much greater heights than that at perigee. Two methods of obtaining information are possible. Firstly, one may examine the perturbation of the orbit during a single revolution. Secondly, one may look for cumulative changes in the orbital elements, just as in the circular orbit use may be made of the progressive change of P.

The first method is unpromising, since the perturbations are so small. With the probable atmospheric density of 4×10^{-15} gm/cm^2 at 300 km, a satellite at this height, moving with the circular velocity of 7.7 km/sec, experiences a retarding force of only 2.4×10^{-3} dynes/cm^2. For a hypothetical satellite with A/M equal to 0.3 cm^2/gm, the acceleration is 7×10^{-4} cm^2/sec. Such an acceleration, assumed to extend over 1200 sec, or about one-fourth the period of revolution, produces a displacement of only about 5 meters, or a displacement of 3 sec of arc if the satellite is 300 km above the earth's surface. Photographic astrometry is probably capable of this accuracy, even for an object with such a rapid angular motion as the projected satellite. However, at the much lower densities to be expected at greater altitudes, the displacement is probably too small to measure with any accuracy.

We turn, then, to an investigation of cumulative changes in the orbital elements. The motion of a body subject both to an inverse-square force and to a resisting medium is a classical problem in celestial mechanics. It is well known that the only elements showing any cumulative changes are the semi-major axis, a, and the eccentricity, e. According to Moulton,[6] the rate of change of these elements is given by

$$\frac{da}{dt} = \frac{P}{\pi} \left\{ \frac{1 + e^2 + 2e \cos \theta}{1 - e^2} \right\}^{1/2} \frac{F(v)}{M} \tag{4}$$

$$\frac{de}{dt} = \frac{P}{\pi a} \left\{ \frac{1 - e^2}{1 + e^2 + 2e \cos \theta} \right\}^{1/2} (\cos \theta + e) \frac{F(v)}{M} \tag{5}$$

where θ is the geocentric position angle of the body in its orbit, as measured from apogee, and F is the force, given by equation (1).

Even if the apogee is some 700 km farther from earth than is perigee, the eccentricity is only 0.05. Under such conditions, v is nearly constant over the orbit, and the dominant variation of da/dt and de/dt throughout the orbit arises from the variation of atmospheric density, ρ, with height. To the lowest order in e we then obtain for Δa and Δe, the changes during one revolution,

$$\Delta a = - \frac{P^2 A^2 v^2}{2\pi^2 M} \int_{h=h_1-b}^{h=h_1+b} \frac{\rho(h)\, dh}{\{b^2 - (h - h_1)^2\}^{1/2}} \tag{6}$$

$$\Delta e = - \frac{P^2 A^2 v^2}{2\pi^2 a M} \int_{h=h_1-b}^{h=h_1+b} \frac{h_1 - h}{b} \frac{\rho(h)\, dh}{\{b^2 - (h - h_1)^2\}^{1/2}} \tag{7}$$

where h_1 is the mean satellite altitude, with $h_1 - b$ and $h_1 + b$ the altitudes at perigee and apogee, respectively. Evidently

$$b = e(r_0 + h_1) = ea \tag{8}$$

where r_0 is the radius of the earth. If $\rho(h)$ varies exponentially, with a scale height H, the two integrals in equations (6) and (7) become $\rho(h_1) I_0 (b/H)$ and $\rho(h_1) I_1 (b/H)$, respectively, where I_0 and I_1 are the familiar Bessel functions of imaginary argument.

One conclusion is immediately evident from the equations. If $\rho(h)$ changes so rapidly over the region of integration that only values of h

close to $h_1 - b$ contribute to the integral, then in equation (7) $(h_1 - h)/b$ may be set equal to unity and Δe becomes equal to $\Delta a/a$. From equation (8) it follows that Δb is approximately equal to Δa, which, in turn, equals Δh_1. Hence, $h_1 - b$, the altitude at perigee, remains constant under these conditions, while $2b$, the difference in altitude between perigee and apogee, steadily decreases. The perigee altitude remains nearly constant until the integral in equation (7) begins to differ appreciably from that in equation (6); i.e., until the difference in altitude between perigee and apogee ($2b$) becomes comparable with the scale height. This result has been derived previously by Davis, Whipple, and Zirker,[7] using a somewhat different set of equations.

In principle, a sufficiently accurate determination of Δa and Δe in successive revolutions should make it possible to determine $\rho(h)$ at all altitudes between perigee and apogee. In practice, observational uncertainties and, in particular, possible variations of $\rho(h)$ with time will limit the distance above perigee at which such a density determination is possible. If the density fluctuates by 10% from time to time, it may be difficult to measure ρ at those heights where it is less than one-tenth of the perigee value. A number of satellite flights would be needed to disentangle effects of density fluctuations from effects produced by the change of average density with altitude.

II. Density from Satellite Orientation

Evidently it would be desirable to measure atmospheric density in a more direct manner than by orbital observations. In principle, a much more sensitive method would be to measure the change of orientation produced by the air drag on a satellite whose center of mass did not coincide with the center of pressure. To illustrate the principle of the method, we consider a dumbbell-shaped satellite, composed of two spheres separated by a distance d. Let one sphere contain nine-tenths of the mass M. Let the other, lighter sphere contain a mass $0.1M$. Each sphere is assumed to have the same cross-sectional area A. If the dumbbell is set in motion initially without rotation, but with its axis of symmetry transverse to the direction of motion, the air drag will produce a displacement of the lighter sphere relative to the heavier one, resulting in a net rotation. Let us assume that a measurable rotation is 0.1 radian, or about $6°$, corresponding to a displacement of 10 cm, for d equal to 100 cm. It may be noted that with conventional photocells the orientation with respect to the sun may be measured* with an accuracy of about $3°$. In computing the displacement the air drag on the heavier sphere

---

* I am indebted to Dr. John P. Hagen of the Naval Research Laboratory for this estimate.

can be neglected, in view of its greater mass. If A and M have the same values assumed above (3×10^3 cm^2 and 10^4 gm) and v is 8×10^5 cm/sec, an angular deflection of 0.1 radian would be produced in 20 min, about one-fourth the orbital period, by an air density of 10^{-17} gm/cm^3, corresponding to a particle density of less than 10^6 atoms/cm^3. For comparison, we have already noted that the mean of the estimated densities at 300 km is about 4×10^{-15} gm/cm^3. Thus we see that with this method the air density can, in principle, be measured down to values several orders of magnitude smaller than the probable value at perigee. A satellite of the assumed A/M, moving in a circular orbit through air of density 10^{-17} gm/cm^3, would have a life of about 50 years.

It may be noted that the "critical level," at which the mean free path of an air molecule equals the scale height, is found where the particle density is about 3×10^7 gm/cm^3—see Spitzer.[5] Above this level lies the exosphere, in which the air molecules move essentially without collision, and in which the density distribution is that of an isothermal gas. Hence, if the kinetic temperature and atmospheric composition are known at the critical level, the density can be computed accurately at all greater heights. Evidently, orientation measures can, in principle, determine ρ well above the critical level.

One practical difficulty with this method of determining air drag is its dynamic complexity. On passage through denser layers the satellite will be given considerable rotational momentum, and analysis of the rotational motion to yield the accelerating forces is an intricate task. Moreover, the accuracy will decrease if the satellite is rotating with appreciable angular velocity. To achieve the greatest sensitivity, the lighter sphere might be replaced by a vane, which would be folded back during launching and which would be opened up only as the satellite approached apogee.

Another possible modification of this general method would be to set the dumbbell in rotation about its axis of symmetry. This rotational speed would then be essentially constant, and the air drag would produce a precession which could then be measured and simply interpreted. We analyze the accuracy obtainable with the scheme.

The angular rate of precession, Ω, under a torque L, is given by the familiar equation

$$\Omega = \frac{L}{I\omega} \tag{9}$$

where I is the moment of inertia about the axis of symmetry and ω is the angular rate of rotation about this axis. The torque may be set equal to the force on a cross-sectional area A, multiplied by the distance, d, of this cross section from the center of mass. The moment of inertia, I, may be set equal to Mr_g^2, where r_g is the effective radius of gyration.

For a solid sphere, r_g is 0.632 times the radius; for the assumed value of A, the radius is about 30 cm, and we shall set r_g equal to 20 cm. For M, A, and v equal to 10^4 gm, 3×10^3 cm^2, and 8×10^5 cm sec^{-1}, as before, and for d equal to 100 cm, we obtain

$$\Omega = 4.8 \times 10^{10} \frac{\rho}{\omega} \text{ rad/sec.} \tag{10}$$

If we require a total precession of 0.1 radian in 20 min, Ω must equal 8.3×10^{-5} sec^{-1}. For a rotational period of 100 sec, corresponding to ω equal to 6.3×10^{-2} sec^{-1}, which may be as low a value as is consistent with the requirement that ω must exceed Ω throughout the orbit, equation (10) indicates that the minimum measurable Ω will be reached for an air density of 1.1×10^{-16} gm/cm^3, an order of magnitude greater than the limiting value found above, but still less by a factor of 40 than the probable density at 300 km.

The sensitivity of the method could be increased in two ways. In the first place, the accuracy of orientation measures could be increased, though it is uncertain whether such an increase could be consistent with the payload limitations of the IGY satellite. In the second place, the torque could be much increased, either by increasing A, the deflecting area, or d, the distance from the deflecting area to the center of mass. Increasing A would have the disadvantage that the life of the satellite would be correspondingly reduced. However, greater sensitivity is primarily desirable if the air density turns out to be relatively low, in which case the satellite life will be long enough so that a substantial shortening of the life would not be serious. Increasing d substantially would not shorten the life, but would pose difficult structural problems.

For appreciable accuracy with a convenient size, the rotational period must be relatively long. Fortunately, eddy currents in the earth's magnetic field will automatically slow down the rate of rotation until such long spin periods are attained. Calculations by the Naval Research Laboratory group, which has pointed out the importance of this effect, indicate that the rotational period will double in about a day for the aluminum-walled sphere envisaged for the IGY program.* A somewhat slower rate of retardation is probably desirable and can obviously be achieved by appropriate use of laminations, nonconducting walls, etc.

Let us now consider some of the problems involved in such an observational program. It is evident that for this technique to be applicable, the rate of change of satellite orientation must be measured over a time interval of some 10 to 20 min. A longer time of measurement is not needed, owing to variations in altitude and, hence, in density during a longer period. A satellite at a 300-km altitude will be above the hori-

---

* I am indebted to Dr. Homer E. Newell, Jr., for this information.

zon for about 10 min, and measures may be telemetered during this time to a single observing station. Moreover, this method is most useful if the vehicle is at apogee, at a greater altitude than 300 km. Since the time above the horizon varies linearly with the altitude, it is evident that observations received at a single observing station would probably provide the needed accuracy.

Finally, we may consider very briefly how the axial orientation of the satellite may be measured. The most accurate method is to use observations made within the satellite itself. The NRL group has developed a system for determining the orientation by means of photo-electric observations. This system, described by Chubb, Friedman, and Kupperian,[8] utilizes a wide-angle photocell to observe the sun, and a narrow-beam photocell to observe the light reflected from the earth. With this system, a probable error of about 3° can most likely be achieved in absolute orientation of the satellite spin axis. While this is probably the simplest, most effective method, other possibilities should be mentioned. With a suitably designed transmitting antenna, measurement of the intensity of the radio signal from the spinning satellite would determine the angle between the satellite spin axis and the line to the ground station. A magnetometer might also give useful information. If many successive determinations of the precession rate, Ω, were made, solar observations alone, or radio intensity measures alone, might be adequate, as the remaining uncertainties in orientation could be assumed random and averaged out in the analysis of the data.

One additional method of determining the orientation should be mentioned. In principle, the orientation of a purely passive spinning satellite may be determined by optical observations from the ground. Suppose, for example, that the satellite is in the form of a cylinder with hemispherical ends, and suppose that the hemisphere and one side of the cylinder are painted uniformly white, while the other side of the cylinder is painted black. The amplitude of fluctuation of the sunlight scattered from the satellite, and received at a ground station, will clearly depend on the orientation of the vehicle, and measurement of this relative amplitude will provide information on the orientation. With intermediate conical sections painted alternately black and white in 90° segments, the received light signal will contain also a first overtone of the fundamental spin frequency. Measurement of the relative intensities of the steady component, the fundamental, and the first overtone would, in principle, determine the orientation of the spin axis in space. These measurements could be made with a recording photocell on the end of a guided telescope. Considerable subsequent analysis would be required to determine the orientation of the spin axis from the known position of the sun and the relative intensities of the three signals.

While this optical method of measuring the orientation has the great advantage of simplifying the satellite, it suffers from severe disadvantages. In the first place, it requires a spin sufficiently rapid so that the relative intensities of the three signals—the constant one, the fundamental, and the first overtone—do not change appreciably during a single spin period. This requirement would seem to rule out any possibility of a period 100 sec long, if this method were to be used, and may even rule out a period as long as 10 sec. In the second place, the method is insensitive if the satellite is nearly between the sun and the ground station. As a result, the time available for this type of measurement is short, and from one station an orientation can be found at only one instant of time. Another station a few thousand miles away would be required to give Ω.

Since the IGY satellite is planned to include telemetering equipment in any case, and since internal measures of orientation are probably at least as accurate as the optical measures from the ground and can be obtained both more frequently and with fewer stations, we may infer that primary emphasis in any such program should probably be placed on the telemetered information.

In conclusion, it appears that orientation measures provide a sound method for determining atmospheric densities at heights far above perigee, provided that the satellite can be launched in a suitably elliptical orbit.

REFERENCES

1. Rocket Panel, "Pressures, Densities, and Temperatures in the Upper Atmosphere," *Phys. Rev., 88:* 1027–1032 (1952).
2. H. Kallmann. *Project RAND Research Memorandum* No. 1047, 1953.
3. D. R. Bates, "The Earth's Upper Atmosphere," *Mon. Not. Roy. Astron. Soc., 109:* 215–245 (1949).
4. D. R. Bates, "The Temperature of the Upper Atmosphere," *Proc. Phys. Soc., B64:* 805–821 (1951).
5. L. Spitzer, Jr. *The Atmospheres of the Earth and Planets.* Chicago: Univ. of Chicago Press, 1949, Chapter VII.
6. F. R. Moulton. *An Introduction to Celestial Mechanics.* New York: The Macmillan Co., 1902, p. 291.
7. R. J. Davis, F. L. Whipple, and J. B. Zirker, Chap. 1 of this volume.
8. T. A. Chubb, H. Friedman, and J. Kupperian, Chap. 17 of this volume.

Pressure and Density Measurements Through Partial Pressures of Atmospheric Components at Minimum Satellite Altitudes

by H. S. Sicinski, N. W. Spencer, and R. L. Boggess
ENGINEERING RESEARCH INSTITUTE,
UNIVERSITY OF MICHIGAN, ANN ARBOR

ABSTRACT

Pressure and density measurements made from a satellite at altitudes of 400 to 900 km are expected to range from 10^{-10} to 10^{-8} mm Hg and 10^6 to 10^8 particles/cm^3. These measurements are initially complicated by the lack of knowledge concerning the gas-composition at these altitudes. Data from ionization-type pressure gages would provide ambiguous results since the responses of these devices vary with the nature of the gas. Until the time when the composition is better known, a measure of the partial pressure of the components will be a more useful approach to defining this region. Knowledge of the composition, density, and pressure can be had simultaneously through the use of a device which, in principle, is a modified "Omegatron" or "Synchrometer" as described by Hipple, Sommer, and Thomas. This device in its later forms is simple in structure and operation, being capable of high sensitivity similar to the conventional ionization gages. Unlike the conventional ion gage, which ceases to function as a pressure gage below 10^{-8} mm Hg, the modified "Synchrometer" continues operation into the range of 10^{-10} mm Hg. The principle of operation is similar to a cyclotron. A small beam of ionizing particles is passed parallel to a magnetic field, causing local ionizations along the beam. These ions are then accelerated by the alternating potential between two parallel plates. As in the cyclotron, when the r-f frequency is equal to eH/M, the ions of mass M and charge e are accelerated in orbits of increasing size and eventually strike an ion collector. If the ionizing beam is kept constant in value along with the electric and magnetic fields, the ion-collector current is a measure of the partial pressure of the gas of this charge-to-mass ratio. A lightweight instrumentation is possible through the use of "tuned gages" having permanent magnets for their magnetic field. This approach reduces the complexity of scanning and its associated field measurements and provides partial pressure for one component. Additional weight reduction follows from the replacement of the filament with a photosensitive source of ionizing radiation. This feature with its dependence on sunlight should serve to separate the ionized population from the unionized, in addition to providing the opportunity to study the earth's atmosphere in the presence and absence of sunlight. (The research reported in this document has been made possible through support and sponsorship extended by the Geophysics Research Division of the Air Force Cambridge Center, under Contract No. AF 19[604]-545.)

Environment for Pressure and Density Measurements

The environment for a satellite about the earth having an elliptical orbit with a perigee of from 300 to 800 km is somewhat speculative; thus an examination of the many possible models will only demonstrate the lack of knowledge concerning this region. The model shown in Fig. 1 is as reasonable as any for the purpose of establishing the orders of magnitude for the composition, particle density, pressure, and temperature. The assumptions fundamental to this model are: (1) temperature distribution with altitude above 100 km is taken with a slope of $4°$K/km; (2) oxygen dissociation starts at the 94-km level and (3) is essentially 100% at the 100-km level, the dissociation increasing linearly. With such assumptions, the region of perigee will expose the instrumentation to pressures in the range $10^{-10} \leq P \leq 10^{-8}$ mm Hg (see

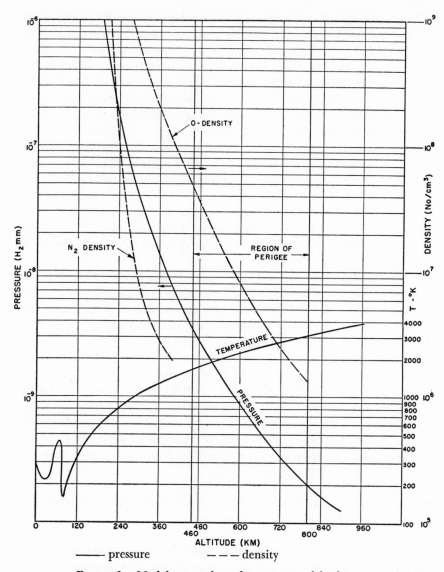

FIGURE 1. Model atmosphere for extreme altitudes.

Fig. 1), temperatures in the range $1500 \leq T \leq 3000°K$, particle density (no./cm³) in the range $10^{+5} \leq \rho \leq 10^8$, and a varying composition of ionized and neutral particles.

Discussion

Pressure measurements made on a minimal-altitude satellite are expected to be of the range $10^{-10} \leq P \leq 10^{-8}$ mm Hg. There are at least three devices which will produce pressure data electrically in this range: (1) the Bayard-Alpert gage,[1] (2) the modified Bayard-Alpert gage developed by W. B. Nottingham,[2] and (3) the mass spectrometer. Both (1) and (2) are modifications in ion-gage configurations such that it is possible to reduce the low-pressure limit of an ordinary ionization gage by a factor of 1000 or more. This is accomplished by reducing the solid angle available to x-rays formed by electrons striking the electrodes of the ionization gage. If gages (1) or (2) were used immediately in a satellite instrumentation, the resultant data would be subject to interpretation according to the assumed gas composition. This follows from the marked sensitivity to the gas composition possessed by ionization gages.

Until the time when the composition of the environment at the extreme altitudes is known, a measure of the partial pressure of the gas components will be a useful approach to defining this region, in preference to ion gages.

Such a device is embodied in a modified mass spectrometer; however, because of the severe weight restrictions on the satellite instrumentations, the conventional d-c and r-f mass spectrometers do not at this time seem suitable since it is desired to identify the gas components while determining the component's pressure and/or density.

At present it does not appear necessary to make preliminary experiments to determine the composition of the gas before proceeding with density and pressure determinations. Density and pressure can be had simultaneously through the employment of a device using cyclotron resonance phenomenon as its principle of operation. In contrast to the usual mass-spectroscopic method, where stringent geometrical conditions are necessary, cyclotron resonance detection requires precision care only in the uniformity of the magnetic field.

Principles of Operation

For purposes of completeness a brief summary of the action of a charged particle under the influence of an electric and magnetic field will be given before discussing the "Synchrometer."

A uniform magnetic field constrains a moving ion to follow a circular path and requires the time for the ion to traverse the circle to be a constant for a given ion and magnetic field with no dependence on the speed of the ion. This is true also for half a circle, so that in cyclotron applications the ion increases its velocity as it progresses such that the length of the path increases in correct relationship to keep the time of travel constant between accelerations. This means that a potential source of constant frequency can be used to make the electrodes alternately plus and minus under the influence of a steady magnetic field. This can be shown analytically by using an ion of charge e moving in a plane normal to the magnetic field B with a velocity v in a space free from electric fields. The magnetic field will exert a force equal to Bev on the ion normal to both its direction of motion and the magnetic field. Using Newton's second law, we have

$$Bev = mv^2/r \qquad (1)$$

where m is the mass of the ion and r is the radius of the circular path. Solving, $v = eBr/m$ and the time required to traverse a full circle is

$$T = 2\pi r/v \qquad (2)$$

or

$$T = 2\pi m/eB \qquad (3)$$

which is independent of the velocity of the ion. Also, the frequency $f(= \omega/2\pi)$ of the alternating potential required for the electrodes is

$$f = 1/T = eB/m2\pi. \qquad (4)$$

The kinetic energy gained by the ions when they have reached the exit at radius R can be expressed in terms of the equivalent voltage V which would give them the same energy.

$$Ve = mv^2/2 \qquad (5)$$

or

$$V = eB^2R^2/2m \qquad (6)$$

which in electron volts would be

$$W = Z^2B^2R^2 (4.8 \times 10^{-5})/A \text{ electron volts} \qquad (7)$$

where Z is the number of electronic charges on the ion and A is the atomic number, B in oersteds, R in cm. Similarly, the frequency

$$f = ZB (1.53 \times 10^3)/A \text{ cps.} \qquad (8)$$

In the discussion so far we have neglected the increase of mass with velocity which from the special relativity theory is

$$m = m_0/\sqrt{1 - (v/c)^2} . \qquad (9)$$

Substituting this change of mass into equation (4) we see that in order to keep the frequency constant as the velocity increases, that is, to maintain the resonance condition, the magnetic field should increase proportionately with the mass m. This effect leads to the defocusing and loss of the ions such that the conventional cyclotron has difficulty attaining adequate resolution in mass measurements; however, a number of important advances in this field make it possible to employ this principle in the construction of a pressure-density gage for use in regions of unknown gas composition.[3-8] As shown in Fig. 2, a small beam of ioniz-

ing particles is passed parallel to a magnetic field, causing local ionizations along the beam. These ions are then accelerated by the alternating
potential between two parallel plates. As in the cyclotron, when the
value of the r-f frequency is equal to the frequency eH/M, the ions of
mass M and charge e are accelerated in orbits of increasing size (Archi-
medes' spiral) and eventually strike an ion collector. If the ionizing

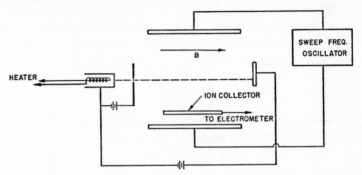

FIGURE 2.   Cyclotron resonance principle for partial-pressure-density
gage.

beam is kept constant in value along with the electric and magnetic
fields, the ion-collector current is a measure of the partial pressure of the
gas of this charge-to-mass ratio.

Under the influence of an r-f electric field $E = E_0 \sin \omega t$ applied
normal to a steady magnetic field B, a particle of charge-to-mass ratio
e/M will describe a spiral locus with an angular velocity of $(\omega + \omega_c)/2$,
where ω_c is the cyclotron resonance frequency. The radius at any instant is given by

$$r = (E_0/B\epsilon) \sin (\epsilon t/2). \tag{10}$$

At resonance for a particular particle, $\epsilon = 0$ and equation (10) becomes

$$r = E_0 t/2B. \tag{11}$$

Given any fixed value of E_0/B, there is a critical value for ϵ, $\epsilon' = E_0/R_0 B$
where R_0 is the distance of the collector from the origin.

Resolution

The resolution can be defined as the mass of the particle divided by
the mass error, or $M/\Delta M$. This is also equivalent to the cyclotron
resonance frequency divided by the frequency error, where the frequency
error is measured at the base of the resonance peaks. It follows that

$$M/\Delta M = R_0 B^2 e/2E_0 M. \tag{12}$$

At the critical value of $\epsilon = \epsilon'$ the time required for the ions to reach the collector is $t' = \pi/\epsilon'$ and the resolution becomes

$$(M/\Delta M) = \omega_c t'/2\pi = n' \tag{13}$$

where n' is the number of revolutions the ions make before reaching the collector.

The maximum radius r_m attained by nonresonant ions differing in mass by ΔM from the resonant ions is given by

$$r_m = 2MR_0/(n_\pi \Delta M). \tag{14}$$

Equation (3) indicates that for a constant magnetic field B the resolution varies inversely with the mass. If E_0 is decreased properly as the mass is increased, the resolution will be constant.

Data Output Characteristics

A typical output curve from which pressure and density can be deduced is shown in Fig. 3. A calibration will provide the mass number associated with each frequency, while the current will provide information for calculating the density and pressure.

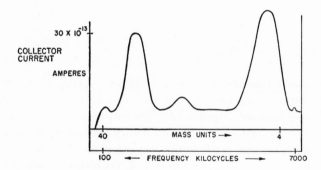

FIGURE 3. Output data.

It can be shown from equation (12) that by scanning magnetically ΔM remains constant. This is an advantage since the width of the recorded peaks remains constant. Thus, the instrument can be set for maximum scanning rate over the entire mass range, and a linear mass scale will be recorded if the magnetic field is made to vary linearly with time. In order to increase resolution, it is necessary either to increase the number of revolutions or to determine more critically a change in phase of the circulating ions. The number of revolutions corresponding to a minimum detectable ion current may be increased by increasing the magnetic field, by increasing the sensitivity of the detector, or by increasing the trapping efficiency.

Satellite Instrumentation

The block diagram in Fig. 4 demonstrates the principles for an instrumentation using a varying magnetic-field intensity and fixed electric-field frequency. The equipment consists of a filament power supply, electrometer and associated d-c amplifier, fixed-frequency oscillator, and

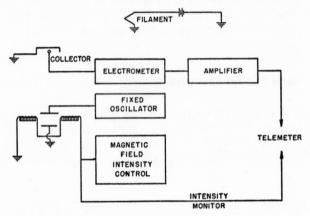

FIGURE 4. Block diagram of apparatus (varying magnetic field, fixed electric field).

a magnetic-field intensity control driving an electromagnet. Fig. 5, on the other hand, using the varying electric-field frequency with a fixed magnetic-field principle, consists of a filament power supply, electrometer and associated d-c amplifier, sweep-frequency generator, and a permanent magnet. Both systems provide the desired data with the resolution as discussed previously. Among the major problems involved in taking density or composition measurements is that of the contamination by the missile. This contamination might be reduced substantially by taking advantage of the sun's heating and the large pumping speeds available for outgassing of surfaces present. If active data sampling is delayed for a period of from several days to a week, the missile could be constructed in such a way that temperature could be elevated several hundred degrees throughout this period so that the contamination would become negligible in time. The gage should be mounted so that the sampling elements are not restricted by the conductance of opening or connecting tubulations, but mounted above the missile surface directly exposed to the environment, leaving the associated equipment below the missile surface. Since the resolutions of both systems are comparable, weight could be the deciding factor for a choice. A very substantial reduction in weight is possible through the use of a permanent magnet

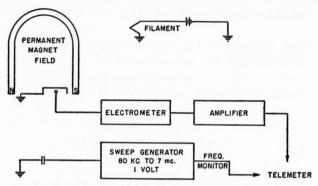

FIGURE 5. Block diagram of apparatus (varying frequency electric field, fixed magnetic field).

as a field source. The magnetic field could, for example, be made to vary in the desired manner by moving the permanent magnet in and out of the magnetic circuit surrounding the sampling chamber.

Ionized and Un-ionized Environment

The presence of extreme ultraviolet radiation at high altitudes suggests the possibility of determining the gas composition with regard to the ionized and un-ionized population through use of a photo-electric source in place of a filament. The work of H. E. Hinteregger[9] and others[10-12] suggests that an ionizing source might be fashioned by using beryllium plates exposed to the sun's radiation. In these circumstances it might be possible to separate the ionized composition from the un-ionized composition each time the satellite rotated to shield the instrument from the sun. Likewise, the device would provide the opportunity to compare the environment of the earth's atmosphere on the dark side of the planet with that of the lighted side with each rotation about the earth.

Tuned Gages

The problems in scanning can be eliminated completely by using several gage systems where the electric and magnetic fields are set to some predetermined value necessary to capture only oxygen or nitrogen, for example. It is conceivable that one magnet could serve all the systems using the air gap to determine the field strength at a particular sampling chamber. A single electrometer-amplifier system could likewise serve all the tuned gages to provide the partial pressure of any component present, by means of high-speed switching or commutating.

REFERENCES

1. R. T. Bayard and D. Alpert, "Extension of the Low Pressure Range of the Ionization Gauge," *Rev. Sci. Inst., 21:* 571–572 (1950).
2. W. B. Nottingham, "Design and Properties of the Modified Bayard-Alpert Gauge," *Vacuum Symposium Trans.,* 1954, p. 76.
3. S. A. Goudsmit, "A Time-of-Flight Mass Spectrometer," *Phys. Rev., 74:* 622–623 (1948).
4. J. A. Hipple and H. A. Thomas, "A Time-of-Flight Mass Spectrometer with Varying Field," *Phys. Rev., 75:* 1616 (1949).
5. P. I. Richards *et al.,* "Magnetic Time-of-Flight Mass Spectrometer," *Phys. Rev., 76:* 180 (1949).
6. J. A. Hipple *et al.,* "A Precise Method of Determining the Faraday by Magnetic Resonance," *Phys. Rev., 76:* 1877–1878 (1949).
7. F. Bloch, "Recent Developments of Nuclear Induction," *Phys. Rev., 79:* 234T (1950).
8. L. G. Smith, "The Mass 'Synchrometer' and Measurement of the Mass of S^{32}," *Phys. Rev., 81:* 295 (1951).
9. H. E. Hinteregger, "Photoelectric Emission in the Extreme Ultraviolet," *Phys. Rev., 96:* 538–539 (1954).
10. J. Weiss and W. Bernstein, "Energy Required to Produce One Ion Pair for Several Gases," *Phys. Rev., 98:* 1829–1831 (1955).
11. C. D. Maunsell, "Measurement of Absorption Coefficients for Photoionizing Radiations in Low-Pressure Gases with a Space Charge Detector," *Phys. Rev., 98:* 1831–1836 (1955).
12. J. D. Craggs and C. A. McDowell, "The Ionization and Dissociation of Complex Molecules by Electron Impacts," *Rept. Prog. Physics, 18:* 374–422 (1955).

Meteorological Measurements from a Satellite Vehicle

by W. G. Stroud and W. Nordberg
SIGNAL CORPS ENGINEERING LABORATORIES,
FT. MONMOUTH, NEW JERSEY

ABSTRACT

The usefulness of an earth satellite in studying the meteorology of the earth is reviewed. The various levels of information available from the various levels of complexity of
instrumentation are outlined. A specific instrumentation suitable for the initial (IGY) satellites is presented and the basic
aspects of the operational problems are outlined. It is shown
that the necessary orientation information can be obtained
from the albedo data.

Introduction

One of the greatest advances in the field of meteorology, and
particularly synoptic meteorology, will take place when man will be able
to make more or less continuous observation of the earth from a station
far above the surface of the earth. No other technique could possibly
do what will ultimately be possible from a satellite. With photography
or television or an observer at 2000 miles altitude, an area equal to the
United States synoptic chart published by the Weather Bureau would

be visible. Then tropospheric weather systems in their entirety could be tracked by means of their associated clouds. The generation, growth, and course of "bad-weather" systems such as hurricanes will undoubtedly be observable. The high-altitude observations of solar radiation, reflected and scattered energy, and out-going long-wave radiation coupled with the surface measurements would permit solution of many of the unresolved theoretical questions revolving about the thermodynamic state of the atmosphere, the mechanism of cyclogenesis, etc. Just the high-altitude observer's ability to fill in the vast gaps of cloud observations over the uninhabited land and ocean areas of the world would be a substantial gain, since at present less that 5% of the earth's surface is covered by observations.

Detailed photographs of the clouds may make possible studies of topographic features that give rise to the so-called "orographic" clouds and of special phenomena such as thunderstorms and, possibly, tornadoes that are revealed through their unique cloud formations. These studies could well give information on the origin, growth, and course of such events and on their related properties—pressure, temperature gradients, vortex slopes, etc.

In general, radiation studies from a satellite would contribute greatly to the studies of other planetary atmospheres,[1] for then observations similar to those made of other planets would be possible from outside the earth's atmosphere.

The extreme-altitude studies will of necessity, at least in the beginning, depend on observations of cloud mass, distribution, and motions for information about the earth's weather.

The clouds are a direct expression of the physical processes taking place in the atmosphere; there is a general relationship between the forms of clouds and their height. And clouds are visible signs of definite schemes of motion followed by the air and reflect the ever-changing conditions of temperature, moisture, and movements of the air at different levels above the surface of the earth. There is quite a bit more that could be said about the cloud-mass distribution over the earth, their motions, their relation to specific air masses and frontal systems. Examples of the types of studies possible may be found in a number of references.[2-6]

The initial satellite and, quite possibly, even the immediate later ones will not carry, in all likelihood, photographic devices, television, or observers, so information on cloud-mass distribution will have to be obtained through telemeterable techniques. Indeed, the first devices must demand only the simplest of internal circuitry and telemetering systems.

One of the less complex measurements that might be made from a satellite would be photodetector (photocell or equivalent) measurement of the solar radiation reflected by the sunlit side of the earth—the albedo of the earth.

Fundamental to a satellite-borne study of the reflectivity of the earth is the need for orientation information. Initially, orientation control will not be necessary as long as one can deduce the relative orientation of the device. By appropriate instrumentation it is possible to obtain the orientation from the albedo data.

The purpose of this paper is to provide the background required for research studies that would begin with albedo measurements from a satellite vehicle capable of giving orientation information and to propose specific instrumentation for these measurements. It is anticipated that preliminary measurements will be carried out with the proposed instrumentation installed in small rockets fired off the east coast of the United States.

Discussion

Theoretical Background

The measurements proposed would consist of determinations of the intensity of radiation from the earth by photodetectors viewing the earth through small solid angles as the satellite spins about a stable axis.

The theoretical background is concerned with two problems: (1) what light intensities will be expected; are they detectable and, roughly, how might they be expected to vary; and (2) how are the measurements to be related to surface or tropospheric phenomena?

The earth's albedo has been computed by Danjon[7,8] from measurements of the intensity of the earth-shine reflected by the moon (new moon in old moon's arms) and by Fritz[9] from measurements and estimates of the individual albedos of ground, sea, forest, snow, clouds, etc. These results agree that the average albedo of the earth is about 36% with fluctuations between 32% (in July) and 52% (in October). However, neither method is very accurate.

The fluctuations are apparently caused by the changes in the amount of cloud cover over the reflecting side of the earth. Ångstrom[10] has pointed out that the albedo of the earth is linearly related to the percentage of cloud cover

$$A = K_1 + K_2 C$$

where K_1 and K_2 are constants, C equals the fraction of cloud cover, and A equals the albedo. Although he gives values of 0.17 and 0.53 for

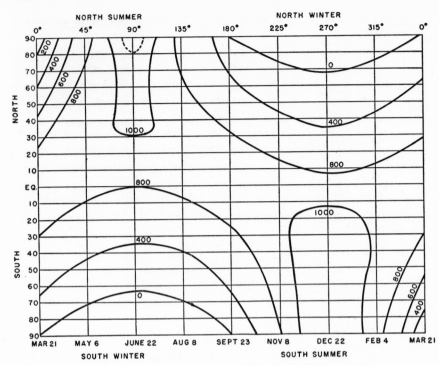

FIGURE 1. Daily insolation in cal cm^{-2} day^{-1} received at earth's surface in the absence of an atmosphere (Ref. 13).

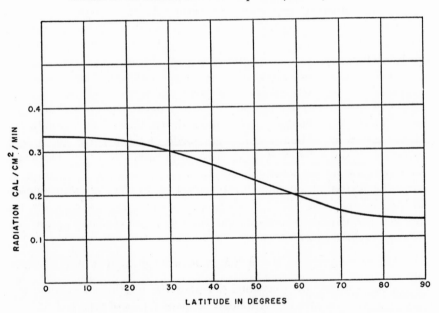

FIGURE 2. Variation of the incoming solar radiation at the earth's surface with latitude.

K_1 and K_2, respectively, it is quite possible that more recent studies would revise these numbers.

Observations would be made in the visible or near-infrared regions of the spectrum for a number of reasons. At shorter wavelengths (4000 A) the intensities of reflected light become too small; above about two microns the response time of the infrared detectors becomes too great to be useful. In short, the most sensitive, fastest response photodetectors are available for the visible region.

The total incoming solar intensity, the solar constant, equals 2.0 cal/cm²/min. However, the amount of radiation falling on each square centimeter of the earth's surface depends on the atmosphere, the time of the day and of the year, and the latitude. The variations for an atmosphereless earth are shown in Fig. 1.

The incoming radiation at the earth's surface as a function of latitude is shown in Fig. 2.

We shall consider 30° N. latitude for some specific computations. The albedos of the various surfaces of the earth vary considerably, as shown in Table I. There is very little information on the spectral reflectivity of these surfaces.

TABLE I [9,11,12]

Albedo variations of earth's surfaces

Surface	Albedo (%)
Fresh Snow	80 to 85
Old Snow	40
Grass	10 to 33
Rock	12 to 15
Dry Earth	14
Wet Earth	8 to 9
Water (sea) *	3 to 10
Forest	5
Deserts	25
Cloud Sea	50 to 75

* The albedo of the sea depends on the roughness. Practically no radiation is reflected by a smooth surface for solar zenith angles less than 40°; the reflectivity then increases from 2% at 43° to about 40% at 85°.

There is some uncertainty about the albedo of clouds (Ref. 9) which may arise in part from the variation of the albedo with cloud thickness, type, water content, and with wavelength. These variations are briefly summarized in Figs. 3 and 4.

The prime question is whether or not enough light is reflected from the surface with lowest reflectivity (the sea) to be detected, since we would like to be able to detect the horizons† when these horizons are

† With a cloudless horizon there is a doubling of the light scattered by the atmosphere just above the horizon, because the path length viewed doubles. This has been observed in many of the rocket photographs (Refs. 2 and 11).

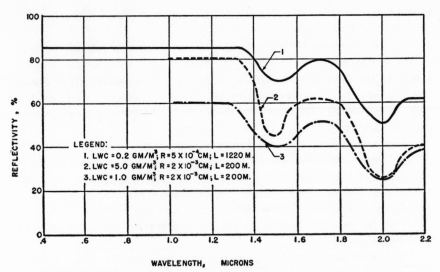

FIGURE 3. The reflectivity of clouds as a function of wavelength (Ref. 14).

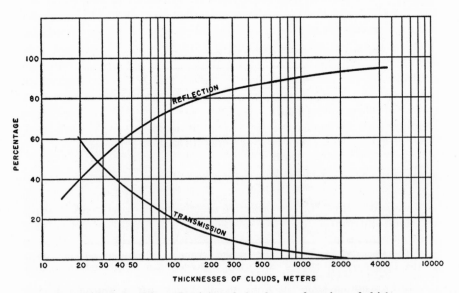

FIGURE 4. The reflectivity of clouds as a function of thickness.

the sea. Using 2% for the albedo for the sea and assuming that the surface scatters isotropically,* then, since

$$R_S = R_E \left(\frac{R}{R + H} \right)^2$$

---

* We do not know how valid this is at this time.

where R_S = radiation density at satellite

R_E = radiation density from earth

R = radius of earth

H = distance above surface = 500 km

the light intensity at 500 km will be 0.15 lumen/cm². Typical photodetector sensitivities are shown in Table II.

TABLE II

Sensitivities of various photodetectors*

Type	Sensitivity
Photomultiplier 1P21	80 amps/lumen
Phototube, Vacuum 929	45 microamps/lumen
Phototube, Gas 5583	124 microamps/lumen
Kodak Ektron Detector	~ 100 microamps/lumen

* With S-4 response, peaked at roughly 5000 A.

It is apparent that there is sufficient light to operate any of these devices. In a private communication, H. Friedman of the Naval Research Laboratory has pointed out that they have been able to detect the horizon very clearly, even at night, using a vacuum-type phototube. The choice of the detector will depend on other, more practical, considerations. One of these considerations is the amount of radiation scattered by the atmosphere in the visible and ultraviolet regions of the spectrum. The rocket-borne photographic studies[3] have been most successful when infrared films and filters are used. The Kodak Ektron Detector with its good response time (400 microsec) and a peak sensitivity at 2.5 microns is tentatively considered the best choice.

Method

Since it is the ultimate objective of an albedo experiment to study the cloud distribution over the earth's surface, it is important to obtain both measurements of the amount of radiation reflected from a limited area of the earth at any given time and exact orientation data of the satellite with reference to the earth.

It is assumed that the vehicle will follow an elliptical nonpolar orbit with an inclination of about 30° and that the vehicle will spin at a high rate (several hundred rpm) about a predetermined axis. It is also assumed that this axis will remain reasonably fixed in space and that the launching will take place along the spin axis. Perigee and apogee are assumed to be 200 and 800 miles, respectively. Most of these assumptions seem well justified because the chances for survival of this specific satellite are very small in the event any one of them is not valid.

Also, it has been assumed that the configuration of photocells planned can be fitted to any vehicle shape. We are not convinced that a spherical shape is the most desirable for the majority of the experiments. A smaller, lighter, and mechanically superior unit would be a

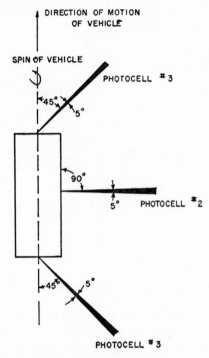

FIGURE 5. Suggested photocell configuration on vehicle.

cylinder with its spin axis coincident with its longitudinal axis (see Fig. 5). No antispin device will be necessary; indeed, it is undesirable. In the long run, only the drag data would profit by a sphere. The damping of the spin by eddy currents will have to be minimized by the use of laminated or nonconducting materials.

A minimum of three photoelectric cells (probably Eastman Kodak Ektron Detectors) will be arranged on the vehicle in such a way that the aperture of Detector No. 1 will look forward at an angle σ of approximately 45°. The three apertures will be placed 120° apart around the circular cross section of the vehicle. Each aperture will be about 5° wide. This means that at an altitude of around 500 km, at least one photocell will always be looking at the earth, independent of the position of the vehicle. If the vehicle is spinning, each photocell will sweep a curved path on the earth's surface. In perigee position, the center path will cover a zone of the order of 15 miles in width and

2500 miles in length (Fig. 6). Each of the three zones will be separated by about 200 miles at the center. In apogee, the width and length of the center zone will be in the order of 60 miles and 4600 miles, respectively. The zone separation will be about 800 miles. For intermediate positions the length(s) and width(s) of the path(s) will vary accordingly, and as long as the vehicle keeps spinning at least one photocell will sweep a portion of the earth.

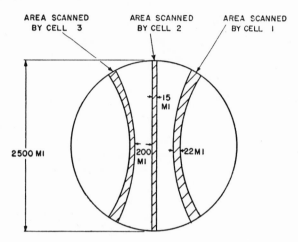

FIGURE 6. View of areas on earth swept out by photocells.

The spin rate can be determined by measuring the repetition rate of the pulses from one individual photocell. The biggest problem will be to determine which portion of the earth each photocell is scanning. This problem can be solved by determining the orientation of the vehicle with respect to the earth directly from the photocell pulses.

The angle between spin axis of the vehicle and the vector **R**, from center of the earth through the vehicle, can be determined with sufficient accuracy from the duration of the sweep of any one photocell (Fig. 7). The sweep duration for each photocell as a function of the orientation of the vehicle is shown in Fig. 8. The curves are based on a spin rate of 90 rpm, an altitude of 300 km above the surface of the earth, and, naturally, on a spherical shape for the earth.

For instance, if the vehicle is oriented so that the spin axis is orthogonal with **R**, the sweep time for cell No. 2 will be 0.270 sec. The sweep duration for both cells No. 1 and No. 3 will be 0.286 sec. As the angle between **R** and the spin axis changes, the sweep duration for cell No. 2 grows shorter. The sweep times for cells No. 1 and No. 3 will become more and more different.

It can also be seen from Fig. 8 that most of the time all three photocells will sweep the earth. Only if the spin axis is within ±20°

of **R,** the radius vector, is there only one photocell which will sweep the earth.

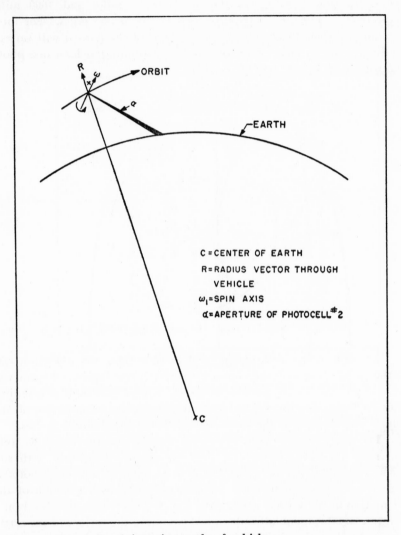

FIGURE 7.   Orientation angle of vehicle.

If the vehicle is at altitudes higher than 300 km, the curves in Fig. 8 will be of essentially the same shape.   However, they will be shifted toward somewhat shorter times.

A spin rate of about 100 rpm is desired because it gives an optimum ratio between number of sweeps during one observation period and resolvability of the orientation angle.   If the spin is too slow, not enough sweeps could be detected from one observation station, and the number of stations would have to be increased. If the spin is too fast, the curves in Fig. 8 would be too flat near the maximum so that a change of about 20° in the orientation angle would correspond to only about a one-millisec change in sweep duration. In this case, a somewhat more complicated photocell arrangement would be necessary.

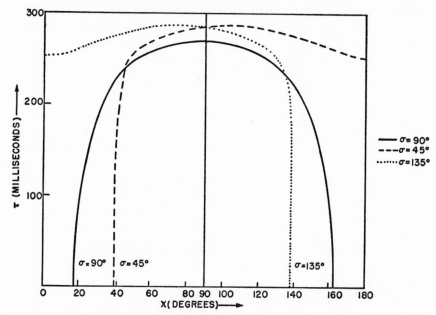

FIGURE 8.   Sweep times as functions of the orientation of the satellite.

Knowing the orientation, we can determine the position of the zone on the earth which has been scanned by a particular photocell. These orientation measurements, obtained strictly by studying the duration of the albedo pulses, may be supplemented by the time of the occasional sweeps of the photocells across the sun. Differentiation between solar and albedo signals will be easy because of the different intensities and durations involved.

After solving the orientation problem, the albedo of the earth can be determined by analyzing the intensity output of the photocell. If photocells of very low time constants are employed, a high degree of resolution can be expected and albedo measurements over areas of roughly 20×100 miles seem definitely feasible.

The Telemetering Problem

Probably the primary limitations for most experiments and instrumentations of the satellite will derive from the telemetering system possible and available in the satellite. The key function of the satellite's transmitter will be to radiate a signal usable in the electronic tracking of the device.

Because there are a number of alternatives possible (for example, if the telemetering interferes with the tracking method, it is possible to separate tracking and telemetry in time and/or geography), we shall outline a telemetry that will satisfy the requirements of this experiment. In other words, the over-all satellite instrumentation shall be considered

FIGURE 9. Idealized pulse shape from photodetector.

as a system that we will design, rather than as fixed in transmitter telemetry.

It seems unlikely that a single telemetry will meet all the requirements arising from the different research instrumentations.

As described, the end information to be telemetered is essentially a square voltage pulse, the amplitude of which is a function of the light intensity received by the photodetector and the duration of which is a function of the earth sweep seen by the detector. Fig. 9 illustrates the expected variations.

The amplitude of the initial pulse would tell which photodetector was active. The width of the pulse, τ, would vary from a minimum of the width of the coding pulse, probably one millisec, to a maximum of about 300 millisecs. It would be desirable to have a response time of about 1/900 sec, i.e., a telemetry capable of handling 1000 pps. This would permit the resolution of information separated by the beam width of the photodetector, 5°. However, this is a rather stringent requirement and it may not be possible to meet it within the framework of low weight, minimum complexity, and minimum power demanded by satellite instrumentation.

A rather broad set of specifications for a telemetry for this experiment in the satellite is given in Table III.

Actual instrumentation bread-boarding will be necessary to fix accurately all the requirements. The potential of transistorized devices with their great saving in power drain will be examined periodically as these devices improve.

Note on Operational Requirements

The operational requirements of the proposed experiment are considered minimal. A set of five or six telemetering receiving stations located along a meridian such as 80° W. longitude would be most reasonable. These stations would consist of a keying transmitter for turning

TABLE III

General specifications for albedo-orientation telemetry

Carrier:	100-mc/sec Band	Temperature:	about 300°K; 50°C
Type:	FM/FM	Response time:	1 millisec
Components:	Subminiature	Amplitude:	Logarithmic; accuracy 2%
Weight:	3 lb	Subcarriers:	One channel at 27 kc
Power life:	4 weeks*		

* Keyed: On 6 min out of 90 min; about one-half this time for an inclined orbit of 30°.

on the satellite instrumentation and a telemetering receiving and recording system. Such a string of stations is consistent with the satellite tracking requirements and plans.

Conclusions

The albedo of various sections of the earth and its atmosphere and the orientation of a spinning satellite can be measured by appropriate photodetector configurations on the vehicle. The initially rough data will be available only over limited areas of the sunlit side of the earth because of the power and telemetering limitations that mean that the telemetering will be keyed from a limited number of sites over which the satellite will pass. As a planned experiment, this technique would seem to have possibilities of success.

REFERENCES

1. S. L. Hess, "Some Aspects of the Meteorology of Mars," *J. Meteor.,* 7: 1–13 (1950).
2. L. F. Hubert and O. Berg, *U.S. Monthly Weather Review, 83:* 119 (1955).
3. C. T. Holliday, "The Earth as Seen from Outside the Atmosphere," in *The Earth as a Planet,* edited by G. Kuiper. Chicago: Univ. of Chicago Press, 1955.
4. D. L. Crowson, "Cloud Observations from Rockets," *Bull. Am. Meteor. Soc., 30:* 17–22 (1949).
5. J. H. Conover, "Observations and Photographs of a Cold Front Made from an Airplane," *Bull. Am. Meteor. Soc., 29:* 313–318

(1948); with S. H. Wollaston, "Cloud Systems of a Winter Cyclone," *J. Meteor., 6:* 249–260 (1949).

6. C. E. P. Brooks, "Mean Cloudiness over the Earth," *Mem. Roy. Meteor. Soc., 1:* 127–138 (1927); "Geological and Historical Aspects of Climatic Change" in *Compendium of Meteorology* (Boston: Am. Meteor. Soc., 1951).

7. A. Danjon, "Albedo, Color, and Polarization of the Earth," in *The Earth as a Planet,* edited by G. Kuiper. Chicago: Univ. of Chicago Press, 1955, p. 726.

8. A. Danjon, *Bull. Astrophysics, 17:* 363 (1954).

9. S. Fritz, "The Albedo of the Planet Earth and of Clouds," *J. Meteor., 6:* 277–282 (1949).

10. A. Ångstrom, "Energiezufuhr und Temperatur auf verschiedenen Breitengraden," *Gerlands Beitr. Geophysik, 15:* 1–13 (1926).

11. M. Luckeish, "The Visibility of Airplanes," *J. Franklin Inst., 187:* 311 (1919).

12. R. Tousey and E. O. Hulburt, "Brightness and Polarization of the Daylight Sky at Various Altitudes above Sea Level," *J. Opt. Soc. Am., 37:* 78–92 (1947).

14

The Radiative Heat Transfer
of Planet Earth

by Jean I. F. King
GEOPHYSICS RESEARCH DIRECTORATE,
AIR FORCE CAMBRIDGE RESEARCH CENTER

ABSTRACT

A method is developed for obtaining the vertical temperature distribution of a planetary atmosphere from the law of darkening of the planet's emission spectrum. The intensity of the radiation emerging from a planet is directly dependent on the vertical thermal structure of its atmosphere. For the monochromatic case the emergent intensity is simply the Laplace transform of the Planck intensity considered as a function of optical depth. Now, for a given wavelength the Planck intensity is a single-valued function of temperature. Thus, in principle, a complete knowledge of the variation of the emergent intensity with zenith angle (law of darkening) suffices to determine the thermal structure of the accessible optical depth.

In practice, to find the Planck intensity we must obtain the inverse Laplace transform, which is mathematically tantamount to solving a Fredholm integral equation of the first kind. An approximate solution to the problem is obtained using the Volterra method which replaces the integral equation by a set of linear simultaneous equations with the Planck intensity expressed as a series of step functions. A sample calculation shows that as few as three values of the limb-darkening function yield quantitative information on the vertical temperature distribution.

Alterations in the theory necessitated by considerations of band, rather than monochromatic, intensity measurements are indicated.

A lightweight, rugged instrument which appears capable of such thermal measurements is discussed. This is the far-infrared filter photometer currently being developed by The Johns Hopkins University under Air Force Contract AF19 (604)-949.

The lower hemisphere of the satellite is bathed in far-infrared thermal radiation emitted by the earth and its atmosphere. Situated, in effect, beyond the atmosphere, the satellite offers a unique platform for the astronomical study of the earth in the light of its own emission spectrum. No other physical parameter accessible to the satellite contains the wealth of information concerning the thermal state of the atmosphere which is inherent in the far-infrared emission of the earth.

A far-infrared thermal-sensing device situated on the satellite would have a readily perceived use in determining upper-atmospheric constituents by a frequency scan of the spectrum. A less obvious but potentially fruitful possibility arises from the variation of the terrestrial emission as the satellite field of view sweeps across the earth's apparent disk.

This intensity variation across the disk (limb-darkening effect) is a measure of the departure of the atmosphere from an isothermal state. This, in turn, suggests that an accurate measure of the infrared limb-darkening would yield information as to the vertical thermal structure. The relation is this: the monochromatic radiant intensity emerging from the top of an atmosphere ($\tau = 0$) at a zenith angle $\theta = \cos^{-1} \mu$ is given from the fundamental equation of transfer as

$$I(0, \mu) = \int_0^\infty B(\tau)e^{-\tau/\mu} \, d\tau/\mu \tag{1}$$

where τ is the optical depth and

$$B(\tau) = \frac{2h\nu^3/c^2}{e^{h\nu/kT(\tau)} - 1} \tag{2}$$

is the Planck intensity, a function of wavelength and temperature. Equation (1) thus relates the emergent intensity to the thermal state of all the layers of the atmosphere within optical reach of the top.

With the emergent intensity presumed known and the desideratum the Planck intensity, the problem reduces to solving a Fredholm integral equation of the first kind. We obtain an approximate solution using the Volterra method, which consists of replacing the integral equation by a set of linear simultaneous equations.

We begin by expressing the Planck intensity as a series of unit step functions whose coefficients a_i we are to determine:

$$B(\tau) = \sum a_i S_i, \quad i = 1, 2, \ldots, n \tag{3}$$

where

$$\begin{aligned} S_i &= 1 & \tau_{i-1} < \tau < \tau_i \\ &= 0 & \text{elsewhere.} \end{aligned} \tag{4}$$

We substitute equation (3) into relation (1) to obtain

$$I(0, \mu) = \sum a_i l_i \quad i = 1, 2, \ldots, n \tag{5}$$

where

$$l_i = e^{-\tau_{i-1}/\mu} - e^{-\tau_i/\mu}. \tag{6}$$

By choosing n values of μ, i.e., $\mu = \mu_j$ where $j = 1, 2, \ldots, n$, equation (5) becomes a set of n simultaneous equations to be solved for the a_i's. Thus

$$I_j = \sum_{i=1}^{n} a_i l_{ij} \quad j = 1, 2, \ldots, n \tag{7}$$

where for conciseness we have written $I_j = I(0, \mu_j)$.

The extension of the formalism to include *band* rather than mono-chromatic emergent intensities is ready and obvious. For a band of moderate spectral width ($\Delta \nu \approx 25 \text{ cm}^{-1}$) we can write equation (1) more generally as

$$I(0, \mu) = - \int_0^{\infty} B(\tau) \frac{\partial \mathcal{F}}{\partial \tau} d\tau \tag{8}$$

where $\mathcal{F}$ is the band transmissivity, the probability that a photon emitted in the band $\Delta \nu$ at optical depth τ emerges to the surface without suffering absorption. The substitution of equation (3) into the generalized equation (8) now yields

$$I(0, \mu) = \sum a_i (\mathcal{F}_{i-1} - \mathcal{F}_i) \quad i = 1, 2, \ldots, n. \tag{9}$$

We obtain as before the set of n simultaneous equations

$$I_j = \sum_{i=1}^{n} a_i l_{ij} \quad j = 1, 2, \ldots, n \tag{10}$$

with

$$l_{ij} = \mathcal{F}(\tau_{i-1}, \mu_j) - \mathcal{F}(\tau_i, \mu_j). \tag{11}$$

By solving the equations (10) for the coefficients a_i, we have obtained the approximate solution (3) for $B(\tau)$. This, in turn, through the use of the Planck relation (2), yields the temperature as a function of optical depth.

Power and weight considerations of the satellite appear to rule out a scanning, gear-driven infrared spectrometer of the conventional design. A rugged, semi-passive, lightweight filter photometer has recently been developed by John Strong of The Johns Hopkins University under AF19 (604)-949 for balloon probing of the atmosphere. The sole power requirements are for the chopper blade and an a-c signal amplification. An instrument of this type could be constructed with interference filters strategically tuned at 6, 9.6, 11, and 15 microns. The 6-micron filter would receive the water-vapor radiation, the 9.6-micron the ozone, the 15-micron the carbon-dioxide emission spectrum, while the 11-micron filter by utilizing a spectral window would see directly to the earth's surface. This would provide a spectral scan of sorts, while a limb-darkening scan would be obtained by a proper distribution of the sensing elements on the satellite surface.

15

Visibility from a Satellite at High Altitudes

by V. J. Stakutis and Capt. Joseph X. Brennan, USAF
GEOPHYSICS RESEARCH DIRECTORATE,
AIR FORCE CAMBRIDGE RESEARCH CENTER

ABSTRACT

The determination of the visual range or visibility at any altitude depends, in great measure, on the contrasting luminances of the viewed object and its background. Methods and instrumentation employed on balloon flights for observing the pertinent physical quantities are proposed for extension to satellite vehicles and altitudes. The simple design of two types of instrumentation for measuring the luminous quantities is described briefly to show their applicability to satellite installation. The essential element of the instrumentation is a Weston photronic barrier-layer cell equipped with a viscor filter which responds to light flux in a manner very similar to that of the human eye. Provision is made for changing the material of lenses and photocells for increased sensitivity and durability under high-altitude conditions. One photometer unit observes sky background luminance directly. The second unit measures the illumination of the viewed surface so that the object's brightness (luminance) is calculable through its surface reflectance. A minimum number of photometer units, arranged for viewing in the azimuth and zenith directions, is suggested for a first effort because the actual limitations of weight and telemetering are still uncertain. The maximum desired arrangement would be a nearly spherical studding of the satellite with photometers. From the observed quantities of luminance and illuminance it should be possible to arrive at directional contrast values, contrast reduction, attenuation coefficients, and an estimate of degree and type of scattering. The effect of altitude on such values can be realized by comparison with similar data acquired at balloon and aircraft levels. The final result of visual range is to be determined from nomogramic methods based on the investigations of the Tiffany Foundation. Examination of the visual spectral distribution and polarization phenomena is not considered for a first series of experimental flights.

Introduction

It is proposed that present experiments relating to visibility in the atmosphere made from high-altitude balloons be extended to satellite altitudes. These experiments involve the direct determination of the sky's and the earth's luminances and their contributions to illuminance in the spherical region about positions of increasing altitude up to 100,000 ft. Indirectly, the experiments afford the data for computing contrast values, contrast reduction, the attenuation coefficient, and the related visual range. From the observed and calculated quantities it may be possible to ascertain the precise light-attenuation phenomena which are encountered as one rises through the atmosphere.

During the course of this work it has often been suggested that the photometric quantities obtained with high-altitude balloons should hold up quite well or change predictably in high regions of the atmosphere. This observation has been based on the presumption that most of the strongly and irregularly scattering atmosphere is far below 100,000 ft. If this were actually the case, it would still be of interest to verify such conclusions at as high an altitude as one could attain. However, photometric data obtained from recent balloon flights indicate that the luminance values and light scattering are not quite of the order predicted by theory based on a Rayleigh molecular atmosphere. Furthermore, at two or three hundred miles above the earth the perturbation of airglow and starlight may add a significant contribution to skylight and visibility. In any case, it is believed that a satellite-borne experiment for mapping the sky's and the earth's luminances and illuminances and for determining the associated quantity of visibility would be of exciting interest.

Instrumentation

The essential element of the balloon-borne equipment for sensing the incident skylight has been a Weston barrier-layer, dry-disk photronic cell. It is capped with a viscor filter which causes the cell to respond in very close approximation to the manner of the human eye. Readings obtained with this cell are then photometric.

To measure the illumination (illuminance) on a surface due to a hemisphere of skylighting above the surface, the modified photocell is merely set into the plane of the surface and covered with a diffusing opal glass or plastic plate. Such an arrangement of photocell and cover plates weighs a scant third of a pound.

To measure luminance or sky brightness, a photometric box 7 in. long and of 5-in.-square cross section was constructed to contain the few, simple, component parts (see Fig. 1). Incident light is admitted at one end of the box through a plastic fresnel lens 4 in. in diameter and of 6-in. focal length. Within the box and at the focal distance of the lens is set an aperture screen. The cell is mounted on axis with the lens and aperture but slightly displaced behind the aperture so that the luminous flux may spread out and not saturate just a small portion of the cell. The size of the aperture determines the angle of view of the photometer box; the size (area) of the lens can be considered as an optical amplifier of light flux. Baffles have been added about the lens and the interior of the box has been properly blackened—both these features to reduce the quantity of scattered light in an attempt to achieve the angle of view as calculated from geometrical considerations. The complete luminance photometer box weighs slightly more than 1 lb and can be fixed in any desired orientation with respect to its vehicle.

For both types of units the outputs of the cells have been measured by microammeters. In flight it was necessary to photograph a bank of meters and then recover the film record. Photometric values corresponding to the meter readings were then obtained from calibration curves of the modified cells.

Telemetering was not utilized on the balloon flights because the gondola and top of the balloon were studded with photometric units in order to get a good mapping of the sky's and the earth's luminances from zenith to nadir. The power pack necessary to telemeter the huge quantity of data would have been prohibitive weight-wise for a balloon lift to high altitudes. With regard to the proposed satellite dimensions it is realized that, even though the individual photometer units are not heavy or large, the same degree of studding will not be possible.

The reduction of the number of units to a few preferred ones for each flight should then permit the telemetering of a vastly reduced quantity of data. Nor does the telemetering have to be continuous; it need only be intermittent at a rate based on the angular sweep of the satellite.

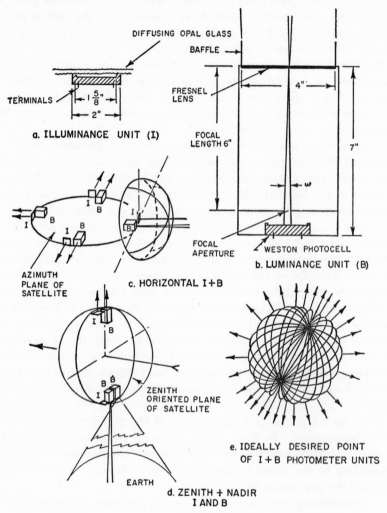

FIGURE 1a, b, c.   Construction and orientation of illuminance and luminance units.

FIGURE 1d, e.   Orientation of intensity and brightness photometers.

At lower altitudes it was expected that the sky's luminance would vary sharply in a small angular sweep, especially in the critical regions near the horizon and near the sun. Strong variations in the sky's brightness could then pass unnoted in the integrating effect of a wide angle of view. An example of such a wide angle of view is the 20° opening of the human eye used in searching. On the other hand, a precise mapping of the sky would be better obtained with an angle of view that is but a few minutes of arc. This, however, would incur the difficulty of low cell sensitivity that could be overcome only by strong electronic amplification and accompanying weight.

A compromise between close mapping and sensitivity was obtained on the balloon flights by opening the angle of view to 5° and employing a 4-in.-diameter fresnel lens for optical amplification. This design proved to be thoroughly satisfactory for measuring zenith sky luminance up to 100,000 ft. Contrary to the reported observations of the crew of Explorer II, the zenith sky was still far from black, being in fact four times brighter than it had been two hours earlier at a seven o'clock morning launch on a September day. The same type of unit has also been found to be sensitive in the region of maximum zenith brightness that might exist at 220 km as derived from a recent[1] Naval Research Laboratory rocket flight. Should greater sensitivity be demanded of the luminance units, improvement may be obtained by expanding the angle of view or employing a similar but more sensitive photocell.

Either or both of these measures may be necessary. It may not be practicable to expose the photometer units on the satellite's skin. They would probably have to be mounted behind a faring of translucent material which would, undoubtedly, reduce the incident luminous flux substantially. However, the attenuation of the translucent faring could be taken into account in calibrating the photocell's response and the sensitivity could be increased as suggested above.

It is presumed, at this time, that the photometric units will be mounted in a vehicle whose orientation could be known although it need not be fixed. This is, perhaps, a stringent requirement and not easily obtained. However, if it were possible to attach direction to the first set of satellite photometric observations, it is believed that the results could then be used for defining satellite orientation with greater ease.

With this type of instrumentation it is suggested that the following quantities relating to visibility from a satellite be measured, at least piecemeal.

Horizon Luminance and Illuminance

The first set of desired observations is of horizon or horizontal luminance and illuminance, in a minimum of four directions, and preferably in the direction of translation, to the rear, and to either side of the line of motion. This horizon region of investigation should be one of the brighter portions of the sky when the sun is the strongest source of light in the sky. Since on any one flight the satellite will run a range of zenith sun positions from sunrise to sunset with respect to itself, it is to be remembered that on one side of the earth the sun will illuminate the missile, its background, or be a part of the background. Observations behind the earth, away from the sun, can be just as useful in determining the extent of the umbra or the intensity of light emanating from sources other than the sun.

Horizon measurements should yield the background sky brightness against which the satellite or any other object will be viewed from a flight level. And sparse though any four simultaneously made observations will be, the results should permit a fair degree of extrapolation as to the variance of horizon sky brightness between the actually obtained values. Quite naturally, a more numerous studding than four units would be preferred. The best boundary-value results would be obtained if the path of the satellite were to lie in the plane or at right angles to the plane of the sun's travel about the earth.

Comparison of the four simultaneously observed horizon luminances may also serve to indicate if a Rayleigh type scattering predominates, i.e., if primary and secondary maxima lie on the sun line and minima are found at right angles to this line. It had been implied earlier that a non-Rayleigh type of scattering was still indicated by the data from balloon flights. Scattering minima had been observed at 120° to 140° from the forward direction of sunlight scatter.

To determine whether or not an object is visible against a given background, one needs also to know the brightness of the object facing the viewer. The brightness of a diffuse surface is proportional to the intensity of illumination incident on the surface. If, therefore, illuminance units are mounted side by side with the luminance photometer boxes, it would be possible to measure the intensity of illumination on a surface due chiefly to light flux issuing from the hemispherical region of the sky and earth subtended by the plane of the surface. The brightness of any object surface subjected to this illumination may then be calculated from

$$B_0 = \rho I \tag{1}$$

where I is the intensity of illumination and ρ is the reflectance of the surface. The difference in brightness values of viewed object and background leads to a contrast figure as defined by

$$C = \frac{B_B - B_0}{B_B}. \tag{2}$$

This, then, is the inherent contrast in a given direction, at the satellite position, and with respect to altitude and sun position. It may be compared to similarly obtained figures at balloon and aircraft altitudes. These comparisons may serve in a small way as a measure of light scattering between these altitudes.

One further quantity is available from this first arrangement of photocells. At a satellite speed of 18,000 mph, a short enough period of time can be chosen so that the path along the arc of flight is approximately linear and the sun's position will not have changed appreciably. The forward- or rearward-pointing luminance units would then have viewed the same relatively unchanged sky background at both ends of this interval. The luminance value measured more distant from the observed sky region is apparent with respect to the closer or inherent value. Neglecting the effect of variations of other added skylight, one can then evaluate the attenuation coefficient from

$$B_A = B_0 e^{-\alpha x} \tag{3}$$

where α is the attenuation coefficient, x the length of the interval, and B_0 and B_A the inherent and apparent luminances, respectively. Again, the horizontal attenuation coefficient can be compared to similarly obtained values at lower altitudes to observe the difference produced by rising higher in the atmosphere or to observe how closely experiment verifies the prediction of theory based on a Rayleigh molecular atmosphere.

Rather than delve too deeply into the method of calculating visibility, it may suffice to state that the quantities of luminance, illuminance, and contrast are enough to make use of nomograms for graphical solutions of visual range. These nomograms were devised by S. Q. Duntley[2] and based on the work of the Tiffany Foundation. They correspond to 95% probability of detection. Each is for a given value of background luminance and for a range of contrast values.

Nadir I and B

Albedo-type apparatus using a nadir-pointing spectrograph have been carried to 90,000 ft to examine the effects of varying terrain texture and increased altitude on reflecting the visual portion of the solar spectrum. Significant intensity variations were observed above New Mexico in passing over terrain such as scrub desert, bare rocky mountains, heavily wooded forest, and the White Sands—at lower levels. Closer to the peak of the flight the angle of view more nearly included all these varied terrains and the individual contributions were not resolvable. Moreover, it was found that the total nadir intensity of illumination due to the upwelling light increased with altitude, presumably due to reflection and scattering from layer discontinuities above the tropopause. This higher-level returned light, it appeared, veiled the actual brightness and brightness differences of adjacent areas on the ground.

A similar visual "albedo" experiment could be extended to the satellite. It has been pointed out that unless an area of uniform texture were unusually large in spread, the angle of view of the luminance units would record the integrated brightness of adjacent differing types of terrain. However, the "albedo" brightness of certain extensive reflecting surfaces can each be measured well within as well as above their perturbing boundaries, and further compared as to the degree of contribution to the total upwelling light illuminating the bottom of a surface 200 or 300 miles above the earth. In general, the surface or low-altitude reflecting surfaces may be reduced to the following: huge bodies of water, the lumped land areas within the angle of view, vast snow or ice fields, and wide cloud undercasts. It would be advisable to employ a nadir-pointed luminance unit to measure, as it were, the visual "albedo" or background brightness of these extended features.

An illuminance unit mounted on the undersurface of the satellite and pointing downward would record the illumination received from the lower hemisphere which includes the earth. The zenith-looking brightness of any object at this point may then be obtained from the product of the received illuminance and its surface reflectance. Comparable data of the same sort are available from balloon flights so that an average attenuation coefficient for the zenith direction from 20 to 200 miles or more may be computed. And with such measurements being made continually, then the ranging effect of the necessary parameter of sun's position will be attained.

The operational difference between luminance and illuminance measurements is that of gathering light flux in a cone of vertical angle smaller than or equal to 180°. The photronic cell with a diffusing, translucent cover plate set in a plane surface and looking downward measures the illuminance on such a surface produced by light upwelling from the earth ball and the scattering atmosphere in the hemisphere below the satellite. If, at the same time such an observation was being recorded, another unit were pointed downward but fabricated and baffled to subtend only the earth ball, then, substantially, a measurement of the earth ball's brightness would be obtained. The difference between this luminance value and the nadir illuminance value could then be attributed chiefly to the air-light outside of the earth-subtending cone. It is suggested that these two observations might be of interest to determine roughly how bright the earth ball appears with changing sun elevation and to estimate the order of illumination derived from the atmosphere outside of the earth-subtending cone.

Zenith I and B

In conjunction with the downward-looking instruments for sensing upwelling light flux, similar photometer units should be used pointed upward to receive the downwelling light. From a zenith-pointed luminance unit would be obtained the quantity of sky brightness as background to the satellite or other object seen directly overhead from lower or ground levels. Combining this background value with the measured undersurface brightness of an object at the same level in the manner of equation (2), one arrives at an inherent contrast figure in the zenith direction. Vertical contrast figures from satellite and balloon altitudes may then be compared for contrast reduction in the air space between these altitudes. An average attenuation coefficient for this atmospheric layer is calculable. The possibility of extending the use of the contrast reduction and attenuation coefficient for predicting a visual range continuing in the zenith presents itself. The zenith and horizontal contrast values can be employed with the pertinent background luminances and the Tiffany data in estimating where a satellite might be visible from the ground.

The brightness of the sky at zenith, when viewed from high altitude, was a matter of conjecture by the crew of Explorer II. The same inquiry has been made at recent date by a group interested in celestial navigation controls using stars that might be visible in a darkened daylight sky. The inquiry could be pushed to ask if a star could produce a noticeable perturbation in the illumination level at satellite altitudes. Occurrence of this phenomenon would be best examined by a modified luminance unit. Its angle of view would have to be reduced considerably so that intrusion of the star in the field would be immediately noted. The unit might even be converted by the addition of condenser lenses in the focal plane of the objective to what is called a Roche system, so that the luminance value recorded by the photocell would be constant as long as the star was held in the field of view.

The downwelling light illuminating the upper surface of the satellite would be measured by a zenith-pointed illuminance photometer unit. This would serve to obtain a record of the changing intensity of illumination as a function of the sun's position on the sunny side of the earth. It would also supply a measure of the light level due to sources other than the sun on the shady side of the earth. In either situation the value of upper-surface illuminance provides the quantity necessary for computing the satellite's brightness, contrasting it to the earth's background and leading to an estimate of its perceptibility from above.

Conclusion

More emphasis has been placed on the physical quantities of luminance and illuminance to be measured from a satellite than on actual visibility. This approach was followed, since the final determination of visibility depends on the actual physical conditions that may be found in the upper atmosphere. It is to these conditions that the seeing eye will probably have to adapt itself.

The arrangement of photometer units as suggested in each case is a minimal one. A luminance and illuminance photometer unit should always be paired, and at least two such pairs should be used together but looking in opposite directions. Since the satellite may have a tumbling or rolling motion, it would be far better if the horizon and zenith rings of photometer units were studded more frequently with units and, weight permitting, if rings of photometers were inserted obliquely between the basic two in order to improve the mapping of the sky.

The discussion has dealt with photometers receiving light intensities only, without regard to spectral distribution. The most interesting spectral investigation was not proposed, since the introduction of filters or filtering mechanisms would lead to marked increases in weight of themselves or in the mass of amplifying equipment to sense the reduced intensities in narrow spectral bands. It was felt that the problem of determining the spectral changes in the received solar spectrum between satellite and lower altitudes was better postponed.

The investigation of the polarization of light was also not proposed in the present paper because the problem of equipment design would mount in complexity. However, the degree of light polarization and its influence on vision as one progresses down through the atmosphere comprise an important area of investigation. Experience derived from measuring the total visual spectral luminance and illuminance could be used to advantage in later investigations of the component polarized and spectral-band parts.

Reference has been made to data acquired in a series of balloon flights which was completed in September, 1955. The data are in a final state of analysis and are not yet published. The quality of the conclusions drawn from these flights is based on confidence of calibration and equipment performance and on the internal consistency of observed results.

REFERENCES

1. Otto E. Berg, "Day Sky Brightness to 220 Km," *J. Geophys. Res., 60:* 271 (1955).
2. S. Q. Duntley, "The Visibility of Distant Objects," *J. Opt. Soc. Am., 38:* 237 (1948).

16

A Lyman Alpha Experiment for the Vanguard Satellite

by T. A. Chubb, H. Friedman, and J. Kupperian
U.S. NAVAL RESEARCH LABORATORY,
WASHINGTON, D.C.

Introduction

The hydrogen Lyman alpha line at 1215.7 A is the most prominent line in the far-ultraviolet solar spectrum. The intensity of the line and its profile are of particular interest in astrophysical theories of the structure of the chromosphere, since these characteristics depend very critically on temperature gradient, scale height, and spicule structure in any model solar atmosphere. It is absorbed in the earth's atmosphere, and it is believed to be responsible for radio fadeout during solar flares. The flare intensity of Lyman alpha may be orders of magnitude greater than its radiation from the entire disk under quiet conditions.[1] Theoretical estimates of the relationship between Lyman alpha intensity and flare magnitude vary greatly, however.

Since 1949 a number of direct observations of Lyman alpha by means of high-altitude rockets have been reported. Photon-counter measurements by Friedman, Lichtman, and Byram[2] were made in a V-2 rocket in 1949 (1–10 ergs cm^{-2} sec^{-1}) and by Byram, Chubb, Friedman, and Gailor,[3] in the Naval Research Laboratory Aerobees 8, 9, and 10 in 1952 (0.1 erg cm^{-2} sec^{-1}). A thermoluminescent phosphor flown by Tousey, Watanabe, and Purcell[4] in 1950 covered a band of wavelengths from 1040 A to 1240 A (0.4 erg cm^{-2} sec^{-1}). In 1952 the first photograph of the Lyman alpha line was obtained by a group from the University of Colorado under the direction of W. B. Pietenpol,[5] using a grazing incidence spectrograph (0.5 erg cm^{-2} sec^{-1}). Johnson, Purcell, Malitson, and Tousey[6] obtained excellent far-ultraviolet spectra, including Lyman alpha, in 1954 and 1955 (0.3–0.6 erg cm^{-2} sec^{-1}). In none of these experiments was there positive evidence of unusual solar activity. The spread of results has been ascribed partly to experimental uncertainties and partly to real fluctuations in solar intensity.

In October and November of 1955 solar Lyman alpha was measured again by an ion-chamber technique developed for use in NRL Aerobees 34, 35, and 36. The data have not yet been fully reduced but the intensities in all three flights exceeded 2 ergs cm^{-2} sec^{-1} and may have been as high as 4 ergs cm^{-2} sec^{-1}. We place a high reliability on these figures.

It is therefore evident from the measurements already made that the Lyman alpha radiation from the sun is highly variable even under conditions of insignificant solar-flare activity. To follow fluctuations in Lyman alpha continuously for any extended period of time, or even to obtain a good statistical sampling, would require a prohibitively large number of rocket flights. A satellite experiment offers the possibility of monitoring the sun in Lyman alpha almost continuously for many days and would be worth hundreds of individual rockets for the same purpose. During the period of maximum solar activity in 1957 and 1958, the chances of observing a flare of class-2 magnitude will be quite good and many small flares will certainly occur during the lifetime of the satellite.

Experimental Plan

Measurement of the solar radiation will be accomplished with an ion chamber sensitive to a narrow region of the spectrum centered about the Lyman alpha line. This type of chamber was developed at NRL for use in rockets and has already been flown in 3 Aerobees, during 1955. The chamber responds to photo-ionization of its gaseous filling. If nitric oxide is used, the threshold response occurs at about 1340 A. The short-wavelength cut-off is determined by the opacity of the lithium fluoride window below about 1100 A. Between these wavelengths more than 95% of the solar radiation is concentrated in the hydrogen Lyman alpha line.

One or more of these chambers mounted with their windows exposed through the skin of the satellite will observe the direct radiation from the sun sometime during each roll period. If the telemetering stations are to be located along one meridian, information can be obtained from the satellite for only a few seconds out of each orbit. The instrumentation will therefore include circuitry for storing the peak signal of the Lyman alpha chamber during each revolution of the satellite around the earth. In addition to measuring the maximum variation of the Lyman alpha emission during the sunlit portion of each orbital period, the circuitry will provide for an interval of directly monitored Lyman alpha during the brief telemetering period. The aspect of the sun (angle between direction of the sun and the normal to the window of the chamber) will be provided by a simple photocell. A block diagram of the experimental apparatus is given in Fig. 1.

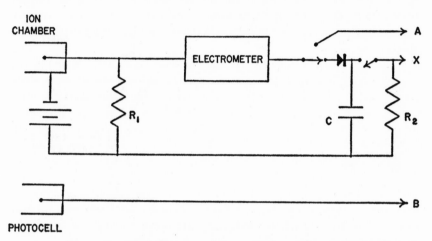

FIGURE 1.   Block diagram of the experimental apparatus.

During the silent period, switch *a* is closed and *x* is open as shown in Fig. 1. When the ion chamber responds to radiation, the voltage developed in resistor R_1 is transmitted via the electrometer and switch *a* to diode *D* and condenser *C*. The diode and condenser form a peak voltmeter and the maximum signal developed during the sunlit orbit will remain stored on the condenser. When the satellite passes over the Minitrack station, telemetering will be switched on. At the start of the telemetering interval, switch *a* transfers the ion-chamber signal to telemeter channel *A* so that instantaneous solar Lyman alpha intensity is transmitted on channel *A*. Simultaneously, aspect information is presented on channel *B*. Sufficient telemetering time should be allowed for these signals to establish the "normal" level of Lyman alpha brightness and to provide roll-period information of interest in connection with the general behavior of the satellite.

Since the stored orbital data can be read out only once per telemetering interval, it is preferable that this read-out occur at the most favorable portion of the telemetering period, i.e., at the point of closest approach to the receiving station. Therefore, after an appropriate delay following the beginning of telemetering, switch x will be closed. Condenser C is thereby discharged through resistor R_2 and the resultant voltage is telemetered on channel X. To provide a large-scale expansion, condenser C will purposely contain "off-scale" information. The duration of the off-scale period and the curve of the "visible" RC discharge should provide a scale expansion of about 100.

The system outlined in Fig. 1 would be assembled from existing components weighing less than 600 gm and would have an operating life in excess of 500 hours.

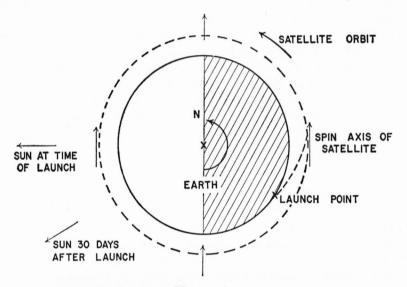

FIGURE 2.   Aspect problem.

Aspect Considerations

The orientation of the satellite at the moment of burn-out of the final stage will determine its aspect relative to the fixed stars for the life of the satellite. Fig. 2 illustrates the aspect problem for the case where the spin axis is tangent to the earth's surface at burn-out. The detector would be mounted with the plane of its window parallel to the spin axis. Since the effective field of view may be made as large as 120°, the detector should see the sun on each roll in the sunlit hemisphere. If the flight of the satellite starts with the spin along a principal axis and with the tube viewing the sun, this orientation should be preserved for several weeks. In the actual launching, conditions may differ somewhat from the simple picture of Fig. 2. The trajectory at burn-out may not be tangent to the earth's surface, the spin axis may not be tangent to the orbit, and, indeed, the spin axis may not be a principal axis of inertia. These factors, coupled with the useful field of view of the detector, would determine the optimum time to launch for the purpose of this experiment.

Conclusion

During the IGY, many phenomena associated with solar activity will be monitored by an extensive network of observatories. The satellite Lyman alpha measurements will relate directly to sudden ionospheric disturbances accompanying solar flares, and these disturbances will be recorded in the forms of radio fadeouts, sudden phase anomalies, cosmic noise absorption, and magnetic crochets. If the permissible satellite payload restricts the possible measurement to just one wavelength, then Lyman alpha would appear to be the most interesting wavelength to study. Additional weight allowance would permit duplication of the experiment in other wavelengths. It would be particularly interesting to follow the variations in the short wavelength X-ray limit of coronal emission.

REFERENCES

1. H. Friedman and T. A. Chubb, "The Physics of the Ionosphere," Report of 1954 Cambridge Conference, p. 58.
2. H. Friedman *et al.*, "Photon Counter Measurements of Solar X-Rays and Extreme Ultraviolet Light," *Phys. Rev., 83:* 1025–1030 (1951).
3. E. T. Byram *et al.*, "Lyman-Alpha Radiation in the Solar Spectrum," *Phys. Rev., 91:* 1278–1279 (1953).
4. R. Tousey *et al.*, "Measurements of Solar Extreme Ultraviolet and X-Rays from Rockets by Means of a $CaSO_4$: Mn Phosphor," *Phys. Rev., 83:* 792–797 (1951).
5. W. B. Pietenpol *et al.*, "Lyman Alpha-Line Photographed in the Sun's Spectrum," *Phys. Rev., 90:* 156 (1953).
6. F. S. Johnson *et al.*, "Emission Lines in the Solar Ultraviolet Spectrum," *Astron. J., 60:* 165 (1955).

A Satellite Experiment to Determine the Distribution of Hydrogen in Space

by T. A. Chubb, H. Friedman, and J. Kupperian
U.S. NAVAL RESEARCH LABORATORY,
WASHINGTON, D.C.

It is proposed to measure simultaneously the intensity of hydrogen Lyman alpha radiation (1215.7 A) received directly from the sun and the resonance radiation of the same wavelength produced by sunlit hydrogen atoms in space. A relatively insensitive photon counter would be used to monitor the intense 1216 A radiation emitted directly by the sun. This radiation pours out through space and is scattered in all directions by hydrogen atoms. At the same time, hydrogen ions are produced from atoms in space by the shorter solar ultraviolet and X-ray radiation or are ejected into space directly from the sun. A fraction of these protons and electrons will recombine into excited states leading to a comparatively slowly varying background of the same Lyman alpha wavelength. An extremely sensitive photon counter can be used to measure the sum of scattered and recombination radiation. When a large flare appears on the sun, the scattered radiation will promptly increase in direct proportion to the growth of Lyman alpha in the flare. The effect on the intensity of recombination radiation will be much slower, so the contribution due to scattering by neutral hydrogen in space can be distinguished from the recombination radiation.

Any theoretical computation of the radiation intensity requires, among other things, a knowledge of the absorption cross section for resonant scattering, the ionization cross section, the recombination co-efficient for radiative capture of electrons by protons, the solar intensity, and, of course, the hydrogen atom and ion densities. Some rough esti-mates have been made using the following numbers:

Solar flux density of Lyman alpha at earth $= 1$ erg cm^{-2} sec^{-1}.

Scattering cross section in core of Lyman alpha line $= 5 \times 10^{-14}$ cm^2.

Recombination coefficient $= 1.5 \times 10^{-12}$ cm^3 sec^{-1}.

Examples of some results derived from these figures are:

1) The scattered intensity in quanta cm^{-2} sec^{-1} from 2π hemi-sphere looking away from the sun is about $10^{10}N_H$ where N_H is the neutral hydrogen density, assumed to be uniform in space.

2) The intensity of recombination radiation varies from $2N_{H+}^2$ to $7N_{H+}^2$ quanta cm^{-2} sec^{-1} looking away from the sun, depending on whether the ion distribution near the earth is inverse square or inverse first power with distance from the sun.

Without knowing the ratio of neutral to atomic hydrogen, a single measurement of Lyman alpha intensity from space will not make it possible to estimate the hydrogen distribution. The correlation with flare activity, however, permits a simple separation of resonant and recombination radiations.

The experimental measurements in the satellite would be per-formed by photon counters.[1] Such tubes operate according to the familiar Geiger counter principle, except that discharges or counts are triggered by ultraviolet photons which photo-ionize the gas contents. A novel feature of the tubes developed by the Naval Research Labora-tory is the elimination of the long wavelength response ordinarily obtained from the cathode surface. This is achieved by using an electro-negative constituent in the gas mixture. Slow electrons photoelectrically ejected from the cathode are quickly attached to form negative ions which drift to the anode without triggering counts. The desired short wavelength threshold is obtained by including a gas component which has its photo-ionization threshold in the far ultraviolet. Nitric oxide serves both functions in a very efficient detector for Lyman alpha. Its photo-threshold is at 1340 A and the ionization cross section at Lyman alpha is very high. In combination with a lithium fluoride window it is sensitive to the spectral region from 1100 A to 1340 A, and it is possible to obtain quantum yields of a few percent at Lyman alpha with comparatively negligible response to longer wavelength solar radiation.

The insensitive photon counter is prepared with chlorine as the negative-ion former. Although chlorine itself is not photo-ionized at Lyman alpha, it forms trace compounds which are ionizable. Instead of obtaining yields of 10^{-2}, as is the case with NO, the halogen-quenched tubes have yields of about 10^{-7} between 1100 A and 1300 A. This low yield is adequate to produce several hundred counts per second when the tube views the solar Lyman alpha radiation directly.

To return to the figure quoted above of $10^{10}N_H$ quanta cm^{-2} sec^{-1} from 2π steradians, a sensitive counter with a yield of 1% and a 1-cm^2 window would produce $10^8 N_H$ counts sec^{-1}. If the field of view is restricted to one-thousandth of the hemisphere, the counting rate will be $10^5 N_H$. A concentration N_H of 10^{-4} cm^{-3} would give a measurable intensity and in the event of a flare the intensity would rise proportionately. The recombination radiation should then be observable if the concentration is about 10 ions cm^{-3} or greater for almost any distribution extending over the dimensions of the solar system. Restriction of the field of view would permit distributed sources of hydrogen in local space to be mapped. It should also detect celestial sources of Lyman alpha radiation in the background. One nighttime rocket flight[2] has already been carried out. This flight showed that high counting rates of Lyman alpha from space can be obtained with a 5° field of view.

Electronics

A block diagram of the circuitry proposed for the satellite is shown in Fig. 1. This system would operate only during telemetering.

At the present stage of development this circuitry, including detectors and batteries to provide five hours of operating life, would weigh less than 900 gm. If the spin rate is to be as high as one per second, the frequency response of the individual channels should be no less than 200 cps. The rate meters indicated in Fig. 1 have a useful dynamic range of over three decades. This is accomplished by counting individual events at low rates and using circuit and counter dead times to give a compressed scale at the highest rates.

Aspect System

A lightweight optical aspect system compatible with single-channel telemetering and low power drain has been developed and used successfully in several rocket flights. The essential features of this system are a highly collimated high-sensitivity photocell for detecting the earth's albedo and a broadly collimated low-sensitivity photocell to provide aspect relative to the sun. Signals from the photocells are modulated by the spin of the satellite; and from the resulting amplitudes and phase relations the orientation of the detector axes relative to the earth can be determined. Since the information is generated by the spin of the satellite, it is desirable that the detectors' axes be perpendicular to the spin axis.

Any set of signals received from the system corresponds to eight

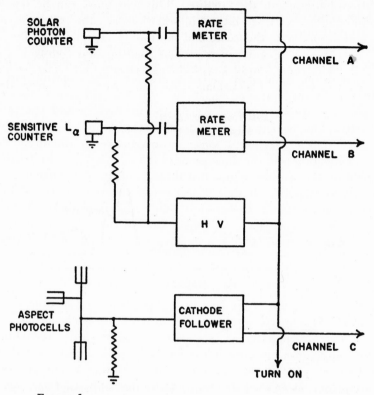

FIGURE 1.

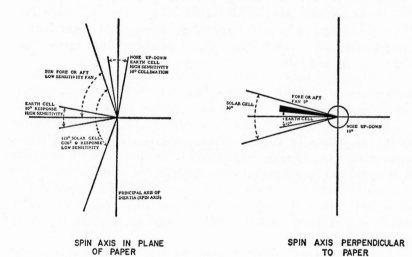

SPIN AXIS IN PLANE
OF PAPER

SPIN AXIS PERPENDICULAR
TO PAPER

FIGURE 2.

possible orientations of the satellite. This ambiguity can be removed with the addition of three bits of information, i.e., the roll sense, nose up or down relative to the earth, and sun fore or aft relative to the spin axis. A schematic diagram of a proposed collimation coding is given in Fig. 2. A one-roll scan of a typical single-channel telemetering input is depicted in Fig. 3. The Lyman alpha detectors are, of course, them-

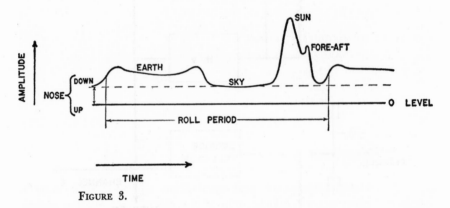

FIGURE 3.

selves sensitive to the sun and can yield the additional information required to give the roll sense.

This system has some blind spots, i.e., the sun near or below horizontal or the sun near zenith, but it should give aspect adequate for our purposes for over 80% of the sunlit orbit. The aspect obtained during the daylight orbit may be followed through the night portion by correlation with Lyman alpha signals resulting from earth shine, the Milky Way, and other celestial sources.

REFERENCES

1. T. A. Chubb and H. Friedman, "Photon Counter for the Far Ultraviolet," *Rev. Sci. Inst.*, *26:* 493 (1955).
2. N.R.L. Aerobee 25, 2:00 A.M., Nov. 17, 1955.

Ultraviolet Stellar Magnitudes

by *Robert J. Davis*
HARVARD COLLEGE OBSERVATORY

ABSTRACT

Computations are performed from which it is possible to construct a tentative map of the sky at 1249 A. For normal stars, it is assumed that the energy distribution can be represented by a Planck function at a temperature depending only on spectral type. Wolf-Rayet stars, nuclei of planetary nebulae, certain peculiar A stars, the sun, and the moon are considered separately. Interstellar reddening is taken into account on the assumption that absorption varies as $1/\lambda$. The limiting magnitude is taken as $+ 2.0$ in the ultraviolet. 218 objects prove to be brighter than this limiting magnitude. Of these 218 objects, only the sun is of spectral type later than A1. 211 of these objects are normal. The results of this survey may form the basis for a rocket experiment.

Since astronomical observations of the sun from without the earth's atmosphere are becoming more common and more precise, it is important to predict the appearance of the sky in the far-ultraviolet region of the spectrum, at present unobservable. I have therefore performed computations from which it is possible to construct a tentative map of the sky at 1249 A.

In order to perform these computations, I have assumed that the energy distribution of any star may be closely approximated by a Planck function $B_\nu(T)$, where T depends only on spectral type. This assumption is based on the observation that the radiation from the sun near the maximum of its intensity curve approximates a Planck function. Very few stars of spectral type later than B8 would appear bright at 1249 A; for earlier stars, the maximum of the intensity curve should lie near to that wavelength.

In accordance with the above assumption, I have defined the ultraviolet magnitude as

$$m_2 = m_1 - 2.5 \log \frac{B\nu_2(T)}{B\nu_1(T)} + C$$

where m_1 is the reference magnitude (photographic or photovisual), $B_\nu(T)$ is the Planck function, ν_1 corresponds to the effective wavelength of the reference magnitude, and ν_2 corresponds to 1249 A. The constant C is chosen so that zero color index corresponds to spectral type A0.

I set the limiting magnitude for these computations at $m_2' = +2.0$, where m_2' indicates that m_2 has been corrected for interstellar reddening. The temperature scale chosen for stars later than type B0 was that given by Hynek.[1] For the O stars, I used the temperature scale given by Vorontsov-Velyaminov.[2] These two scales agree at type B0. R. M. Petrie[3] gives slightly higher temperatures for the O stars.

For every spectral type I computed a limiting photovisual magnitude that I then applied to the entries in the Yale *Catalogue of Bright Stars* (Schlesinger and Jenkins[4]) and to the list of O stars in Payne's *The Stars of High Luminosity*[5] to obtain a finding list of interesting objects. To this list I added all Wolf-Rayet stars and nuclei of planetary nebulae brighter than photographic magnitude 8.5, noting that even at 100,000°K fainter objects would not need to be considered. The sun and moon completed the list.

For every star on the finding list, Stebbins, Huffer, and Whitford,[6] Plaskett and Pearce,[7] or Merrill and Burwell[8] provided revised spectra. I used the photovisual magnitudes given by Payne-Gaposchkin,[9] and checked the results by a set of computations based on the photographic magnitudes given in the *Henry Draper Catalogue* (Cannon and Pickering[10]). The effective wavelength was taken as 5400 A for the photovisual magnitudes and 4102 A for the photographic magnitudes. For all stars except the peculiar objects discussed below, the resulting ultraviolet magnitudes are believed to be accurate to $\pm 0^m.5$ p.e.

The temperatures and spectral intensity curves of the Wolf-Rayet stars presented the most difficult problems in this study. Beals[11] and W. Petrie[12] found from measurements of the continuum that the mean effective temperature of these stars was about 13,000°K, although it was almost impossible to separate out the effects of interstellar reddening.

Excitation and Zanstra temperatures were near 60,000°K. Vorontsov-Velyaminov[13] found a relation from which he could compute the relative contributions of the bright lines and of the continuum to the measured photographic magnitude of a Wolf-Rayet star, given the excitation temperature. Bappu[14] has also discussed the temperatures of Wolf-Rayet stars.

For most of the northern Wolf-Rayet stars, individual excitation temperatures have been published (Beals[11] and W. Petrie[12]). For those objects without published temperatures, I adopted the mean excitation temperature, $T = 60,000°K$. Any more elaborate assumption would be beyond the scope of this paper. Relatively few objects are affected, since only three Wolf-Rayet stars remained above the limiting magnitude of +2.0 after correction for interstellar absorption. However, two of these stars—ζ Puppis (HD 66811) and γ Velorum (HD 68273)—became the brightest objects in the sky, with the sole exception of the sun, so that a rocket photograph of the Puppis-Vela region of the sky would give valuable and interesting information concerning Wolf-Rayet stars. The third star is HD 152408, which is estimated to have exactly the limiting magnitude of +2.0 after correction for 1.7 magnitudes of absorption. All three of these stars are southern objects, lying south of declination $-40°$. None of them has an individually measured temperature. The brighter two have recently been studied by Smith.[15] Each of the three has a normal O spectrum superposed on the Wolf-Rayet spectrum; I have assumed that each component has contributed equally to the photographic magnitude.

Two stars on this program have highly peculiar spectra. Gamma Cassiopeiae (HD 5394) is listed by Morgan and Keenan[16] as B0IV. This star is also known to be an emission-line object. I have taken the temperature as normal for a B0 star: 25,000°K. Eta Carinae (HD 93308) has a spectrum that defies classification. The continuum indicates a temperature of perhaps 20,000°K, the value used in my computations. In addition, this latter star is a nova-like variable, at present lying about 2.5 magnitudes below its last (1843) outburst. The corresponding ultraviolet magnitude is $m_2' = +1.0$.

A large class of peculiar A stars, many of which are spectrum variables, is known to contain abnormally blue stars (Deutsch[17] and Davis[18]). Two of these stars—ϵ Ursae Majoris (HD 112185) and θ Aurigae (HD 40312)—are A0p; I have assumed a temperature of 13,000°K, as compared to 11,000°K for normal A0 stars.

No nuclei of planetary nebulae were found to approach the limiting magnitude of $m_2' = +2.0$, even at temperatures of 100,000°K. The few known hotter objects were considered separately, and also fell far below the limit. Temperatures for planetary nebula nuclei were obtained primarily from Vorontsov-Velyaminov[19] and from Liller.[20]

For all other stars I have used the temperature scales given by Hynek[1] and Vorontsov-Velyaminov,[2] as indicated in Table I.

TABLE I

Temperatures of stars according to spectral type

Spectrum	O5	O6	O7	O8	O9	B0	B1	B2	B3
T (°K $\times 10^{-3}$)	35	33	31	29	27	25	22.5	20.3	18
Spectrum		B4	B5	B6	B7	B8	B9	A0	A1	A2
T (°K $\times 10^{-3}$)		16.8	15.6	14.6	13.6	12.8	11.8	11	10.3	9.7

Since the absorption coefficient of the interstellar medium is known to vary inversely as the wavelength throughout the observable region of the spectrum (Liller[20] and references listed therein), the ultraviolet extinctions at 1249 A may be obtained by extrapolation. For most of my stars, the E_1 color excesses of Stebbins, Huffer, and Whitford[6] are an easily applied uniform criterion. Applying the $1/\lambda$ law of interstellar absorption and neglecting negative E_1, we obtain the corrected value of the ultraviolet magnitude,

$$m_2' = m_2 + 19.2E_1.$$

For objects lying south of $-40°$ declination, there is no extensive uniform survey of color excess. I have therefore relied on the parallaxes (mostly spectroscopic) as given in the Yale *Catalogue of Bright Stars* (Schlesinger and Jenkins[4]), and have used the mean extinction in the galactic plane as given by Allen,[21] applying the $1/\lambda$ law of absorption.

The resulting probable errors are believed to be within $\pm 25\%$ of the correction for stars for which E_1 has been measured, and $+100\%$ or -50% for other objects.

Reddening was applied to the sun on the basis of rocket observations of the spectrum near Lyman alpha (Johnson, Malitson, Purcell, and Tousey;[22] Friedman, Lichtman, and Bryan;[23] Tousey, Watanabe, and Purcell[24]). Reddening was applied to the moon and planets by applying a $1/\lambda$ law to their observed color excesses, which in this case are due to reflectivity and not to absorption.

The results of the calculations described above are given in Table II. In addition, the ultraviolet magnitude of the sun (spectral type G1V) was found to be $m_2' = -13.2$.

In all, 218 objects proved to be brighter than $m_2' = +2.0$. Of these, 23 were brighter than $m_2' = -1.0$. An additional 160 objects, including 19 Wolf-Rayet stars, would have been brighter than $m_2' = +2.0$ had it not been for interstellar reddening.

The distribution, according to spectral type, of stars that are bright

TABLE II

Ultraviolet stellar magnitudes (m_2')

HD No.	Spectrum	m_2'	HD No.	Spectrum	m_2'
358	B9p	1.7	37128	cB0eI	−2.3
886	B2IV	−0.5	37202	B3e	−0.1
1337	O8	1.9*	37209	B1	1.8
3360	B2.5IV	0.4	37438	B3	1.9
3369	B3	1.6	37468	B0	0.5
5394	B0eIV	−0.7*	37490	B3e	1.9
10144	B9	0.0	37711	B3	2.0
10516	B0e	1.5	37742–3	B0e	−2.5
11415	B5III	1.1	37756	B3	1.9
16582	B2	0.4	37795	B8e	1.6
19356	B8V	1.0*	38771	cB0II	−1.0
20336	B3e	1.7	40111	B0II	1.9
23630	B5eIII	1.0	40312	A0p	1.6
24760	B0.5III	−1.2	40494	B3	1.5
24912	O7e	1.1	41117	B1eI	1.8
25204	B3	1.1*	41753	B3	1.3
25940	B3e	2.0	42525	B3	1.8
29248	B2	0.5	42560	B3	1.3
30614	O9.5e	1.5	42690	B3	2.0
30836	B2	0.2	42933	B1	1.6?
31237	B2	0.2*	44402	B5	1.1?
32630	B4V	0.5	44743	cB1I–II	−1.3
33328	B3	1.8	45542	B5e	1.7
34085	B8Ia	−0.8	45546	B3	1.9
34816	B1	0.4	45725–6–7	B3e–B3–B3e	1.1
35039	B3	1.6	46328	B1	0.4
35149	B3	1.9	46487	B3	2.0
35411	B0V	−1.0	47105	A0IV	1.9
35468	B2IV	−1.9	47839	O7	−0.2
35497	B7III	0.3	48915	A1V	−1.1
35708	B3	1.8	50013	B2e	0.6
35715	B2	1.1	50707	B0	0.6
36267	B4	1.8	52089	B1III	−2.1
36486	B0	−1.9*	52918	B3	1.8
36512	B2	1.5	53138	B3I	0.4
36591	B2	1.7	54893	B3	2.0
36695	B2	1.8*	55879	O9	1.4
36822	B0III	0.9	56139	B3e	1.0
36861–2	O8	−0.3	57060	O7.5	−0.2*
36960	B1	0.8	57061	O9	−0.2
37018	B2	1.3	57150	B3e	1.9
37041–2	O9–B1	1.8	58350	B5I	1.3
37043	O8.5	−1.9	58715	B8eV	2.0

TABLE II

Ultraviolet stellar magnitudes (m_2') (cont'd)

HD No.	Spectrum	m_2'	HD No.	Spectrum	m_2'
58978	B2pe	1.9	120307	B2	0.3
63462	B3e	1.7	120315	B5V	−0.5
63922	B0	0.3	120324	B3e	0.4
64503	B3	1.7	121263	B3p	0.2
64760	B2	1.4	121743	B3	1.2
65575	B3	0.7	121790	B3	1.3
65818	B2p	1.4*	122451	B3	−2.2
66811	O5 + WC8?	−3.0	122980	B3	1.7
68273	O6 + WC6?	−3.0	125238	B3	1.3
70930	B2	1.8	126341	B3	1.9
71129–30	K0 + B	0.3	127381	B3	1.8
74195	B3	0.9	127972–3	B3e + A2p	0.5
74280	B5	2.0	128345	B5	2.0
74375	B1	0.9	129056	B2	−0.5
74575	B1	0.0	129116	B3	1.2
74956	A0	2.0	132058	B3p	−0.1
75311	B3e	1.8	132200	B2	0.0
79351	B3	0.7	133242–3	B5	1.9
79447	B3	1.3	133935	B3	1.5
80007	A0	1.8?	135240	O8	1.5
81188	B3	−0.3	135591	O9	1.7
83953	B3e	1.8	135742	B8V	1.7
87901	B7V	−0.2	136298	B3	0.5
91316	cB1	0.1	136504	B3	0.9
91465	B5e	1.5	136664	B3	1.8
93030	B0	−1.1	138690	B3	0.1
93308	Pec	Var*	138749	B5e	1.9
105435	B3e	−0.2	139365	B3	0.8
105937	B3	1.2	141637	B3	1.9
106490	B3	0.0	142114	B3	1.8
106625	B8III	1.7	142669	B1I	0.3
106983	B3	1.3	142983	B3p?	1.6?
108248–9	B1–B3	−2.5	143018	B3	−0.1
108483	B3	1.3	143118	B3	0.7
109026	B5	1.9	143275	B1IV	−1.4
109668	B5	0.7	144217–8	B1IV–B2	−0.4
110879	B3	0.4	144470	B2	1.1
111123	Ble	−2.2	145482	B3	2.0
112091–2	B3e–B3	1.8	147165	B1III	1.3
112185	A0p	0.5	147394	B5IV	1.6
113791	B3	1.6	148605	B3	1.8
116658	B1III–IV	−2.7	148703	B3	1.6
118716	B2	−0.9	149438	B0V	−1.5

TABLE II

Ultraviolet stellar magnitudes (m_2') (cont'd)

HD No.	Spectrum →	m_2'	HD No.	Spectrum	m_2'
149757	O8	−0.4	173948	B3	2.0
150135–6	O6–O7	1.3	175191	B3	−0.8
151890	B3p	0.3*	188209	O8	1.9
151985	B2	0.0	191610	B3e	1.7
152236	B1e	2.0	192685	B3	1.9
152408	O8 + WC8?	2.0	193924	B3	−0.9
156633	B3	1.5*	200120	B3e	1.7
157056	B2IV	−0.2	202904	B3e	1.8
157246	B1	0.1	203064	O8	1.5
158408	B3	−0.1	204172	B0	2.0
158427	B3e	0.0	205021	B1IV	−0.6*
158926	B2IV	−1.8	207330	B3	1.8
160578	B3	−0.4	209952	B5	−0.2
160762	B3IV	0.7	212571	B1e	1.3
165024	B1p	0.2	214680	O8.5	0.2
166182	B2	0.8	214993	B1III	1.5
169467	B6	2.0	218376	cB1	1.6
172167	A0V	0.1	224572	B2	1.9

* Indicates maximum magnitude of variable stars with range of less than 0.7 magnitude, and of β Persei (HD 19356). Eta Carinae (HD 93308) is discussed separately in the text.

in the ultraviolet is entirely different from that of stars that are bright in the ordinary photographic region, as is shown in Table III.

TABLE III

Distribution of stars according to spectral type

Spectrum →	W	O	B	A	F	G	K	M	Pec	Other
% Stars brighter than $m_{pg} = 6.5$	0	0+	10	22	19	14	32	3	0	0+
% Stars brighter than $m_2' = 2.0$	2	10	84	4	0	0+	0	0	0+	0

Owing to the $1/\lambda$ law of interstellar absorption, space is not nearly so transparent at 1249 A as at 5000 A; therefore, the number of stars in a given magnitude interval increases more slowly with decreasing ultraviolet brightness than with decreasing photographic brightness.

Because of the high preponderance of early-type stars in this survey, the galactic equator is strongly accentuated in the ultraviolet. A large clustering of nonreddened stars appears in Orion and the Centaurus-

Carina region, a large clustering of reddened stars in Cygnus, and a partially reddened clustering in Scorpio. Of the 23 brightest objects in the ultraviolet, only two lie north of the celestial equator.

The results of this survey should prove valuable in the selection of the most interesting regions for study when extraterrestrial photometry of high resolution, either from rockets or from artificial satellites, becomes possible.

I wish to thank Dr. F. L. Whipple for suggesting this problem and for assistance in various aspects of the investigation; my thanks also go to Dr. R. N. Thomas and Dr. C. H. Payne-Gaposchkin for many helpful suggestions.

REFERENCES

1. J. A. Hynek (ed.). *Astrophysics.* New York: McGraw-Hill Book Co., 1951.
2. B. Vorontsov-Velyaminov. *Gasnebel und neue Sterne.* Berlin: Verlag Kultur und Fortschritt, 1953.
3. R. M. Petrie, *Pub. Dom. Astrophys. Obs. Victoria, 7:* 321 (1947).
4. F. Schlesinger and L. F. Jenkins. *Catalogue of Bright Stars.* New Haven: Yale Univ. Observatory, 1940.
5. C. H. Payne. *The Stars of High Luminosity.* New York: McGraw-Hill Book Co., 1930.
6. J. Stebbins *et al.,* "The Colors of 1332 B Stars," *Astrophys. J., 91:* 20 (1940).
7. J. S. Plaskett and J. A. Pearce, "A Catalogue of the Radial Velocities of O and B Type Stars," *Pub. Dom. Astrophys. Obs. Victoria, 5:* 99–165 (1931).
8. P. W. Merrill and C. G. Burwell, "Catalogue and Bibliography of Stars of Classes B and A Whose Spectra Have Bright Hydrogen Lines," *Astrophys. J., 78:* 87–140 (1933); *ibid., 98:* 153 (1943).
9. C. H. Payne-Gaposchkin. *Harvard Mimeograms,* Series III, No. 1 and No. 2, 1938.
10. A. J. Cannon and E. C. Pickering. *The Henry Draper Catalogue,* Vols. 91–99, Annals of the Astronomical Observatory of Harvard College. Cambridge: The Observatory, 1918–24.
11. C. S. Beals, "On the Physical Characteristics of the Wolf Rayet Stars and Their Relation to Other Objects of Early Type," *J. Roy. Astron. Soc. Canada, 34:* 169–197 (1940).
12. W. Petrie, *Pub. Dom. Astrophys. Obs. Victoria, 7:* 383 (1947).
13. B. Vorontsov-Velyaminov, *Zeits. f. Astrophysik, 10:* 353 (1935).
14. M. K. V. Bappu. Thesis, Harvard Univ., 1951.
15. H. J. Smith. Thesis, Harvard Univ., 1955.

16. W. W. Morgan and P. C. Keenan. *An Atlas of Stellar Spectra.* Chicago: Univ. of Chicago Press, 1943.

17. A. J. Deutsch, "A Study of the Spectrum Variables of Type A," *Astrophys. J., 105:* 283–304 (1947).

18. R. J. Davis. Undergraduate Thesis, Harvard College, 1951.

19. B. Vorontsov-Velyaminov, *Astr. Zhur., U.S.S.R., 11:* 40 (1934).

20. W. Liller, "The Photoelectric Photometry of Planetary Nebulae," *Astrophys. J., 122:* 240–255 (1955).

21. C. W. Allen. *Astrophysical Quantities.* London: The Athlone Press, 1955.

22. F. S. Johnson *et al.,* "Emission Lines in the Solar Ultraviolet Spectrum," *Astron. J., 60:* 165 (1955).

23. H. Friedman *et al.,* "Photon Counter Measurements of Solar X-Rays and Extreme Ultraviolet Light," *Phys. Rev., 83:* 1025–1030 (1951).

24. R. Tousey *et al.,* "Measurements of Solar Extreme Ultraviolet and X-Rays from Rockets by Means of a $CaSO_4$: Mn Phosphor," *Phys. Rev., 83:* 792–797 (1951).

Quantitative Intensity Measurements in the Extreme Ultraviolet

by H. E. Hinteregger
GEOPHYSICS RESEARCH DIRECTORATE,
AIR FORCE CAMBRIDGE RESEARCH CENTER

The expression "Extreme Ultraviolet" (E.U.V.), as used herein, refers to any electromagnetic radiation from about fifteen hundred down to a few angstroms in wavelength. With this understanding, the E.U.V. covers the interesting region of overlapping ultraviolet and soft X-ray, in which a particular radiation of a certain wavelength actually may be called by either name, depending on the nature of its physical origin. In terms of energy per radiation quantum, the E.U.V. in our liberal definition represents the range from about eight electron volts up to a few thousand.

Any illustration of the various regions of electromagnetic radiation, using a linear scale for quantum energies rather than for wavelengths, shows clearly that the energy range covered by all the infrared, visible, and near ultraviolet radiation together is truly quite small as compared with that of the E.U.V. This picture is not used here with any tendency to minimize the importance of infrared, visible, or ordinary ultraviolet spectroscopy; it should simply illustrate the contrast between the extent of the energy range and the extent to which this range has been covered by studies in the past.

The present body of knowledge about the E.U.V. and its interactions with matter is relatively meager, not only with regard to quantitative data but even with regard to the basic understanding of certain interactions. This situation seems strange because it could not possibly be attributed to any lack of high efficiencies in the interaction of this radiation with matter; on the contrary, E.U.V. radiation is extremely effective, reacting with practically everything, so that any solid or liquid stops it completely within extremely short pathlengths; also, the E.U.V. includes the regions of maximum cross sections for photo-ionization of gases; and the photoelectric emission from solids in the E.U.V. has been found to exhibit yields which strongly exceed even those of alkali metals at their peak response in the near ultraviolet or visible.

Considering these prominent aspects, the weak position of the E.U.V. as to its scientific exploration in the past becomes intelligible only from a historic view, taking into account the considerable experimental difficulties, lack of appropriate technical equipment, and possibly the abundance of attractive problems in other fields of physical research. Also, a merely psychological factor may tempt us to underestimate the role of E.U.V.: in contradistinction to many other types of radiation, E.U.V. never is "loose" in our laboratories or anywhere else on earth, because it takes only very little material to absorb it completely, so that its terrestrial activities are strictly confined to the inside of evacuated components such as tubes.

E.U.V. interactions with matter still present a wide-open field for fundamental research and technological development. Therefore, its eventual importance cannot be fully appreciated at the present time. Based on some recent investigations, the following tentative assessment, however, seems to be reasonable:

1) For terrestrial technology, a strong linkage of E.U.V. studies can be expected with problems of gaseous discharges, with certain phenomena in vacuum tubes, and particularly with various aspects of solid-state physics and solid-state technology;

2) For the technology dealing with objects beyond the earth's atmosphere, the importance of E.U.V. studies is even more obvious, because no longer is this radiation confined to the inside of tubes as under terrestrial conditions; it is now "loose."

Rocket experiments carried out by the Naval Research Laboratory and the University of Colorado have already provided evidence of E.U.V. radiation from the sun. Most of the questions such as what E.U.V. could or could not do to various materials on a satellite, how it might affect other measurements, whether or not it might interfere with certain mechanisms, and any similar problems will have to wait for an answer until appreciable progress has been made toward the following two objectives: quantitative intensity measurements from a satellite and an increased knowledge of E.U.V. interactions with matter, well beyond its present stage of preliminary probing. To a large extent, the two objectives may turn out to be inseparable for reasons which will be discussed later.

The "ideal" goal of intensity measurements over any region of the electromagnetic radiation is to find the absolute spectral-intensity distribution in terms of energy per unit of area, unit of time, and unit of wavelength, or frequency differential, taken as a perfectly resolved function of wavelength or frequency. In order to approach this goal we should have:

1) A dispersing unit (monochromator), whose transmission as a function of wavelength has been determined, and

2) An "absolute" detector, which is wavelength independent, absorbing totally any incident radiation and converting its energy into heat which, in turn, could be subjected to a calorimetric measurement (at least in principle).

How closely this approach can be followed for any practical analysis of some given radiation depends mainly on the available intensity. The lower the average spectral intensity the more has to be sacrificed as to both the obtainable dispersion and the "absolute" character of the detector. Even for radiation of some easily accessible wavelength range and for intensities many times higher than those which can reasonably be expected in the case of E.U.V. on a satellite, the experimenter generally has to settle for much less than the above ideal goal. For the measurement of E.U.V. radiation seen from a satellite, two major obstacles must be considered:

1) The use of any monochromator in the E.U.V. necessarily entails an appreciable loss of intensity (because of the poor reflectivity of gratings in this region);

2) Unless the overall E.U.V. intensity under the conditions met by a satellite is many times higher than actually expected, the total intensity of E.U.V., integrated over its entire range (not dispersed), would hardly be enough for an "absolute" measurement by the most sensitive thermocouple.*

Fortunately, quantitative measurements can still be made at intensities which would be quite insufficient for an "absolute" method, provided there can be developed an adequately sensitive "secondary" detector which is capable of calibration against an absolute one; in addition, it must be verified that its calibrated response can be rightfully extrapolated toward the smaller intensities. In principle, any measurable interaction of our radiation with matter could be used as

---

* The term "absolute" is generally not reserved for the "really absolute" black-body calorimetry method (which, in most of the cases, is practically not workable), but is applied also to any thermoelectric, bolometric, or radiometric detectors provided their receivers may be considered "black" for the entire region, and their response adequately proportional to the incident energy flux.

the basic mechanism of a secondary detector. For the E.U.V. two effects provide a natural basis for the development of sensitive intensity detectors:

1) photo-ionization of gases and
2) photoelectric emission from solids.

As the primary ion and/or electron currents are very small, it is convenient that both effects can be used as triggering mechanisms in connection with an appropriate counting technique ("photon counter"). A systematic scientific approach to the development of photon counters is somewhat difficult, because the real counting mechanism of any experimental counter tube may easily turn into a complex variety of diverse effects. Actually, any counter intended to be of the photoelectrically triggered type can also be triggered by photo-ionization of the gas filling as long as the quantum energy of the incident radiation is sufficient. The admixture of any quenching vapor obviously increases the complexity further. Likewise, a counter which is supposed to be triggered only by the gas filling (photo-ionization) is subjected to the effects of photoelectric emission from the cathode, and possibly from the window material. In spite of the complicating facts just mentioned, the continuation of efforts in the development of improved or new types of photon counters for the E.U.V. seem to be well justified.

Photoelectric emission as a basic mechanism for the development of secondary intensity detectors has the advantage that it can avoid the complications brought about by gas filling and the necessity of a window. It can simply be combined with secondary electron multiplication. The development of such intensity detector tubes (without a window) seems to be most promising for measurements from a satellite. An appropriate grid between radiation receiver (cathode) and first dynode even provides a possibility for discriminating between different quantum energies using a "retarding potential method."

In connection with our plans to use photoelectric emission for the development of windowless detectors for the E.U.V., it should be emphasized that the photoelectric effect of the E.U.V. is strikingly different from the well-known external photoeffect at longer wavelengths, which has been studied extensively in the past and which is satisfactorily explained by the "free electron—potential barrier—surface effect" model. This effect becomes quite unimportant as soon as the quantum energy of irradiation rises beyond about nine or ten electron volts; then, a deeper-level photoelectric emission effect[1] predominates. The yields of this "Deeper-Level Interaction" photoeffect are much higher, and its entire behavior has been shown to be fundamentally different from the ordinary external photoeffect. Within the purpose of this discussion it may suffice to state that this deeper-level photoeffect provides a much easier experimental basis for the development of sensitive intensity detectors, as materials can be chosen as cathodes which exhibit very high photoelectric yields in the E.U.V. without having any noticeable sensitivity to visible or near ultraviolet radiation.

REFERENCE

1. H. E. Hinteregger, "Photoelectric Emission in the Extreme Ultraviolet," *Phys. Rev., 96:* 538–539 (1954).

20

Cosmic-Ray Observations in Earth Satellites

by James A. Van Allen
STATE UNIVERSITY OF IOWA

ABSTRACT

Part A. *Geographical Dependence and Temporal Variations of Cosmic-Ray Intensity in the Vicinity of the Earth*

A single Geiger tube or scintillator carried in a satellite will make possible the study of the cosmic-ray intensity above the atmosphere on comprehensive geographical and temporal bases for the first time. The interpretation of expected data is outlined with respect to the following: determination of the effective geomagnetic field; the magnetic rigidity spectrum of the primary radiation; time variations of intensity and their correlations with solar and magnetic observations and with the observed intensity of secondaries observed in ground stations; and cosmic-ray albedo of the atmosphere. The monitoring function of a satellite will be especially valuable for providing an understanding of the extensive ground observations planned for the IGY period. The ideal data-transmission system and several practical compromises are discussed with regard to their consequences on the fullness of the data.

Part B. *Relative Abundance of Heavy Nuclei in the Primary Cosmic Radiation*

Satellite-borne instrumentation is uniquely able to solve one of the outstanding problems of the astrophysical nature of the primary cosmic radiation—namely, the abundances of Li, Be, and B nuclei. It is proposed to use a Cerenkov detector for this purpose. The technique has been developed and used intensively by this laboratory in balloon experiments. (See Reference 15.) Balloon apparatus suffers from the serious handicap of the residual atmosphere overhead; conventional rockets spend much too little time above the appreciable atmosphere. It appears to be feasible to fly a simplified version of this type apparatus in a satellite. Data can be accumulated for a complete revolution and played back in a 10-sec interval centered around passage over a meridian chain of telemetering receiving stations. The initial objective will be to measure the ratio of the sum of intensities of Li, Be, and B nuclei to the sum of the intensities of all heavier nuclei.

Part A.   Geographical Dependence and Temporal Variations of Cosmic-Ray Intensity in the Vicinity of the Earth

1) *Introduction*

In a series of many rocket firings over the past ten years, the author and his colleagues have made a survey of the cosmic-ray intensity at high altitudes over the complete range of north geomagnetic latitude from the equator to the pole. Directional intensity measurements have yielded a determination of the primary cosmic-ray spectrum.[1] Measurements with single counters have provided a considerable body of knowledge on the total cosmic-ray intensity "above the atmosphere" over a wide range of latitude. A summary and an interpretation of these measurements have been published recently.[2] Fig. 1 gives an up-to-date summary of the total cosmic-ray intensity above the atmosphere as a function of geomagnetic latitude λ; this figure contains data from Reference 2 and from more recent work.

2) *Apparatus for Use in a Satellite*

It has been demonstrated in the work referred to above that a considerable variety of basic information on geophysical and astrophysical aspects of the primary cosmic radiation can be obtained with very simple rocket-borne apparatus—namely, a single Geiger tube whose output pulses are telemetered to a ground station. Such apparatus has been successfully flown in rockets whose accelerations exceeded 250 g; and laboratory tests show that accelerations up to 1000 g are of no significant concern. The apparatus is quite light in weight and, apart from the

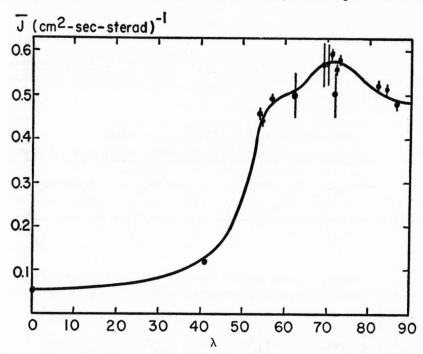

FIGURE 1. Absolute values of average unidirectional intensity of charged cosmic rays above the atmosphere as a function of geomagnetic latitude. (See Ref. 2 for fuller explanation.)

telemetering transmitter, need have a power drain of only a few milliwatts. Furthermore, a cylindrical Geiger tube of a length-diameter ratio of about three is a sufficiently omnidirectional detector so that the angular aspect of the apparatus need be neither controlled nor measured, and the operation of the equipment can be made insensitive to a wide range of temperatures.

Thus, such an apparatus is admirably adapted to use in small satellites.

3) Simplifying Assumptions

For the purposes of the immediately ensuing analysis the following simplifying assumptions are introduced:

a) The orbit of the satellite is circular.

b) The earth is a sphere with density a function of radius only.

c) Atmospheric drag is negligible.

Under these assumptions the apparatus is carried around the earth at constant altitude and the orbit remains fixed in space. (See Section 8 for a brief discussion of the effects of removing these assumptions.)

4) *Nature of Observed Data*

With the help of the information contained in Fig. 1, a foundation for discussing the observations made with such equipment in a satellite is provided in Figs. 2 and 3.

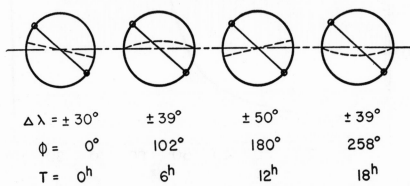

INCLINATION OF ORBIT, $\alpha = 40°$

INCLINATION OF GEOMAGNETIC EQUATOR, $\beta = 10°$

$\Delta\lambda = \pm 30°$	$\pm 39°$	$\pm 50°$	$\pm 39°$
$\phi = 0°$	$102°$	$180°$	$258°$
$T = 0^h$	6^h	12^h	18^h

FIGURE 2. A family of relationships among the plane of the orbit, the geographical equator, and the geomagnetic equator at intervals of six hours of sidereal time. See Table I for basic assumptions. The horizontal line through the diagram represents the geographical equator; the inclined lines with small circles at their ends, the plane of the satellite's orbit; and the dashed lines the geomagnetic equator.

Fig. 2 shows a succession of relationships among the plane of the orbit, the geographical equator, and the geomagnetic equator at intervals of six hours of sidereal time. The figure represents the special case described in Table I, which appears later in the text.

In Fig. 3 is given a schematic plot of the total cosmic-ray intensity at the position of the satellite as a function of flight time. The counting rate of a single Geiger tube is proportional to the intensity as presented in Fig. 1 and Fig. 3. The number of observed counts per second of a typical Geiger tube can be had by multiplying the arbitrary scale of ordinates of Fig. 3 by ten.

It will be noted that the complete curve of Fig. 3 will be traced out once each sidereal day.

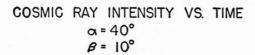

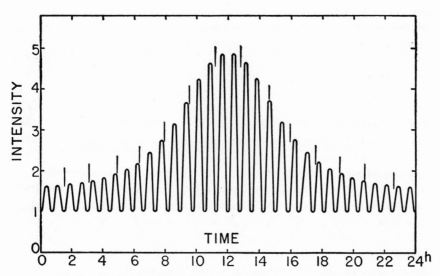

FIGURE 3. A schematic plot of the total cosmic-ray intensity at the position of the satellite as a function of flight time in sidereal hours. The number of observed counts per second of a typical Geiger tube can be had by multiplying the arbitrary scale of ordinates by ten.

5) *Interpretation of an Idealized Set of Data*

For the purpose of the present section, it is assumed that the counting rate of the Geiger tube is transmitted and received continuously. In this case there will be received *for each loop of Fig. 3* a total of some 65,000 counts at the phase $t = 0^h$ or some 150,000 counts at $t = 12^h$. Hence, the data for each loop can be subdivided into, say, ten equal time intervals, in each of which the statistical uncertainty is less than 1.5%.

Thus:

a) *Geographical Distribution.*—The data from a single 24-hour period will assign an intensity figure with an accuracy of better than 1.5% to each one of a net of 300 segments of the orbit distributed over a circumferential belt of the earth extending from 40° N. to 40° S. geographical latitude. Such a body of data exceeds by at least an order of magnitude the presently existing knowledge of this subject (cf. Fig. 1). And, of course, the body of data continues to grow at the same rate so long as the observations continue. An observing period of three weeks will reduce the statistical uncertainties by a factor of over four (or it can be thought of as providing a network of twenty-one times as many segments of the same accuracy as provided by one day's observations).

b) *Geomagnetic Field.*—It is expected that a first-order analysis of the network of data will be made as follows. The locus of the positions of the satellite at the times of occurrence of the minima of counting rate will outline the effective geomagnetic equator. One day's data should serve to locate the axis of the corresponding magnetic dipole to an accuracy of about 1° in latitude and about 3° in longitude.

c) *Terrestrial and Interplanetary Magnetic Fields.*—The results of (b) can be cross-checked by north-south symmetry of the other data of Fig. 3. Indeed, the detailed nature of the effective geomagnetic (and perhaps extraterrestrial) magnetic field, insofar as it affects the arrival of cosmic rays, can be determined in a comprehensive way by a full analysis of all the observed data. For example, the eccentricity of an assumed dipole can be determined by the resulting undulation (24-hr period) of the magnitudes of the minima and maxima in Fig. 3 (undulation not shown). And the lack of north-south symmetry or other detailed features may indicate the lack of applicability of the simple dipole model. There are already suggestions, in fact, from recent data[3,4] that the latitude effect on cosmic rays cannot be adequately attributed to the field of the earth itself, as has been ordinarily done for many years. A comprehensive, homogeneous set of data as herein envisioned may open up an entirely new attack on the determination of interplanetary magnetic fields.[5]

d) *Temporal Fluctuations and Causes.*—A satellite-borne Geiger tube is an ideal monitoring instrument for recording temporal fluctuations of the primary cosmic-ray intensity. For example, a 24-hr set of observations will possess a statistical uncertainty of 1 part in 1000. And the absolute accuracy of the deduced intensity can be about 1%. A powerful new approach to the study of temporal fluctuations will be provided. The nature of the subject may be gathered from two important papers.[6,7]

A notable case of a very large fluctuation was observed by J. W. Graham and J. W. B. Barghausen of the Applied Physics Laboratory, Johns Hopkins University, with an ionization chamber at sea level near Thule, Greenland, on 25 July 1946. Fig. 4 is taken from the published paper describing the results.[8]

It is probable that the intensity above the atmosphere fluctuates by a considerably larger fraction than does that at ground stations. The International Geophysical Year period is an especially interesting one for the observation of such fluctuations and for the correlation of them with solar and geomagnetic data. There is already planned a considerable network of ground observatories which are to be in continuous operation during this period. Observations of the fluctuations above the atmosphere (and of the latitude dependence of those fluctuations) will provide a fresh basis for understanding the cause of such fluctuations and, in particular, the role of the sun in producing them.

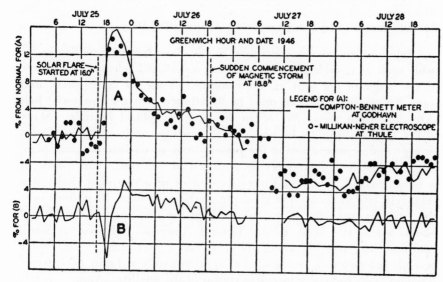

FIGURE 4. Sea-level observations of the great cosmic-ray storm of 25 July 1946. Curve A represents hourly means of cosmic-ray ionization at Thule and at Godhavn, Greenland. Curve B represents hourly means at Godhavn less hourly means at Cheltenham. (After Graham and Forbush, Ref. 8.)

Moreover, the rapid geographical coverage by a satellite observing station may make it possible to plot out "solar impact zones" on the surface of the earth to a degree of satisfaction not yet approached.[9] And the simple latitude dependence of the fractional fluctuation will give a measurement of the rigidity spectrum of the particles responsible for the fluctuation.

By means of absolute measurements of the total cosmic-ray intensity above the atmosphere a start will be made on the study of long-term changes of the intensity of the primary cosmic radiation—for example, the 11-year cycle and perhaps other changes of a longer-term nature.

6) Remark on the Choice of Orbit

For a variety of practical reasons it is planned that the initial IGY satellites will be placed in orbits having an inclination of about 40° to the geographical equator. It is evident that pole-to-pole orbits are much more desirable for cosmic-ray purposes in order that a complete survey of the geomagnetic sphere can be obtained. It is of special interest to plot systematically the latitude of the "knee" and to investigate the variations of intensity at higher latitudes.

It may be hoped that orbits of this nature will be provided as the satellite program progresses.

7) *Interpretation of Less Completely Transmitted Data*

In order to receive continuously the data from a satellite in an orbit such as considered in this paper, a radiated telemetering power of the order of 0.2 watt at, for example, 74 mc/sec is required; *and* some 200 receiving stations must be distributed over the equatorial belt extending from about 36° N. to 36° S. geographical latitude. Many of the stations must be located at sea. Such an array of stations must be regarded as impractical at the present stage of satellite program planning, though it will probably be arranged in due time. Meanwhile, it is more realistic to expect the establishment of a meridian chain of a relatively few stations. For example, a chain of some 10 stations over the latitude range 36° N. to 36° S. along the east coast of the United States, across the West Indies, Central America, and western South America (i.e., roughly along the 75th West Meridian) would make possible telemetering reception for approximately a 1-min period centered on every successive meridian transit of the satellite. Approximately 15 such meridian transits will occur during every 24-hr period. Moreover, much less average power dissipation in the satellite is required since, in principle at least, the transmitter need be operated only for brief periods.

In order to obtain a clearer idea of the observational situation in such a case, Table I has been prepared for a simplified case in which the period of revolution of the satellite is exactly 1/15 of the period of rotation of the earth. (See also Section 3.) The instants at which the satellite crosses the fixed meridian are also shown by vertical lines above the upper envelope of the curves in Fig. 3. Several possible types of data transmission may now be discussed.

a) *Electronic Tabulation of Total Number of Counts in, Say, Equal 5-min Intervals and "Read-out" of the Tabulation at the Time of Each Transit.*—This scheme, if practical, will give substantially as much information as the idealized continuous transmission system (see Section 5), though accuracy may be sacrificed with a miniaturized system of integration.

b) *Electronic Totaling of All Counts Observed between Transits and "Read-out" of Totals at Time of Transit.*—A large amount of detailed information is lost in this case. In effect, one obtains a time average of the curve of Fig. 3, the average being taken over successive time intervals of about 1.63 hours length. The equipment in this case can be very simple, however. Fluctuations can be studied with good satisfaction, though longitudinal dependence is lost. The plotting-out of the effective magnetic field suffers considerably in comparison with paragraph 5 or 7(a). The longitude of the pole of an assumed dipole field is well determined, but auxiliary data are necessary to establish the latitude of the pole (cf. Fig. 1). Detailed analysis of the effective magnetic field will not be very fruitful.

TABLE I

Transits of satellite across a geographical meridian fixed on the earth
(Longitude = 0°)

Inclination of plane of orbit to geographical equator, $\alpha = 40°$	
Inclination of geomagnetic equator, $\beta = 10°$ (centered dipole model)	
Geomagnetic pole at longitude of 90° W. of fixed meridian	

At $t = 0^h$, satellite crosses geographical (and geomagnetic) equator at longitude 0°, in the direction from south to north (i.e., pole of orbit momentarily at longitude 90° W.)

Period of satellite = 1.50 sidereal hours

Orbit assumed circular

Earth assumed spherical with density a function of radius only

Transit Number	Time (sidereal hours)	Instantaneous West Longitude of Pole of Orbit	Geographical Latitude of Transit	Geomagnetic Latitude of Transit
0	0.00	90° W.	0.0°	0.0°
1	1.63	114.4	19.1° N.	18.8° N.
2	3.23	138.5	32.1	31.6
3	4.82	162.3	38.6	37.9
4	6.39	185.9	39.8	39.1
5	7.97	209.6	36.1	35.5
6	9.57	233.5	26.5	26.1
7	11.18	257.7	10.1 N.	10.0 N.
8	12.82	282.3	10.1 S.	10.0 S.
9	14.43	306.5	26.5	26.1
10	16.03	330.4	36.1	35.5
11	17.61	354.1	39.8	39.1
12	19.19	17.9	38.6	37.9
13	20.77	41.7	32.1	31.6
14	22.37	65.7	19.1 S.	18.8 S.
15	24.00	90° W.	0.0	0.0

c) *As in* (b), *Plus Reading of Ambient Counting Rate during a 1-min Period Centered on Meridian Transit.*—Interpretation possibilities similiar to (b) except that auxiliary data on latitude dependence (at a single fixed longitude) will be obtained with the same apparatus. It will likely be desirable to use a counting-rate meter with an integrating time of several minutes for an instantaneous "read-out." The statistical accuracy will be improved and the time necessary to transmit the reading will be reduced thereby.

d) *Reading of Ambient Counting Rate at Time of Meridian Transit Only.*—Such data will be of value in studying temporal fluctuations and in making a simple latitude survey at a fixed longitude.

Finally, it may be remarked that three meridian chains provide a great improvement in data collection. Even a scattered array of only a few stations, well distributed in longitude and latitude, will fill in the array of data importantly.

8) *Considerations Pertaining to a More General Orbit*

Any actual orbit will not be accurately circular but will be elliptical to a good approximation. The altitude of the satellite will vary cyclically. In addition, due to the oblateness of the earth, the orbit of the satellite will not remain fixed in space but the line of nodes will regress and the line of apsides will advance—the cyclic periods for both motions being about two months.

The consequences of these effects on the interpretation of cosmic-ray data have not yet been worked out in detail. But it is evident that the gross result is to provide a three-dimensional array of counting-rate data—that is, the total cosmic-ray intensity will be obtained as a function of latitude, longitude, *and* altitude (as well as a function of time). The interpretation of the observed data will still proceed along the broad lines of Section 5. In addition, the altitude (or radial) dependence will be obtained. It has been found in previous work with conventional rockets that there is a negligible dependence of cosmic-ray intensity on altitude up to at least 100 miles. But such a high-altitude plateau cannot be expected to continue indefinitely. There are three causes for the expected altitude dependence:

a) The geomagnetic cut-off diminishes with increasing altitude.

b) The geometrical shadow of the earth on an omnidirectional detector diminishes with increasing altitude.

c) The cosmic-ray albedo of the earth, insofar as it consists of charged particles, is confined to the vicinity of the earth as suggested by Fig. 5. In this figure the unshaded, lune-shaped regions represent the meridian cross sections of the allowed regions for albedo particles of magnetic rigidity 1×10^9 volts. Any such particles which emerge from the earth's atmosphere are constrained by the earth's magnetic field never to escape from this region. Two cases are shown—one, on the left, for geomagnetic latitude of origin of the albedo radiation 20°;

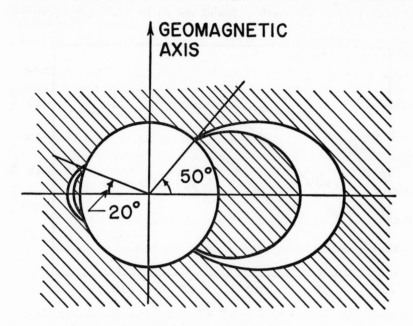

ALBEDO REGIONS — R = I BV.

FIGURE 5. Two sample plots showing the confinement of charged albedo particles to the vicinity of the earth (shown as a circle) by the geomagnetic field. The case on the right is for particles of magnetic rigidity 1 Bv originating at $\lambda = 50°$; the case on the left is for particles of the same magnetic rigidity originating at $\lambda = 20°$. The unshaded regions are meridian cross sections of the allowed regions in which such particles are constrained to remain (courtesy E. C. Ray).

the other, on the right, for 50°. The theoretical foundation for Fig. 5 has been given by Treiman[10] on the basis of the Störmer theory.

Since for a known or assumed primary spectrum, effects (a) and (b) can be calculated, it is evident that an observed radial dependence of total cosmic-ray intensity will yield information of unique value in the study of the cosmic-ray albedo of the earth. In this manner it will be possible to improve knowledge of the primary spectrum. Otherwise stated, it should be possible to obtain separately the primary spectrum and the albedo spectrum by a full analysis of this type of data. Estimates of the radial dependence of total cosmic-ray intensity at several latitudes have been worked out previously[11] and are shown in Fig. 6.

Finally, it should be remarked that the analyses of the present section and those of Section 5 are interlocked; and if, for example, the magnetic field of the earth is found not to be the single controlling

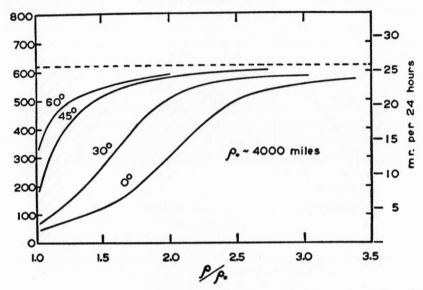

FIGURE 6. Estimated radial dependence of total cosmic-ray intensity in the vicinity of the earth for several geomagnetic latitudes; ρ_0 is the radius of the earth (Ref. 11).

magnetic field, then the analysis which has been sketched in this section must be modified accordingly.

The first step is to obtain a large mass of reliable observations by means of which any hypothesis can be submitted to test. The interpretation of the data will be a step-wise one of successive approximation to a full understanding of the various significant elements.

Part B. Relative Abundance of Heavy Nuclei in the Primary Cosmic Radiation

1) *The Nature of the Problem*

One of the most controversial and interesting aspects of the primary cosmic radiation is the intensity of lithium, beryllium, and boron nuclei relative to that of the heavier nuclei. Astrophysical interest in the subject stems from the following facts. On the basis of spectroscopic data, the three elements Li, Be, and B are found to have an astronomical abundance of the order of 10^{-8} of "universal matter."[12-14] But in spite of the fact that the relative intensities of most of the nuclear species in the primary cosmic radiation have a general resemblance to their relative astronomical abundances, the sum of the intensities of Li, Be, and B nuclei in the cosmic-ray beam at an equivalent atmospheric depth of 18.5 gm/cm² (95,000 ft altitude plus apparatus thickness) is over half the sum of the intensities of all heavier nuclei.[15,16] It is known that the lighter nuclei are often fragmentation products of the collision of heavier nuclei with matter. Such fragmentation will occur in the residual atmosphere above balloon-borne equipment, in the apparatus itself, and *in interstellar space.* Using the meager data presently available on the subject of fragmentation,[17] the directly observed data can be corrected to the top of the earth's atmosphere. The situation is well summarized by the following table (Table II, after Webber[16]):

TABLE II

Composition of the primary cosmic radiation

(after Webber)

$\lambda = 41.5°$ N.

Component	Directional Intensities $(m^2 \text{ sec sterad})^{-1}$		Relative Cosmic Ray Intensities	Relative Astronomical Abundances[12-14]
	Observed at 18.5 gm/cm²	Corrected to Top of Atmosphere		
Protons	<447	<522	<0.86	0.88
Alpha Particles	57.3 ± 3.5	74 ± 5	0.12	0.12
Li, Be, B	3.56 ± 0.33	2.80 ± 0.25	0.005	10^{-8}
Z ≥ 6	5.98 ± 0.90	10.7 ± 2.0	0.018	0.0012

Thus, if it be assumed that the primary cosmic radiation originates in a "typical" astronomical region, it must be concluded that it has traversed a path length of interstellar matter sufficient to result in the production, by the fragmentation process, of the intensity of Li, Be, and B nuclei estimated at the top of the atmosphere. In quantitative form, the corresponding path length of interstellar material may be expressed as the "age" of cosmic rays of $(4 \times 10^6/n)$ years of travel at a velocity c, where n is the average number density of hydrogen atoms (in cm⁻³) along the path. Astrophysicists estimate n as of order one atom of H per cm³. Hence, an upper limit for the age of the primary cosmic radiation arriving at the earth is 4×10^6 years.

But in view of the great uncertainty in extrapolating balloon observations to the top of the atmosphere,* and in view of the far-reaching significance of the result (no other observational method of estimating the age of cosmic rays has yet been reduced to practice), it is believed worthwhile to obviate the need for such corrections by directly observing the intensity ratio Li, Be, and B to $Z \geq 6$ at zero thickness of atmosphere. The intensity of these heavy nuclei is so

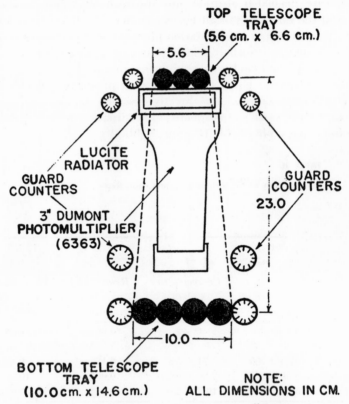

FIGURE 7. Schematic of a balloon-borne Čerenkov detector system for measuring the absolute intensities of heavy nuclei (after Webber).

low that conventional rockets are inadequate for the purpose, in terms of length of time spent above the atmosphere.

2) *Proposed Experiment*

The Čerenkov detector method of McDonald and Webber appears to be adaptable to use in a satellite. The data are readily transmitted

* Other authors, using independently determined fragmentation parameters, estimate *no* Li, Be, and B at the top of the atmosphere.

by radio telemetering (in contrast to methods requiring physical recovery of photographic emulsions). And the Čerenkov method gives excellent resolution in Z. A schematic diagram of the Iowa balloon apparatus is given in Fig. 7 and a sample set of results is shown in Fig. 8.

On the basis of this experience, a simplified version of this apparatus has been designed for satellite use. The weight of the apparatus, apart

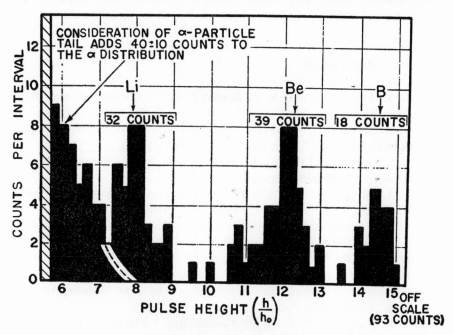

FIGURE 8. A sample set of observed data on the intensities of Li, Be, and B nuclei obtained at 95,000-ft altitude with the apparatus of Fig. 7 (after Webber).

from telemetering, is about 8 lb, including battery power for several weeks' operation. The geometric factor of the telescope proposed is 5 cm² sterad. Hence an average of some 7 nuclei of $Z \geq 6$ will pass through the telescope per hour for a satellite on an orbit such as that considered in Part A. (Actually, an inclination α of not greater than 30° would be desirable in order not to encounter nonrelativistic primaries.) This estimate is based on the roughly known momentum spectra of the heavy particles and on the assumption that the angular orientation of the telescope will be random with respect to a co-ordinate system fixed on the earth.

Thus a week's observations will yield a total of some 1000 nuclei of $Z \geq 6$ and a corresponding number of nuclei of Li, Be, B.

The result will be a new determination of the ratio of Li, Be, B to Z ≥ 6 far surpassing any reasonable expectation of any other method, both in respect to basic certainty as referring to the primary beam (uninfluenced by the earth's atmosphere) and in respect to statistical accuracy.

Since the method is an integrating one, it is only necessary to transmit the data occasionally, as for example on meridian transit. And since the method is a comparative one, no detailed knowledge of the orbit or of the orientation of the satellite body is necessary.

REFERENCES

1. J. A. Van Allen and S. F. Singer, "On the Primary Cosmic-Ray Spectrum," *Phys. Rev., 78:* 819 (1950) ; *ibid., 80:* 116 (1950).
2. L. H. Meredith *et al.,* "Cosmic-Ray Intensity above the Atmosphere at High Latitudes," *Phys. Rev., 99:* 198–209 (1955).
3. J. A. Simpson and D. C. Rose, International Cosmic Ray Conference, Guanajuato, Mexico, September, 1955.
4. J. A. Simpson *et al.,* "Effective Geomagnetic Equator for Cosmic Radiation," *Phys. Rev., 102:* 1648–1653 (1956).
5. J. A. Simpson *et al.,* "On Deriving Geomagnetic Dipole-Field Co-ordinates from Cosmic-Ray Observations," *J. Geophys. Res., 61:* 11–22 (1956).
6. H. Elliot, Chapter VIII, "Time Variations of Cosmic Ray Intensity," of *Progress in Cosmic Ray Physics,* edited by J. G. Wilson (Amsterdam: No. Holland Publ. Co., 1952), pp. 453–514.
7. S. E. Forbush, "World-Wide Cosmic Ray Variations," *J. Geophys. Res., 59:* 525–542 (1954).
8. J. W. Graham and S. E. Forbush, "Solar Flare and Magnetic Storm Effects in Cosmic-Ray Intensity near the Geomagnetic N Pole," *Phys. Rev., 98:* 1348–1349 (1955).
9. J. Firor, "Cosmic Radiation Intensity-Time Variations and Their Origin. IV. Increases Associated with Solar Flares," *Phys. Rev., 94:* 1017–1028 (1954).
10. S. B. Treiman, "The Cosmic-Ray Albedo," *Phys. Rev., 91:* 957–959 (1953).
11. J. A. Van Allen, Chapter XIV, "The Nature and Intensity of the Cosmic Radiation," *Physics and Medicine of the Upper Atmosphere,* edited by C. S. White and O. O. Benson, Jr. (Albuquerque: Univ. of New Mexico Press, 1952), pp. 239–266.
12. H. C. Urey, "The Abundances of the Elements," *Phys. Rev., 88:* 248–252 (1952).
13. J. L. Greenstein and E. Tandberg-Hansen, *Astrophys. J., 109:* 113 (1949).

14. L. Spitzer, Jr., "Upper Limits on the Abundances of Interstellar Li and Be," *Astrophys. J., 109:* 548–550 (1949).

15. W. R. Webber and F. B. McDonald, "Determination of the Intensities of Low-Z Components of the Primary Cosmic Radiation at $\lambda = 41°$ Using a Čerenkov Detector," *Phys. Rev., 100:* 1460–1467 (1955).

16. W. R. Webber, private communication of results obtained subsequent to those given in Ref. 15.

17. J. H. Noon and M. F. Kaplon, "Interactions of the Heavy Nuclei of the Cosmic Radiation," *Phys. Rev., 97:* 769–779 (1955).

21

Study of the Arrival of Auroral Radiations

by James A. Van Allen
STATE UNIVERSITY OF IOWA

ABSTRACT

The soft radiation discovered by the Iowa group above 50 km at auroral latitudes in 1953 (Reference 1) and further studied during 1954 and 1955 provides a novel foundation for plotting out the auroral zone by direct observation. A satellite in a nearly pole-to-pole orbit is a splendid vehicle for this purpose. If such orbits are not available in the near future, a good start on the problem can be made by means of balloon-launched, two-stage, solid-fuel rockets, fired along a meridian over a 10° span of latitudes including the auroral zone.

Introduction

The soft radiation discovered by the Iowa group[1] above 50 km at auroral latitudes in 1953 and further studied during 1954 and 1955 provides a novel foundation for plotting out the auroral zone by direct observation.[2-5] Typical sets of raw experimental results of rockoon flights in the Arctic are to be found in Reference 1. Fig. 1 contains the results of one of the more interesting flights of the 1954 series. Fig. 2 shows the geographic distribution of 42 successful rockoon flights made by the Iowa group during the past three summers for various purposes.

These flights were made possible by the Office of Naval Research, the Atomic Energy Commission, and the National Science Foundation. It has been planned to continue this work by the rockoon technique during the IGY period. But the possibility of doing this type of experiment with the satellite technique is a very appealing one.

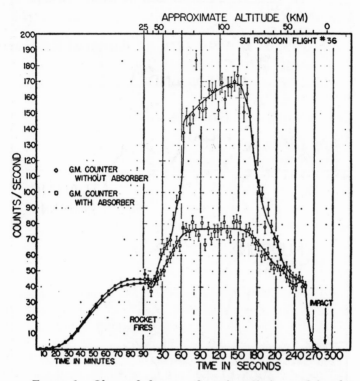

FIGURE 1. Observed data on the soft radiation and its absorption in an aluminum shield. S. U. I. Rockoon Flight 36. Rocket fired at 1404 G.C.T. on 25 July 1954 ($\lambda = 70°$). The "shielded" Geiger tube was encased in an additional absorber of aluminum of thickness 140 mg/cm². Normal cosmic-ray counting rate at high altitudes at this latitude is about 39 counts/sec.

In Fig. 3 is given a summary of the maximum observed counting rates (i.e., intensities) of radiation observed in the twenty-two successful rockoon flights during 1953, 1954, and 1955 which used essentially identical single Geiger tube equipment. The abscissa is geomagnetic latitude. The flights have been distributed from 54° to 89° N. The intensity at the lowest and highest latitudes is believed to be due entirely to cosmic rays (as conventionally defined). The great peak of intensity in the vicinity of $\lambda = 67°$ is attributed to auroral radiation.

The radiation detected in this region is now believed to be X-rays (bremsstrahlung from auroral electrons), on the basis of the most recent flight results and of the laboratory simulation of these results. All observed data are consistent with the detected radiation being X-rays of

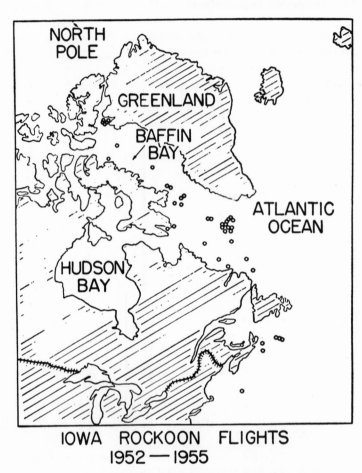

IOWA ROCKOON FLIGHTS
1952 — 1955

FIGURE 2. A chart of the positions of launching 42 successful Iowa rockoon flights during the summers of 1952, 1953, 1954, and 1955.

energy 10 to 100 kev and intensity of order of magnitude 10^4 photons/cm^2/sec.

At the highest altitudes thus far attained in the auroral zone (~100 km) it is presumed that the primary auroral electrons themselves are incident on the rocket apparatus with intensity of order of magnitude 10^7 electrons/cm^2/sec and energies in the range 10 to 100 kev.

If this is true, then it would also be true at the higher altitude of a satellite orbit.

Proposed Experiments

The data given above make it evident that a novel method of plotting out the auroral zone by direct observation is provided by this new discovery. Equipment suitable for a satellite consists of a single Geiger tube, a simple RC integrating circuit of time constant about 1 sec,

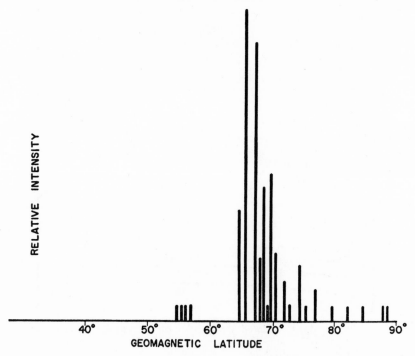

FIGURE 3. Peak counting rates of "unshielded" Geiger tubes observed at high altitudes in 22 rockoon flights of essentially identical equipment 1952–1955, showing latitude dependence of incidence of the soft radiation.

a time base with respect to which the counting rate can be stored, a magnetic storage drum, and a telemetering system suitable for reading out the data periodically.

It is obviously necessary to have the satellite orbit inclined by at least 70° to the geographic equator. A nearly pole-to-pole orbit would be the most desirable. It should be noted that both north and south auroral zones would be scanned thus at frequent intervals and could be compared nearly simultaneously. There is little doubt that the successful execution of this experiment will help immensely in plotting out the zones of incidence of auroral radiations and in studying the time dependence of their arrival in correlation with other pertinent observations.

If it is impractical to obtain suitable satellite orbits in the near future, we propose to continue the study of the problem by the use of

LAUNCHING ANGLES FOR
MAXIMUM RANGE VS.
INITIAL VELOCITY

		V_o	θmax.
CURVE	A	5000 ft./sec	44.5°
"	B	8000 "	43.5°
"	C	10,000 "	42.5°
"	D	12,000 "	41.5°

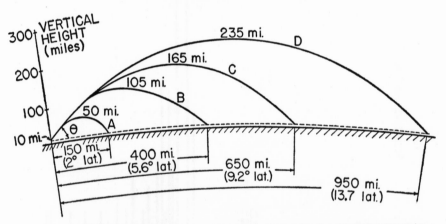

FIGURE 4. Calculated trajectories of one- and two-stage rockoons which are suitable for observing the latitude distribution of incidence of the soft radiation.

conventional rockoons and by the development of two-stage rockoons of considerably greater range.

The potentialities of rockoons for this purpose are shown by the calculated trajectories of Fig. 4. Trajectory A is for a one-stage rockoon; trajectories B and C are for two-stage rockoons made up of solid-fuel rockets which are in existence and are suitable for the purpose; trajectory D corresponds to a reasonable extrapolation of solid-fuel rocket technology over the next several years.

It is evident that a single flight (of Type C, for example) along a meridian will scan a large fraction of the usual zone of incidence of auroral radiation. A detailed latitude plot should be obtained.

REFERENCES

1. L. H. Meredith *et al.*, "Direct Detection of Soft Radiation above 50 Kilometers in the Auroral Zone," *Phys. Rev., 97:* 201–205 (1955).
2. F. B. McDonald *et al.*, "Rocket Observations on Soft Radiation at Northern Latitudes," *Phys. Rev., 99:* 609 (1955) (A).
3. J. A. Ellis *et al.*, "Double Geiger-Tube Study of Soft Radiation at Northern Latitude," *Phys. Rev., 99:* 609 (1955) (A).
4. R. A. Ellis, "High-Altitude Rocket Measurements with Scintillation Counters at Northern Latitudes," *Phys. Rev., 99:* 609 (1955) (A).
5. J. A. Van Allen, "Interpretation of Soft Radiation Observed at High Altitudes in Northern Latitudes," *Phys. Rev., 99:* 609 (1955) (A).

22

Proposed Measurement of Solar Stream Protons

by Willard H. Bennett
U.S. NAVAL RESEARCH LABORATORY,
WASHINGTON, D.C.

The magnetically self-focusing solar proton stream hypothesis used since 1953 as a basis for a theory[1,2,3] of aurorae and magnetic disturbances has been examined further, using a laboratory tube called the Störmertron which produces scale models of proton orbits in the earth's magnetic field. Observations with the Störmertron have shown that there are two classes of orbits which must be considered.

The first class may be called the free orbits and are those of protons approaching the magnetic dipole field from infinity. Many of these free orbits have been calculated by Störmer and others during the past fifty years. Many others of those orbits have been too complicated to calculate, and these also have been observed in the Störmertron.

A second class of orbits, not recognized before, has been revealed by the Störmertron. These may be called the captive orbits.[4] In these, a proton moves from the vicinity of an auroral zone of magnetic latitude near one pole, past the magnetic equatorial plane to the vicinity of the auroral zone around the other pole, and back again, repeatedly, advancing substantially in longitude in the same direction for each such passage either way. In passing from near one auroral zone to near the other in one of the above passages, the proton changes radial distance from the earth with changes in magnetic latitude in approximately the same way that a magnetic line of force of the earth's dipole field does, but the proton does not follow such a line of force. Instead, the proton advances in longitude while changing latitude. Protons cannot come in from infinity and enter such a captive orbit directly, but they must be deflected somewhat in a collision in order to get into such a captive orbit. Escape from such a captive orbit must then be by another collision.

The proton energies which are assumed in applying the solar proton stream hypothesis are those required by Meinel's observation of H-alpha radiation at 80 and 100 km altitude in the earth's atmosphere; that is, 0.5-mev protons can penetrate to 100 km while 2.5-mev protons can

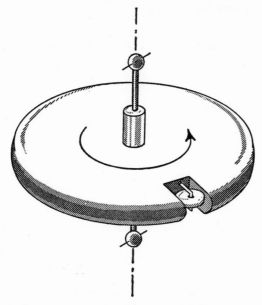

FIGURE 1.

penetrate to 80 km. The likelihood of such energetic protons being scattered out of a free orbit into a captive orbit is negligible in ionized matter at the densities usually assumed to be present in interplanetary space. This likelihood becomes significant only in the upper portions of the earth's atmosphere where the protons have lost much of their energy and in so doing have been deflected into a captive orbit. This puts the origin of any protons in captive orbits at about 100 km altitude.

The solar protons in their initial approach in free orbits and any protons traveling later in captive orbits can be detected and measured only in the vicinity of the auroral zones of magnetic latitude, and an artificial satellite which passes approximately over the two poles of the earth will be needed for this purpose.

The numerical flux densities of solar stream protons to be expected at times of strong aurorae or strong magnetic disturbances are in the range of zero to 10^8 protons/cm^2/sec. It is proposed that both the numerical flux densities and the energy distributions of the solar protons be measured as follows.

An ionization chamber is to be used at an exposed position at an edge of the satellite away from the axis of rotation of the satellite, as illustrated schematically in Fig. 1. The ionization chamber is illustrated in Fig. 2 and is to have a window consisting of 0.000025 in. of nickel

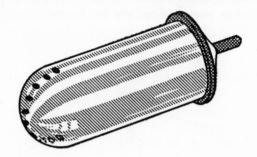

FIGURE 2.

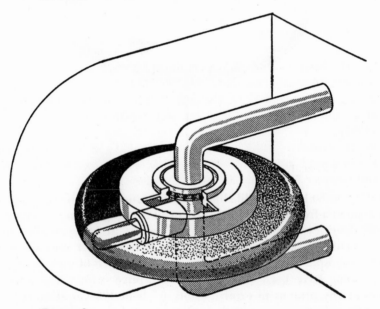

FIGURE 3.

over a row of 0.03-in. holes arranged in a semi-circle in the hemispherical end of the ionization chamber, the row to be convex outward from and in a plane containing the axis of rotation of the satellite. Over the ionization-chamber window is to be a half-toroidal absorbent screen as shown in Fig. 3, the thickness of the screen to vary azimuthally from zero to 0.004 in. of nickel. This toroidal screen is to be made to rotate at a frequency differing from that of the satellite as a whole so that the thickness of absorber in the path of the protons being counted varies in a saw-tooth manner from the window thickness up to 0.004 in. of nickel. Some of an alpha-emitter is to be put inside the thicker part of the screen for calibrating the ionization chamber in flight.

The signal from the ionization chamber is to be amplified with a 5750 penta-grid (ruggedized 6BE6) located also inside the screen, the output clipped to make all pulses have the same height, and only a pulse rate transmitted to the ground stations. The saw-tooth change in absorbent gives the number of protons with range greater than the absorber at that point of the saw-tooth. The rotation of the satellite sweeps out the full sphere of solid angle so that averaging corresponding points on the number of successive saw-teeth traversed in one revolution of the satellite gives a nondirectional intensity of all protons having range greater than the corresponding thickness of absorber. If the satellite rotates much faster than the screen, such averaging is carried out automatically.

REFERENCES

1. W. H. Bennett and E. O. Hulburt, "Magnetic Self-Focusing of Auroral Protons," *Phys. Rev., 91:* 1562 (1953).
2. W. H. Bennett and E. O. Hulburt, "Theory of the Aurora Based on Magnetic Self-Focusing of Solar Ion Streams," *ibid., 95:* 315–319 (1954).
3. W. H. Bennett, "Self-Focusing Streams," *ibid., 98:* 1584–1593 (1955).
4. Editor's note: Compare S. B. Treiman, *Phys. Rev., 91:* 957 (1953); and Chapter 20, Section 8(c) of this volume.

23

Exploring the Atmosphere with a Satellite-Borne Magnetometer

by E. H. Vestine
CARNEGIE INSTITUTION OF WASHINGTON,
DEPARTMENT OF TERRESTRIAL MAGNETISM

ABSTRACT

The various electric-current systems suggested for explaining the known geomagnetic variations at ground level are briefly described. Their influence upon measured signals of magnetic intensity aboard a satellite is estimated for motion below, within, and above the current systems. In the case of currents causing magnetic disturbance or storms, it seems likely that estimates of currents flowing beyond the atmosphere can be made, as has previously been pointed out by Chapman. For instance, if a satellite provides new magnetic data, measurements within the F-region may suffice to separate the so-called ring-current effect from that due to currents flowing near or within the E-region. Since there must be dynamo effects in the ionosphere, magnetic fields of both poloidal and toroidal types can be measured. The toroidal fields will not ordinarily be detectible at ground level. The local irregularities in electric-current flow will produce time fluctuations which may be difficult to interpret, but with the help of ground observations, these fluctuations may indicate important dynamic and spatial properties of ionized regions. Estimates of precision of measurements required are supplied in the case of the various supposed current systems, taking into account the earth's main magnetic field. The desirability of measuring X-ray and other radiation simultaneously with the magnetic changes is emphasized. Finally, the possible relationship of potential successes in magnetic measurements is discussed briefly with regard to time fluctuations in other phenomena such as ionospheric motions, cosmic rays, and aurorae.

Introduction

It was shown by Schuster and others[1,2] that the major time changes in the geomagnetic field, other than secular changes, are due to varying electric currents flowing within or beyond the earth's atmosphere; these varying currents also induce substantial current systems within the earth. The locations in space and the strengths of these overhead current systems are of course of considerable interest in themselves; they are of special high interest because it is known now that their time changes are often closely paralleled by equally interesting and simultaneous changes in cosmic rays,[3] aurorae,[4] ionic motions within the ionosphere,[5] and are less directly paralleled by changes which can be seen visually upon the sun,[6] and by radio waves from active solar areas.[7] Presumably the magnetic and electric fields of the current systems also affect the orbits of cosmic rays. The motions of the aurora may likewise be a manifestation of the deflecting influences of such changing fields, and it is probable that many aurorae are in fact a secondary effect of such changing fields acting to drive the auroral particles. The connections now established with solar phenomena are less specific and ill-defined, presumably because the thick blanket of terrestrial atmosphere below may shield cogent phenomena from view which can be readily detected from aboard a satellite moving above this obscuring region.

By using the magnetic-field patterns at ground level, when these are especially strong locally, it is possible to estimate the distance overhead to concentrated electric currents. This has been done for the polar regions near the auroral zone,[8,9] as well as at low levels of the atmosphere near the magnetic equator.[10,11] An early suggestion that electric-current sheets in the ionosphere might be located by a rocket-borne magnetometer traversing them[12] was followed by a brilliant rocket experiment by Singer, Maple, and Bowen[13] which seems to have located a current layer near a height of 100 km at the magnetic equator, in the case of the solar daily magnetic variation. The discontinuity found, even though not completely measured, indicated that somewhat more current was present than that actually required to explain the solar daily variation; in fact, some currents flowing near the same level or above and causing a magnetic storm simultaneously occurring may have contributed to the measured field. It is understood that this pioneering experiment will be amply supplemented by new rocket measurements planned by the Upper Atmosphere Rocket Research Panel, which, by many direct rocket measurements, has made such great advances in our knowledge of the upper atmosphere. It is clear that these numerous rocket-borne magnetometers of the IGY flown in low, middle, and high latitudes will add greatly to our store of knowledge respecting electric-current systems of the upper atmosphere. Yet the heights they attain, and the short duration of measurements within or in close proximity to the electric currents, suggest that similar measurements made aboard a satellite may also promise success. It is the purpose of the present paper to discuss the more obvious advantages and disadvantages of this type of exploratory endeavor. The availability of instrumentation of suitable weight is assumed, although satellites of sufficient size may not be available for many years.

Idealized Electric-Current Systems of the Atmosphere Estimated from Magnetic Measurements on the Ground

It may be stated at once that almost all of the rather exhaustive discussion by Chapman[14] of the use of rocket-borne magnetometers in the investigation of the electric-current systems of the upper atmosphere will be immediately applicable to the use of similar equipment mounted within a satellite. In this paper Chapman indicated estimates of the signals expected near current systems deduced from surface data for the solar daily magnetic variations (S), the lunar daily magnetic variation (L), and the electric-current system of disturbance (D); he conveniently denoted these electric-current systems, S, L, and D. He also discussed in some detail the principal uncertainties respecting them which it was proposed might be removed by means of rocket experiments. In particular, he pointed out that the polar and equatorial electrojets merited special attention in view of their incorporation of more intense electric currents and magnetic fields locally; the equatorial electrojet he then considered as an effect found only in S and L, and he did not then know that there was likewise an equatorial jet associated with the D-field, which was demonstrated by Sugiura[10] for sudden commencements, and by Vestine[11] for the initial phase of magnetic storms, a secure statistical basis for both findings being established in a more complete recent study by Forbush and Vestine[15]. The writer has also found evidence, to be reported separately, which indicates that a

FIGURE 1. Worldwide distribution of ionospheric current flow averaged for the equinoxes, appropriate to the solar daily magnetic variation (S); 10,000 amperes flow between successive current lines, and meridians are to local time in hours (after Bartels).

manifestation of the D-field known as geomagnetic bays appears at times to show a jet effect near the equator, associated with electric currents flowing within the atmosphere. This merely means that unquestionably there should be found evidence of magnetic-storm effects in low latitudes associated with atmospheric current systems, but the major issue as to whether or not there is a principal part flowing in the equatorial plane in the form of a current ring at a distance of a few earth radii still remains. Finally, another difference makes some revision of Chapman's results desirable, and this is the need for considering the alteration in signal estimated for mainly horizontal trajectories, rather than that for the mainly radial motions discussed by Chapman. Some of these differences have in fact already been reported by Singer[16] in a discussion of the use of a satellite-borne magnetometer.

The Electric-Current System S

Fig. 1 shows the electric-current system deduced from Chapman's analysis[1] for the solar daily variation S and though done long ago it cannot readily be improved today by including the omitted equatorial electrojet; in fact, present plans of the IGY do not appear at this writing to include stations adequate to permit formal derivation of the equatorial electrojet, which must seem a strange omission. This is a sheet-current representation of this necessarily three-dimensional current system. It shows eastward-flowing electric currents near the equator by day, and westward-flowing currents by night. As Chapman[14] noted, the mode of analysis would not have revealed a uniform electric current flowing from west to east, which might be detected by rocket-borne magnetometer, during a magnetically quiet day. A satellite-borne magnetometer moving rapidly in an equatorial orbit, and above the height of current system S, in conjunction with a few ground stations along the magnetic equator would in principle permit estimates of this uniform electric current, since the measured total magnetic intensity would be opposite in sign on either side of the current sheet, when averaged around the earth. This is an experiment, however, which would demand rather precise and successful removal of the contribution of the earth's main magnetic field, requiring not only precise location in space of the satellite, to about one-half mile, but also precise magnetic measurements.

Another way of indicating the height is afforded if the satellite moves within a sheet current with ionization patchwise distributed horizontally, as well as vertically. Local intensifications and rarefactions in ionization seem likely from the observed scattering of radio waves and sporadic E at lower levels. The effect expected in the presence of the net current predicted from the ground observations should be a noise signal of amplitude the same as or greater than for the main signal, perhaps 100 gammas or more (one gamma equals 10^{-5} cgs). However, this presupposes that a trajectory in the E-region can be expected in the early and later stages of the satellite's flight history, assuming the present information respecting the distribution of electric conductivity with height to be correct.

The Electric-Current System L

Fig. 2 shows the electric-current system L, likewise due to Chapman.[1] There should also be shown an electrojet near the magnetic equator which present data fail to define. The same considerations for S apply also to L, though a steady current flowing from west to east could not, if present, be distinguished from that for S, presumably a distinction of little consequence. It will be noted that the current intensity, and therefore the field discontinuity across the layer L, is considerably less than that for S; in fact, less than a tenth of that of S. The amplitude is so small that prospects of detecting the L currents are poor. It seems likely that a signal arising from current flow within patchily ionized

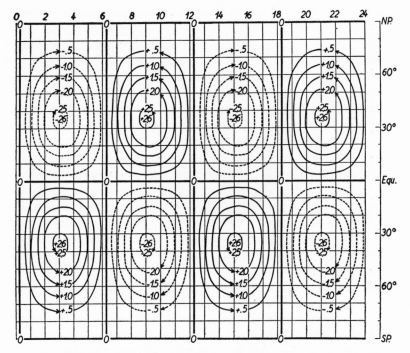

FIGURE 2. Ionospheric current systems for the lunar daily magnetic variation (L); Mean of lunation at equinoxes; 1000 amperes flow between successive lines, and meridians are to local lunar time in hours (after Chapman and Bartels).

regions would offer the greatest hope of height location. A semi-diurnally varying noise signal identified for an equatorial trajectory might help identify the current.

The Electric-Current System D

This electric-current system was derived in the idealized form of a current sheet by Chapman,[17] discussed further by Vestine and Chapman,[9] and there was a later extension to actual hours of magnetic storm by Vestine[18] and others. The results were based on measurements of the Second International Polar Year, 1932–33. Fig. 3 shows a sheet-current representation for two hours of the storm of May 1, 1933. It will be seen that the electric currents during a magnetic storm attain values many times as intense as those shown for S in Fig. 1, and much stronger

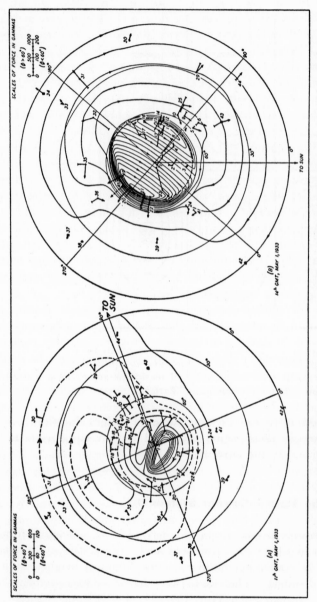

FIGURE 3. Mean hourly disturbance vectors and corresponding electric current systems for height 150 km for main phase of magnetic storms; view from above geomagnetic north pole (legend as in Fig. 4).

than the equatorial electrojet for any system. In the polar regions, two electrojets along the auroral zone are shown, and these are much stronger than the equatorial electrojet for S or D.

Again, as in the case of S, the effects of patchy ionization are likely to produce irregularities in current flow and should give a marked noise signal which it should be possible to identify with the region of current flow. In particular, the polar areas show such marked local differentiations in current that identification of atmospheric currents should be simplified. Finally, during flight along a trajectory the main field varies more gradually with distance than will magnetic fields within or adjacent to current systems—the sources for the main field, though large, are far away.

Fig. 4 shows current systems derived for the initial phases of a magnetic storm, although there was not in these a definition of any equatorial electrojet, perhaps because of paucity of data.[12,18] According to the Chapman-Ferraro theory of magnetic storms,[19] the actual current system should be located several earth radii above the earth in the initial phase of the storm. In view of the usual presence now established of an equatorial electrojet on the day side of the earth during this phase, in which there must be electric currents flowing near the E-region, it is of high interest to locate and define the atmospheric component of current responsible.

If about 20 sudden commencements of magnetic storms occur yearly,[15] it would be necessary for the satellite-borne magnetometer to record for about 20 days on an average before one sudden commencement could be expected. This expectation perhaps might be doubled, if care were taken to fire the satellite at a time when active and large sunspot groups were in evidence. If the sudden commencement and the initial phase of magnetic storms were due to electric currents surging beyond the atmosphere, as Chapman and Ferraro suggest, the signal noted during flight through the F-region may be several times as large as that noted at ground level, below the electromagnetically screening E-region. For this experiment, the magnetometer must be able to measure fields as small as about 10 gammas. Three or four times each year there are magnetic storms with field changes of several hundred gammas at the equator, and though measurements at such time are of great interest, such storms are difficult to predict in advance with better than a 50–50 chance. The median size of sudden commencements in low latitudes is only about 20 gammas, and though it might easily be as great as 40 gammas if due to extraterrestrial sources outside, it may be difficult to measure so small a value; the surges in current which occur later in magnetic storms will be easier to measure and will be no less interesting, at least in early attempts. Fig. 5 illustrates observed values for a large storm.

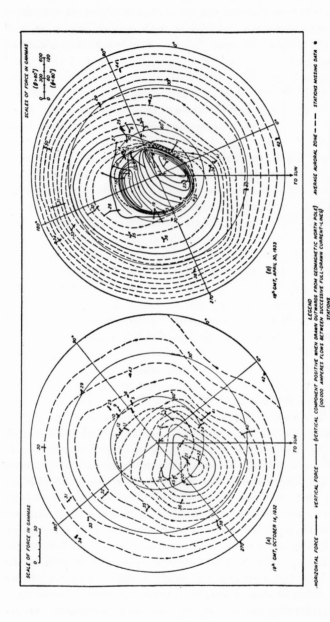

FIGURE 4.   Mean hourly disturbance vectors and corresponding electric-current systems for height 150 km for maximum of initial phase of magnetic storms; view from above geomagnetic north pole.

The electrojets shown at the right of Fig. 3 are to be found in polar regions during intensifications of the D-field known as magnetic bays.[12] Bays occur in measurable form on at least half of all days. These sometimes start, when locally intense, with the simultaneous occurrence of a homogeneous auroral arc,[20] which is a form often associated with incoming protons within the arc.[21,22,23] It has hence been suggested

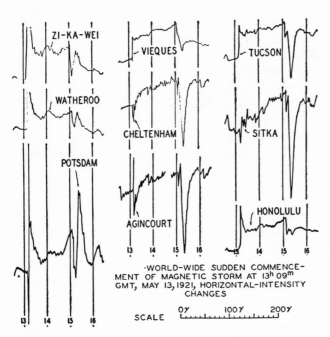

FIGURE 5.   Magnetic storm of May 13, 1921.

many times that these electrojets might be generated somehow by dynamo action, the most detailed calculations on this point being due to Fukushima.[24] Of course, electric fields associated with incoming charges will give rise to horizontal or vertical electric doublets, which must also drive some currents in low and middle latitudes, though the radial component of a vertical doublet could presumably give rise only to a pulse of current, from the crossed electric and magnetic fields in low and middle latitudes. It would be of interest to know whether or not the electric currents in low latitudes during a bay are located within the atmosphere, since it is difficult to trace a dependence on electric conductivity as deduced from ionospheric measurements. According to Wulf,[25] a rapidly flowing gas will generate its own ionization, and the currents would then be generated by dynamo action at levels of high collisional frequency. Bays also have sudden beginnings like sudden commencements,[26] which are listed routinely by Bartels along with indices of geomagnetic activity. The presence of electric fields acting upon the F-region at times of bay-like disturbance in low latitudes has been suggested by Martyn,[5] and such electric fields will of course drive electric currents within the E-region. Measurements aboard a satellite during a magnetic bay hence would provide much information of high interest, when studied and compared with the usual magnetic measurements recorded at ground observatories. Since the ionization is again likely to be patchy, a rough signal should be experienced when the satellite moves within the current.

If winds have a part in the production of magnetic disturbances,[9,24,25,27,28] zonal air flow is normally expected as a dominant characteristic, since the earth is in rotation. A vertical gradient in zonal wind velocity, of the type found by Whipple,[29] would then generate meridional current flow near and within the E-region. The magnetic fields may then be toroidal[28] or the magnetic lines of force may close within the atmosphere. At ground level the observable magnetic field due to a meridional circulation would then be seen in the Hall current component, in which electric current is driven nearly perpendicular to the geomagnetic main field. Within the F-region the separation of the ordinary and extraordinary waves obtained during radio soundings of the ionosphere does not seem to indicate the presence of toroidal fields that are detectable there. Another region where toroidal fields are expected will be near the junction between the outer region which must slip relative to the earth and its atmosphere. This will be expected several earth radii out, where the kinetic energy of streaming coronal gas has about the same energy as that per unit volume for the magnetic and electric field. In other words, the geomagnetic field sufficiently far out will be wound up within the region which does not move with the earth. This magnetic field will then reflect some degree of symmetry relative to the axis of the earth's rotation and exert a profound influence upon any auroral-type particles or cosmic rays, if it is large enough. It is also possible that the zonal motion of solar streams near the earth will give rise to some form of toroidal field;[7] also, at such times the paths of radio whistler signals will be lengthened, or rendered complex at times of magnetic disturbance, as in the "dawn chorus," in the event turbulent scattering conditions are present.

Other Current Systems

Fig. 6 illustrates phenomena known as micropulsations of the geomagnetic field.[1] Some types of these are of frequent occurrence throughout low and middle latitudes. Another type known as giant pulsations is occasionally noted (a few times per year) near the auroral zone.

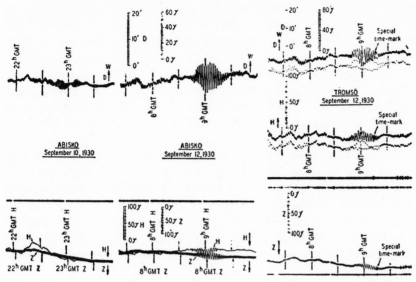

FIGURE 6. Micropulsations recorded at Abisko, Sweden, and at Tromsö, Norway (after B. Rolf).

Less perfect sinusoidal changes, however, occur frequently and may be measurable aboard a satellite. Fig. 7 shows an example of the ionosphere responding in unison with a giant pulsation in some way. This record was obtained by Harang, in Norway. It is not necessarily true that the

FIGURE 7. Echoes recorded on 11.0 mc/sec indicating an ionized or scattering region, at virtual height 650–800 km showing, during occurrence of oscillations in magnetic curves, pulsations of like period in the reflecting power in the ionized region (after L. Harang).

heights of radio reflection are those shown—the reflected signals actually may arise near the E-layer. But hydromagnetic waves propagated within the F-region should be detectible aboard a satellite.

The Earth's Main Magnetic Field at Satellite Level

It was indicated above that if the satellite had a trajectory sufficiently high above the earth, the region of measurement would then be one in which the main field would be wound up. The amount of winding depends on the very high electric conductivity there, as well as on the velocity of the streaming gases undergoing a relative motion with respect to the earth. But below this level, which may be as far as 10 earth radii out, the main magnetic field is determined by a sufficiently accurate knowledge of the main field measured on its surface. Unfortunately, this accurate knowledge of the surface magnetic field has never been obtained. Instead, there is available only a moderately accurate knowledge of the surface magnetic field, which has been used to compute the earth's main field and its secular magnetic change upward to a distance of 5000 km. This is done by the method of spherical-harmonic analysis, although there also exist formal integral methods which might be used with modern electronic computers. In terms of spherical co-ordinates (r, θ, λ), where r is the distance from the earth's center, with origin at the earth's center, θ the colatitude, and λ the longitude, the magnetic potential over the earth's surface $(r = a)$ may be expressed

$$V = a\sum (a/r)^{n+1}(g_n{}^m \cos m\lambda + h_n{}^m \sin m\lambda)P_n{}^m (\cos \theta) \tag{1}$$

where $g_n{}^m$, $h_n{}^m$ are constants determined from the surface magnetic data, and $P_n{}^m (\cos \theta)$ is the associated Legendre polynomial of integral degree n and order m.[1] The space gradients of V give the magnetic-field components, and the possible presence of an external magnetic field of the earth has been neglected.

Series of the form (1) have been fitted to the earth's surface magnetic field, and bearing in mind that the earth's equatorial field is about 30,000 gammas and the polar field is about twice as great, a comparison of observed minus computed values yields an average difference of about 150 gammas or so, throughout low and middle latitudes. The fit could of course be improved using values of m and n greater than the value 6 actually supposed here to terminate what is really an infinite series, but the uncertainties in the measured ocean values are at least of this order, and the transient variations such as the daily variation are sometimes as large as this. However, there are about 100 magnetic observatories over the earth, providing continuous measurements; so in the engineering sense the noise level is of the order 20 gammas or so, in low and middle latitudes, and variable from one day to the next.

Field components have been computed at the 300-km and 500-km levels, and the error is likely to be about 150 gammas, as at ground level. The actual error could be measured on magnetically quiet days aboard a satellite; so difference corrections depending on r, θ, and λ could be set up as a function of time; good spacing of monitoring stations on the ground would be needed, if defects in spherical-harmonic extrapolation are to be removed even coarsely.

Another scheme which, unlike spherical harmonics, depends more on the magnetic field observed locally is to extrapolate and interpolate from measured and estimated values, using a three-dimensional Taylor series such as

$$F(x + h) = e^{h(d/dx)}F(x) \tag{2}$$

where x means symbolically x_1, x_2, x_3, and the exponent is also treated symbolically.[30]

In practice, it probably will be unnecessary in many cases to rely on such cumbersome schemes, because advantage can be taken of measured differences from, say, one two-hour period to the next, or from one day to the next, in actual studies of upper-air phenomena.

Finally, it is clear that magnetic measurements made aboard a satellite will improve the existing knowledge of the earth's main field, and that the effects of the main field in at least special cases can be removed from observed signals to obtain estimates of desired signals related to transient phenomena.

Tentative Summary of Satellite-Borne Magnetometer Explorations for Consideration

In a new project of this kind it is not unlikely that attempts to undertake one line of investigation will end up by doing something quite fascinating of an entirely unsuspected and different character. At any rate, the obvious problems which everyone will have already thought of as amenable to solution can be listed in part as follows:

1) Investigate the spatial distribution of the earth's main magnetic field within the ionosphere and exosphere.

2) Estimate the spatial distribution and height of the electric-current systems which flow within the ionosphere and beyond, by comparison of measured signals with those obtained by ground-based stations, and from transient signals associated with irregularities in the distribution or patchiness of ions. In auroral regions the latter may prove particularly interesting.

3) Obtain more definite descriptions of the current flow within the polar and equatorial electrojets.

4) From the time fluctuations in magnetometer signal, by auto-correlation or other methods, deduce the blob size of ionized patches, and hence deduce, if possible, particulars such as the state of turbulence of the ionosphere; it may be convenient to telemeter values measured at higher sensitivity if low-frequency signals are removed or transmitted at lower sensitivity on an intermittent coded basis.

5) Closely related to (4) would be the search for hydromagnetic waves and toroidal magnetic fields.

6) During the initial phase of magnetic storms it would also be of interest (as at other times) to detect a possible burst of radiation such as X-rays, because ground observations show that an enhancement in current seems to occur at times on the sunlit half of the earth.

It appears likely from the preceding discussion that significant contributions to our knowledge of the earth's main magnetic field will result from the satellite measurements, with improvements in its spherical-harmonic representation. These improvements will also be of interest in problems concerning the earth's fluid central core. In particular, since total intensity, F, will be measured, which at the magnetic equator will be the same as the horizontal intensity, H, there should result from equatorial measurements an improved determination of one-half of the terms of equation (1); at any rate, a boundary condition will have been established for potential analyses, even though F itself is not a potential function.

Under (2) it is very difficult to improve upon the estimates made by Chapman[14] for the case of rocket-borne magnetometers, and for methods of making estimates reference should be made to that paper. In those experiments also, F is assumed to be the quantity measured. Using as the field of a current sheet the value $2\pi i$, independent of distance to it for points of measurement nearby, Chapman found the contrast in F across the westward-directed polar electrojet of the D-field to be as much as 0.27 gauss, if flow took place within a homogeneous auroral arc. To experience a field change of this size, the satellite would move in a meridional orbit near the 100-km level, during the most intense part of a magnetic storm. Even at the 300-km level, the change in F should be several hundred gammas, and in a sense similar to values observed at ground level.

If the so-called ring-current effect were due to westward-flowing electric currents near the E-region, the equatorial contrast in the transient field in F would be about 200 gammas in the case of a moderate magnetic storm, such as that for Fig. 3, the disturbance in F at the ground being in opposition to the main field at the ground, and adding to it at the F-region. The signal contrast would be expected to be largest near 6 p.m. and smallest near 6 a.m.; near noon and midnight the effects would be due mainly to the ring-current effect, after removing effects due to the S and the L current systems. A diurnal variation of about 100 gammas, opposite in phase between ground and satellite, would be expected, if the currents flow near the E-region.

It may also be recalled here that during magnetic storms there exist occasional large transitory surges in field, susceptible to measurement aboard a satellite.

Observations while traversing auroral curtains showing progressive wave motions may reveal the presence of hydromagnetic waves; it would be of interest to determine whether or not these are engendered by transient zonal winds near the E-layer.[28]

Acknowledgment is made to Dr. J. P. Heppner, Naval Research Laboratory, for bringing some of the opportunities for measurement to the writer's notice.

REFERENCES

1. S. Chapman and J. Bartels. *Geomagnetism.* Oxford: Internatl. Series of Monographs on Physics, 1940. Vols. I and II.
2. B. N. Lahiri and A. T. Price, "Electromagnetic Induction in Nonuniform Conductors and the Determination of the Conductivity of the Earth from the Terrestrial Magnetic Variations," *Phil. Trans. Roy. Soc. London, A, 237:* 509–540 (1939).
3. S. E. Forbush, "Cosmic-Ray Effects Associated with Magnetic Storms," *Terr. Mag., 43:* 203–218 (1938).
4. L. Harang. *Aurorae.* New York: John Wiley and Sons, 1951.
5. D. F. Martyn, "The Physics of the Ionosphere," Report of the Physical Society Conference, 1955, pp. 260–264.
6. A. G. McNish, "Terrestrial-Magnetic and Ionospheric Effects Associated with Bright Chromospheric Eruptions," *Terr. Mag., 42:* 109–122 (1937).
7. H. W. Dodson *et al.,* "Solar Flares and Associated 200 mc/sec Radiation," *Astrophys. J., 118:* 169–196 (1953).
8. Kr. Birkeland. *The Norwegian Aurora Polaris Expedition 1902–1903.* Vol. I, part 1 (1908), pp. 39–315; part 2 (1913), pp. 319, 551. Christiania: H. Aschenhoug and Co.
9. E. H. Vestine, "Asymmetrical Characteristics of the Earth's Magnetic Disturbance-Field," *Terr. Mag., 43:* 261–282 (1938).
10. M. Sugiura, "The Solar Diurnal Variation in the Amplitude of Sudden Commencements of Magnetic Storms at the Geomagnetic Equator," *J. Geophys. Res., 58:* 558–559 (1953).
11. E. H. Vestine, "The Immediate Source of the Field of Magnetic Storms," *J. Geophys. Res., 58:* 560–562 (1953).
12. E. H. Vestine *et al. The Geomagnetic Field, Its Description and Analysis.* Carnegie Inst. of Washington, Publ. 580, 1947.
13. S. F. Singer *et al.,* "Evidence for Ionosphere Currents from Rocket Experiments near the Geomagnetic Equator," *J. Geophys. Res., 56:* 265–281 (1951).
14. S. Chapman. In *Rocket Exploration of the Upper Atmosphere.* London: Pergamon Press, 1954, p. 292.
15. S. E. Forbush and E. H. Vestine, "Daytime Enhancement of Size of

Sudden Commencements and Initial Phase of Magnetic Storms at Huancayo," *J. Geophys. Res., 60:* 299–316 (1955).

16. S. F. Singer. In *Rocket Exploration of the Upper Atmosphere.* London: Pergamon Press, 1954, pp. 368–370.

17. S. Chapman, "Electric Current-Systems of Magnetic Storms," *Terr. Mag., 40:* 349–370 (1935).

18. E. H. Vestine, "Disturbance Field of Magnetic Storms," *Bull. Int. Union Geod. and Geophys., 11:* 360–381 (1940).

19. S. Chapman and V. C. A. Ferraro, "Theory of Magnetic Storms," *Terr. Mag., 36:* 77–97, 171–186 (1931); *ibid., 37:* 147–156 (1932); "New Theory of Magnetic Storms," *ibid.,* pp. 421–429; *ibid., 38:* 79–96 (1933); "Theory of the First Phase of a Geomagnetic Storm," *ibid., 45:* 245–268 (1940); "Geomagnetic Ring-Current. I. Radial Stability," *ibid., 46:* 1–6 (1941).

20. J. P. Heppner, "Time Sequences and Spatial Relations in Auroral Activity During Magnetic Bays at College, Alaska," *J. Geophys. Res., 59:* 329–338 (1954).

21. L. Vegard, "Hydrogen Showers in the Auroral Region," *Nature, 144:* 1089–1090 (1939).

22. C. W. Gartlein, "Aurora Spectra Showing Broad Hydrogen Lines," *Trans. Am. Geophys. Union, 31:* 18–20 (1950).

23. A. B. Meinel, "Doppler-Shifted Auroral Hydrogen Emission," *Astrophys. J., 113:* 50–54 (1951).

24. N. Fukushima, *J. Fac. Sci. Tokyo Imp. Univ., 8:* 293–412 (1953).

25. O. R. Wulf, "On the Relation Between Geomagnetism and the Circulatory Motions of the Air in the Atmosphere," *Terr. Mag. Atmos. Elect., 50:* 185–197 (1945); *ibid.,* pp. 259–278; "On the Production of Glow Discharges in the Ionosphere by Winds," *J. Geophys. Res., 58:* 531–538 (1953).

26. J. P. Heppner, "Note on the Occurrence of World-Wide S.S.C.'s During the Onset of Negative Bays at College, Alaska," *J. Geophys. Res., 60:* 29–32 (1955).

27. S. Matsushita, *J. Geomag. Geoelect., 5:* 22 (1953).

28. E. H. Vestine, "Winds in the Upper Atmosphere Deduced from the Dynamo Theory of Geomagnetic Disturbance," *J. Geophys. Res., 59:* 93–128 (1954).

29. F. L. Whipple, "Evidence for Winds in Outer Atmosphere," *Proc. Natl. Acad. Sci., 40:* 966–972 (1954).

30. A. Zmuda and L. McClung, "Vertical Extrapolation of Geomagnetic Field Components," *Trans. Am. Geophys. Union, 36:* 939–942 (1955).

24

Measurements of the Earth's Magnetic Field from a Satellite Vehicle

by S. F. Singer
UNIVERSITY OF MARYLAND

ABSTRACT

We discuss here the application of satellite observations to magnetic measurement on three different time scales:

Part A. *Measurement of the Earth's Main Field and Its Secular Variations*

The main advantages of a satellite over other methods are described. We conclude that it should be possible to get a better description of the main field and to study in greater detail the motions of eddies in the earth's core.

Part B. *Short Time Variations of the Field and Atmospheric Current Systems*

The satellite magnetometer by being located above the ionosphere observes the magnetic fields produced by atmospheric current systems in opposite phase when compared to a sea-level magnetometer; both instruments, however, observe currents external to the earth's atmosphere (the presumed Störmer ring current) in the same phase. This technique therefore allows determination of the location and strength of the currents responsible for magnetic storms at low latitudes and in the auroral zones, as well as for the disturbed and quiet diurnal variations.   Such measurements allow us to decide between different theories for the magnetic-storm currents.

Part C.   *Transient Variations*

Aside from quasi-steady-state effects, transient variations produced by rapid motions of ionized gas near the earth are of interest.   They produce sudden magnetic commencements and other rapid variations of the earth's field.   A physical model is presented in which the approach and penetration of a magnetohydrodynamic shockwave gives rise to a sudden commencement increase.   Satellite observations can give us information of crucial importance by locating the position of the SC currents and by overcoming the ionosphere shielding effects.

Appendix I discusses the proton free-precession magnetometer, operating principles, sources of error, problems of data storage and telemetering.

Appendix II discusses a proposed model experiment to verify some crucial points of the magnetohydrodynamic shockwave model advanced in Part C.

Appendix III discusses some parameters of this shockwave in the interplanetary space.

A. Measurement of the Earth's Main Field and Its Secular Variations

We will attempt to evaluate here the effectiveness of a satellite in carrying on measurements of the earth's main field, in comparison to other methods, e.g., an airplane equipped with a magnetometer.

Measurements

What we require is:

1) A worldwide survey covering the earth uniformly.

2) A means of de-emphasizing the higher harmonics and local anomalies.

3) A nearly simultaneous measurement over the whole earth, and a large number of these so as to average out effects due to external currents.

4) The possibility of repeating the measurements at regular time intervals.

5) A measurement precision as high as possible (a few gamma or better).

6) Finally, all this should not require an unreasonably great cost and effort.

A satellite equipped with a magnetometer satisfies these requirements:

1) In a polar orbit it will cover all of the earth's surface. We can make the net as fine as we please by choosing an orbital period such that the orbit trace over the earth is not repetitive. A 96-min orbit would give rapid coverage, a 93-min orbit would give a finer mesh, etc.

2) A peculiar advantage of the satellite is its high operating altitude. The effect on higher-order harmonics and local anomalies can be seen as follows. At an operating altitude of 500 km, the dipole field has decreased by a factor $[6370/(6370 + 500)]^3 = 0.798$; at the same time, e.g., $[6370/(6370 + 500)]^9 = 0.507$. Consider now a large magnetic anomaly near the surface extending over about 100 km; if we represent it by a dipole, its contribution would be reduced by a factor $(100/500)^3$, i.e., less than 1%. From this point of view a somewhat higher operating altitude, e.g., 1000 km, would be even better.

An important comparison would be between the observed field at 1000 km and the field as extrapolated from sea level and from 500 km by use of spherical-harmonic analysis, in the manner of Vestine.[1] This comparison may reveal a *time-invariant* contribution of the atmosphere.

A related problem is to find what portion, if any, of the earth's field is of external origin.

3) In order to eliminate effectively *time-varying* contributions to the magnetic field from the outer atmosphere and extraterrestrial currents, it is important to carry on observations over a large number of days, or even several weeks. It would be technically difficult to do this with an airplane but relatively simple for a satellite once it has been put into operation.

It is important also to make these survey measurements over nearly the same period of time so as not to introduce the secular variation into the determination of the dipole and higher-order components (see below).

4) To study the secular variation, the measurements must be repeated periodically. To get an order-of-magnitude estimate of the time scale, we consider that the westward drift of the main features of the nondipole field and of the secular variation is about 1° in 5 years, well within the space resolution of the satellite. The maximum secular rate of change of any component of the earth's field is about 150 γ per year.[1] Thus it may be possible to measure the variation at certain locations even within the space of a few weeks. According to Vestine these maximum variations occur south of Capetown, west of Deception Island, and in other rather inaccessible places.

5) As discussed in Appendix I, the free-precession magnetometer is capable of extremely high precision. Its major drawback lies in the fact that it measures the scalar value of the field rather than its separate components. A possible way of remedying this difficulty is to bring in also data from ground and airplane magnetometers, particularly changes in the inclination and declination.

6) Here we must compare cost and effort with ground and aircraft observations of comparable accuracy, coverage, time duration, etc. This comparison amounts to an educated guess, but it would seem that even today the satellite looks better and that this advantage will increase markedly with time as problems of satellite technology become solved. In addition, the satellite method has the unique advantages outlined under (2).

Applications

The central problem is to understand the origin of the earth's field. In this connection, the study of the secular variations is of major importance. Bullard has pointed out that the horizontal scales of the secular variation[1] and of the nondipole field[2] are similar, of the order of several thousand kilometers. They both drift westward at a rate of 0.2° per year while the dipole field drifts more slowly, and perhaps not systematically.

The information from the satellite may enable us to disentangle the nondipole (spatial) variation from the temporal variation. It should be possible to obtain significant information in a matter of years instead of decades. If we adopt the point of view that we are dealing here with the motion of large eddies in the earth's liquid core,[3] we may use the data to study the energy and angular momentum transport and compare it with our expectation from theoretical models of a rotating core with thermal convection.

Finally, there are some more practical applications to other geophysical studies, e.g., in the study of cosmic rays we need to know the geomagnetic field, especially the dipole field, as precisely as possible. We also want to know the higher-order fields in order to calculate the shifts in the Störmer cones,[4] albedo trajectories,[5] and the high-latitude cut-off.

B. Short Time Variations of the Field and Atmospheric Current Systems

Here we discuss measurements on a time scale intermediate between secular variations (Part A) and transient variations (Part C). The time scale for Part B varies then from a time commensurate with the solar rotation period (27 days) down to a time where the induction effects of the atmosphere are of importance (fraction of an hour).

The purpose of these measurements is mainly to understand the influences of the atmosphere and the regions beyond, on the earth's magnetic field.

In 1947, the proposal was made by Vestine[6] to investigate ionospheric currents by shooting a rocket through the layer. These proposals have been amplified by Chapman.[7]

Measurements of the earth's magnetic field at high altitudes (E-layer) have been carried on by the writer and his colleagues[8,9] in the past to measure mainly the S_q system; they have led to the following results:

1) They have established experimentally the fall-off of the earth's magnetic field with altitude; this provides an important check on the analysis of the sea-level field by means of spherical harmonics, such as has been carried out recently by E. H. Vestine.[1]

2) The later measurements[9] led to the discovery of a thin (10 km high) current layer in the equatorial region in the lower E-layer of the ionosphere. Previously, it had been supposed that the current would have to flow in an altitude interval from about 70 km to 300 km.

3) These findings have led to an important revision of our ideas about the conductivity of the ionosphere,[10] about the effects of the magnetic field on the conductivity, and about the winds necessary in the ionosphere to produce the observed currents.

It seems important to carry out similar rocket experiments during quiet and disturbed periods, to measure not only currents at low latitudes but also in the auroral and polar regions, at various times of day, and during various phases of the moon. In addition, it is important to make such measurements during the different intervals of a magnetic storm. Clearly, the approach to continuous measurements using sounding rockets is very costly and would consume a tremendous amount of effort. For this reason, the writer proposed in 1951 the application of a small ("minimum") satellite to this investigation.[11]

The satellite magnetometer, by being located above the ionosphere, observes the magnetic fields produced by atmospheric current systems in opposite phase when compared to a sea level magnetometer; both instruments, however, observe currents external to the earth's atmosphere (the presumed Störmer ring current) in the same phase.[12] This technique therefore allows determination of the location and strength of the currents responsible for magnetic storms at low latitudes and in the auroral zones, as well as for the disturbed and quiet diurnal variations.

The satellite in an orbit near 500 km could then be used to measure on a worldwide basis and continuously,

1) the solar quiet day (S_q) variations,

2) the lunar quiet day (L_q) variations,
3) the auroral current belts, and
4) the currents over the polar caps.

As discussed in Appendix I, the accuracy of the instrument is adequate, although determination of the vector field would be more desirable.

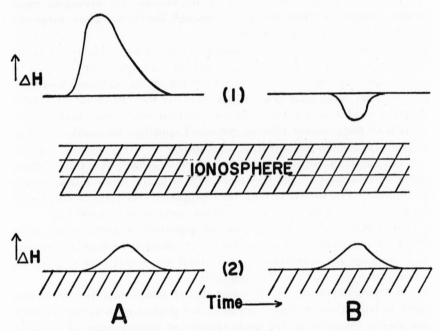

FIGURE 1. Schematic diagrams of magnetic variations (ΔH) observed by: (1) magnetometer above ionosphere; (2) magnetometer below ionosphere. (A) Variation due to external current. (B) Variation due to current flowing in earth's ionosphere.

Of particular interest for satellite measurements, however, are observations during magnetic-storm periods. The current systems can be divided into a D_{st} (storm time) and an S_d (solar time) part. It seems likely that at least the S_d currents flow in the ionosphere.[13] The D_{st} currents which decay away quite slowly are assumed by Chapman and Ferraro to be associated with the extraterrestrial ring current.

The "ring current" has been assumed variously as a line or as a cylindrical sheet whose axis is parallel to the earth's dipole axis. This may not at all be the case. In recent work not yet published (R. Rhodes, master's thesis, University of Maryland, 1955), we have investigated efficient mechanisms of trapping low-energy particles in the geomagnetic field for long times. Application of perturbation calculations shows that these particles drift so as to produce a ring-current effect. The trapping time is also consistent with the decay time of magnetic storms ($\sim$ several days). Our model allows calculation of the current distribution as a function of both latitude and altitude.[14]

The solution to this question of the location of the D_{st} current is, of course, precisely what the satellite data could furnish us. It was assumed at one time that the ring current would also account for the decrease of the cosmic radiation which is often observed during magnetic storms. Closer examination has shown this not to be the case, but the effects of a possible ring current on the orbits of cosmic rays and auroral particles are still of the greatest interest.[15]

C. Transient Variations

One of the most interesting applications of the satellite magnetometer is to the measurement of transients. It is here where the shielding effects of the earth's atmosphere are most important and where measurements above the ionosphere can add much to our knowledge of the cause of the variations and the location of the currents producing them.

We will be concerned here with the following points:

1) Listing significant observations of the onset of magnetic storms: the SC, the SC*, pre-SC disturbances, the enhancement of SC and of the initial phase, and their relation to S_q.

2) An attempt to explain these phenomena in a coherent physical picture; mathematical considerations will be only sketched in. (A description of a model experiment to verify some crucial points of (b) below is given in Appendix I.)

3) Tie-in with satellite observations.

1) *Observations*

(a) Newton[16] has derived a time lag of 22 hours for great magnetic storms (and 34 for storms of smaller intensity) between the central meridian passage of active sunspots and the commencement of a great storm.

(b) A worldwide sudden commencement (SC) is observed; it consists of a rise in the magnetic field within a short time interval (of the order of a few minutes).

(c) The SC varies considerably from place to place. A careful statistical analysis by Forbush and Vestine[17] has established that the SC (and the initial phase, IP) is enhanced during the daylight hours at Huancayo, thus indicating an atmospheric source for SC and IP. These suggestions had been made previously by Vestine[18] and Sugiura.[19]

Even earlier Chree[20] had given evidence that the sizes of SC's are larger in the auroral regions than elsewhere (by perhaps a factor of 4) and Fukushima[21] in analyzing the storm of August 3, 1949, concluded that SC is enhanced in the auroral zone and on the daylight side. Measurements with induction magnetometers also show a daytime enhancement of SC.[22]

(d) In his discussion of the diurnal variation of SC, Newton[23] points to the occurrence of SC*, a reverse impulse in the horizontal force component which precedes the SC increase by about a minute or so. A careful study of the distribution of SC* with respect to local time and latitude has been published by Nagata,[24] who concludes that it can be represented by a high-latitude, upper-atmosphere current system consisting of a strong clockwise vortex (at about 14^h) and a weaker counter-clockwise vortex (centered at 6^h).

(e) Fukushima[21] has called attention to a pre-SC bay-like disturbance at high latitudes. It precedes the onset of the magnetic storm by about an hour. During the magnetic storm, disturbances are observed which take place intermittently along the auroral zone;[25] these are attributed to occasional concentrations of corpuscular radiation.

(f) A phenomenon possibly related to (e) has been discussed by Heppner, who related high-latitude bay disturbances to changes in the appearance of the aurora.[26]

2) *Physical Picture of Sudden Commencement*

The Chapman-Ferraro theory[27] attempts to explain the initial phase of magnetic storms through the behavior of a neutral ionized corpuscular stream moving in a magnetic field which has an inverse-cube distribution in the direction of the motion of the beam. Ferraro[27] also calculates the build-up of the compressed magnetic field as the beam is retarded, and tentatively identifies it with the SC; he does not calculate the effects to be observed, although he mentions the importance of ionospheric shielding currents. The CF theory, however, cannot account simply for the observational facts listed above.

We are tempted therefore to develop the following physical picture to account for the observational data of the SC:[14]

(a) We first adopt the point of view that we are dealing here with an interplanetary shockwave, a suggestion advanced by Gold[28] to explain the high degree of collimation in time of the worldwide SC, even after a long travel time from the sun [points (a) and (b) above].

(b) We also adopt the view, advanced most strongly by Vestine, that the SC currents actually flow in our atmosphere [cf. (c) above].

There is little doubt that a shockwave will develop. In Appendix III we estimate the disturbance velocity to be ~50 times the velocity of sound. The mean free path we estimate as ~10^{-6} of the sun-earth distance.

(c) An interesting interpretation can now be added. From the theory of strong shocks, we deduce also the velocity to which the gas behind the shockwave is accelerated, namely, $\frac{3}{4} V_{\text{Shock}}$. This leads to

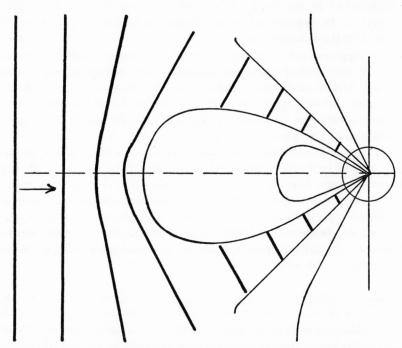

FIGURE 2. Position of the shock front in the earth's dipole field at successive intervals. Note the bending of the shock front as it interacts with the earth's field.

the result that the gas arrives in the vicinity of the earth about 7–10 hours after the SC, i.e., just about at the beginning of the main phase. We believe that this is a significant result and identify the SC and IP (initial phase) with the shockwave and the main phase with the corpuscular stream.

(d) We now consider what happens when the shockwave impinges on the earth's dipole field. The gas and, therefore, the field in the equatorial plane are compressed by the shockwave. Since the conductivity is finite, the field lines will snap out again, a process which can be described by a diffusion equation. In front of the shockwave, induction effects will screen the observer on the earth, until finally the induced currents extend to the lower base of the ionosphere, at which time he may be able to observe a very slight build-up due to the compressed field.

(e) However, the gas behind the shock has now been set in motion perpendicular to H_0 and experiences therefore a body force and a retardation. The resulting expansion waves will catch up with the shock and stop it. This process should occur some earth radii out, well above the ionosphere. Above and below the equatorial plane the field is not perpendicular to the shock velocity; therefore, less or no retardation will be experienced by the shock. It appears therefore that the shock front will curve. (In Appendix II we discuss an experiment designed to verify this effect in the laboratory.)

(f) Applying the reasoning of (e) in a continuous manner, we find the shock split and entering the northern and southern auroral zones. Confined within an annular region (of the magnetic lines of force) whose area shrinks rapidly, the velocity of the shockwave and gas increases, causing high ionization in the auroral ionosphere. We regard the reaction of the gas on the confining magnetic field as the cause of the SC* events. The charge separation of the gas under the influence of the earth's field acts as the driving force for the atmospheric SC currents in the lower latitudes.[14]

(g) To explain the pre-SC high-latitude disturbances, we bring in high-velocity particles, perhaps traveling in streams in the manner described by Bennett and Hulburt.[29] The emission of high-velocity beams during solar eruptions[30] has been observed with radio methods; their smaller interaction enables them to arrive ahead of the shockwave.

It is obviously not feasible to describe the sequence of processes by a simple mathematical model; we must forego, therefore, a very elegant and satisfying treatment in the manner of Chapman-Ferraro. Some progress has been made with a one-dimensional model by Burgers.[31] The model experiments may add further knowledge. It will be necessary also to consider more physical points, such as polarization and Hall current effects in the shock. But geophysical data, from satellites as well as other sources, will be needed to test the picture proposed here.

3) *Satellite Observations during SC and IP*

The main job of the satellite will be to establish (by the methods described in Part B) the location of the SC and IP currents, particularly at low latitudes. We will be interested also in observing the possible induction effects above the ionospheric shielding.[32]

In the auroral zones we may be able to measure a variety of physical effects, by optical means (i.e., luminous excitation of gas) and by corpuscular counters or other ionization detectors (for high-velocity particles).[33] A magnetometer will be able to measure what portions of the SC or SC* currents flow in the ionosphere and determine their exact geographical distribution.[33]

ACKNOWLEDGMENTS

It is a pleasure to acknowledge some stimulating discussions on shockwaves with Professors J. Burgers and E. L. Resler of the University of Maryland.

APPENDIX I
Description of Experimental Approach

In the past the magnetic field of the earth has been measured in rockets by the writer using fluxgate techniques.[8,9] We will review here (following M. Packard and R. Varian) the use of nuclear induction methods which have the advantage of high precision and simplicity.[34]

Proton Free-Precession Magnetometer

All nuclear induction measurements of magnetic-field strength are possible because the nucleus has an intrinsic magnetic moment and spin angular momentum and, therefore, will precess about a magnetic field at a frequency which is proportional to the field strength. This precession is analogous to the precession of a gyroscope in the earth's gravitational field and can be calculated using as a model a classical gyroscope having angular momentum A and being acted on by a torque $M \times H$ produced by the interaction of magnetic moment M and the magnetic field H. Under these conditions the magnetic moment will precess about the magnetic field at a frequency

$$\omega = MH/A = \gamma H \tag{1}$$

independent of the angle between the magnetic field and magnetic moment; γ is a constant which is called the gyromagnetic ratio. For the proton γ_p has been measured as $2.6752 \pm 0.002 \times 10^4$ sec^{-1} gauss^{-1}.

To obtain a coherent precession, some mechanism must be provided to cause the proton moments to be oriented near a direction perpendicular to the field. In the usual nuclear magnetic-resonance experiments this is accomplished by the addition of an RF magnetic field at right angles to the polarizing field. This technique works well for the measurement of high magnetic-field strength; however, for fields less than about 25 gauss the sensitivity of the method becomes too low. It is then necessary to use a slightly different application of the nuclear resonance principle which has recently been developed by Varian Associates, Palo Alto, California, the so-called free nuclear precession magnetometer. This device uses the principle of nuclear induction to preserve the inherent high precision of the method but utilizes a fundamentally different method for producing an orientation perpendicular to the precessing field and for increasing the sensitivity. A strong polarizing field H_0 is used to polarize the nuclear magnetic moment M_0 to a value many times its earth's field value. This polarizing field, which is perpendicular to the earth's field, is suddenly turned off with the result that the nuclear moment is left perpendicular to the earth's field H_e and so will precess about it at the Larmor frequency given by equation (1). The precessing moment induces a voltage in a pickup, or receiver, coil oriented approximately at right angles to both the polarizing field and the earth's field, and the frequency of this voltage gives the magnitude of the earth's field. Using protons, the resonant frequencies corresponding to fields of the order of the earth's field are about 2 kc/sec. The system is highly accurate because the precessional frequency will depend only upon H_e and the constant γ_p. For protons in water γ_p has been measured to an absolute accuracy of about 1/40,000. Relative measurements can be even more accurate. The effects of external parameters are very small; for example, the resonant frequency will change as a function of temperature by less than one part in 3 million for a 100°C temperature change.

The high accuracy of the field measurement is maintained independently of the orientation of the coils because the nuclear precession takes place about the total field. The magnetometer reading will be correct even if the orientation is incorrect; however, the signal amplitude will fall off since it is proportional to the sine of the angle between the earth's field and the axis of the coil. The functions of polarization and pickup could be performed by the same coil.

Instrumentation

Under development now is a modification of the Varian free nuclear precession magnetometer for use in sounding rocket experiments. This unit should be ideally adaptable to satellite measurements. It is small, lightweight, and uses a minimum of power. It is capable of giving a reading of the earth's magnetic field independent of orientation every few seconds. The signal is large enough to be telemetered directly and consists of an audio-frequency tone which can be directly superimposed on an RF carrier. All of the elaborate instrumentation needed to measure precisely the precession frequency of the protons could be placed into the ground station and not into the satellite.

The details of the supporting instrumentation, i.e., telemetering and power supply, cannot be discussed in a very definite manner until such matters as payload, orbit, and receiving stations are settled.

For example, if the orbit is from pole to pole, the output of the magnetometer will vary in frequency by about a factor of 2. Means must be provided either for transmitting the information continuously and, therefore, receiving it continuously on the ground or for storage and release of the information over the polar regions. For equatorial or near-equatorial orbits the variation in the audio frequency to be

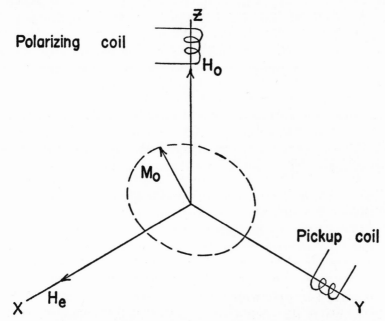

FIGURE 3. Principle of free precession nuclear resonance magnetometer showing orientation of coils, and of earth's field H_e. The field used to polarize the protons is H_o. During operation the polarizing field is turned off and the protons then precess about the earth's field H_e.

telemetered will be quite small; furthermore, in order to achieve useful scientific results, it may not be necessary to obtain continuous coverage. In order to investigate the location of magnetic-storm currents, a large number of isolated readings will be adequate. However, to study the properties of the sudden-commencement increase, it will be desirable to approach as nearly as possible continuous observations.

Sources of Error

The free-precession magnetometer is capable of extremely high precision. Varian Associates quote an absolute accuracy of about 1 γ with as much as 15 measurements per minute, and a sensitivity of 0.1 γ. It has also an inherently high stability, shows no drift, and therefore requires no in-flight calibration. The limitation to its accuracy is likely to be given by extraneous factors, chiefly inhomogeneities of the local field in the satellite which produce gradients over the volume of the magnetometer. This leads to a decoherence of the signal produced by the precessing protons, shortens the time during which the measurement can be conducted, and therefore lowers the precision.

A major source of error is the altitude uncertainty of the satellite. Since $\Delta H = -3(M/R^4)\Delta R$ (at the equator), we have $\Delta H/\Delta R = -(3/R)H_0$. Therefore, at an altitude of 500 km,

$$\Delta H = -\frac{3}{6370 + 500} \times 3 \times 10^4 \, \Delta R.$$

A variation of 1 km thus produces a ΔH of $\sim 13 \, \gamma$ at the equator, and 26 γ near the poles. In order to make the altitude error comparable to the others, we must know the altitude to better than 0.02 km (or 60 ft). The problem is twofold:

1) We must determine the altitude of the orbit (assumed to be circular) to this precision. This means determining the orbital period to the precision as follows:

$$\because T = 2\pi (GM_E)^{-1/2} R^{3/2};$$

$$\Delta T = \frac{3}{2} T_0 \frac{\Delta R}{R_0} \sim \frac{3}{2} \times 6000 \sec \frac{\Delta R}{6370 + 500} = 1.3\,(\Delta R).$$

For $\Delta R \sim 0.02$ km, $\Delta T = 0.026$ sec.

2) In reality the satellite orbit will be slightly elliptical. Due to the nonsphericity of the earth, a perturbation will be produced resulting in a motion of the line of apsides. In the equatorial plane this motion will be a uniform regressive rotation. In the polar plane the motion is quite complicated and contains periodic terms as well as progressive terms.[35]

APPENDIX II
A Model Experiment on Interplanetary Shockwaves in the Geomagnetic Field*

We wish to reproduce in the laboratory some of the conditions which are believed to occur when a shockwave produced by solar corpuscular emission impinges on the earth's magnetic field. We are particularly interested in observing the shock front to detect a possible curvature produced by the differential propagation velocity.

---

* With Prof. E. L. Resler, Jr., Institute of Fluid Dynamics and Applied Mathematics, University of Maryland.

In order to simulate the actual conditions as closely as possible, we apply suitable scaling factors. The distance involved is ~8 earth radii (in the equatorial plane), i.e., 5×10^9 cm. Our laboratory dimension is ~5 cm, giving a scaling factor of 10^9 which must be applied to H, the conductivity σ, and electron concentration n_e. H varies from 10^{-4} gauss to 0.5 gauss, $n_e \sim 10^2$ up to 10^5; we will leave σ out of consideration for the time being, since the gas will be highly ionized (~50%).

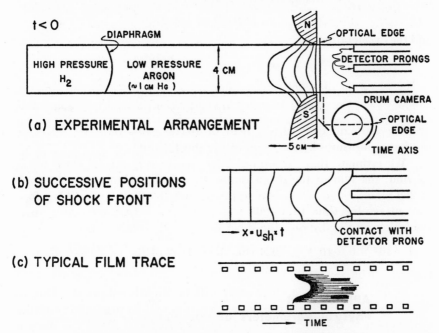

FIGURE 4. Proposed experiment for verifying the effect of a non-homogeneous magnetic field on a shockwave. (a) Experimental arrangement showing the shock tube, the inhomogeneous magnet, the detector prongs, and drum camera. (b) Showing the successive positions of shock front as it interacts with the inhomogeneous magnetic field. Note the bending and the time of contact with the various detector prongs. (c) A typical film trace such as might be taken by the drum camera if the shockwave positions are as shown in (b). The detector prongs will blow brightly and give the three dark streaks in the picture.

We should therefore produce fields of at least 10^5 gauss and n_e of 10^{11} to $10^{14}/\text{cm}^3$.

Two methods suggest themselves for producing the high ionization: an RF discharge, or a strong shockwave. The RF discharge leads to a high electron temperature, while the second method may give a more realistic presentation, since $T_e \sim T_{\text{gas}}$.

An incident strong shockwave itself can produce an electron density of 10^{16} or $10^{17}/\text{cm}^3$; therefore with a Mach number of 10 we can achieve a conductivity of 1 mho/cm.*[36]

We will now construct a nonhomogeneous field to simulate the earth's dipole field $(H \sim 10^4$ gauss$)$, and calculate roughly the distortion of the shock front. The gas behind the shock has velocity ~ 4 km/sec; then

$$\sigma(v \times H) = \frac{10 \text{ mhos/cm } (3 \times 10^5 \times 10^4)}{10^8} = 300 \text{ amps,}$$

and the deceleration is

$$\frac{i \times H}{\rho} = \frac{\frac{300}{10} \times 10^4}{.0001} = 3 \times 10^9 \text{ cm/sec}^2$$

$$s = \tfrac{1}{2}at^2 = \tfrac{1}{2} \times 3 \times 10^9 \times (2 \times 10^{-5} \text{ sec})^2 = 0.6 \text{ cm.}$$

We estimate that with a field of 10,000 gauss or more we could produce a measurable distortion of the shock front.

We estimate that the optical edge (see Fig. 4) can be lined up to 0.1 mm; the film in the drum camera is spinning about a vertical axis at 200 m/sec. We can resolve approximately 80 lines/mm. Therefore, we can resolve time to $1/(200 \times 10^3 \times 80) = 6 \times 10^{-8}$ sec. Our space resolution is: the distance the shockwave travels in this time:

$$4 \times 10^5 \times 6 \times 10^{-8} = 0.024 \text{ cm, about } 1/30 \text{ of the estimated effect.}$$

APPENDIX III
Physical Parameters of Interplanetary Shockwaves

We start by establishing first some basic facts: the disturbance causing an SC propagates to the earth in some 20 hours, therefore, with a velocity $\sim(1.5 \times 10^{13})/(3600 \times 20) = 2 \times 10^8$ cm/sec.

If we assume the IP matter at rest before the disturbance reaches it, we have the typical condition for the establishment of a shockwave, since the disturbance velocity is supersonic; we estimate the velocity of an Alfvén wave as $\sim 4 \times 10^6$ cm/sec. We can now compute the Mach number and, therefore, the strength of the shock.

Next we investigate whether or not the mean free path is small enough to allow a shock front to be formed between the sun and the earth; the width of the shock front can be taken as 3–4 times λ; $\lambda = 1/nS$. If we assume a very high degree of ionization to exist, then

---

* If it seems desirable, the conductivity could be increased by a factor of 10, if we raise the Mach number to 15; but this requires a somewhat more elaborate instrumentation.

S is determined by the Coulomb interaction between ions and electrons:

$$S = 2.4 \times 10^{-5} \frac{Z^2}{T_e^2} \, \text{cm}^2.$$

We will take $Z = 1$, and assume $\log T_e$ in IP ~ 4–5, $\therefore S = 2.4 \times 10^{-13}$ to 2.4×10^{-11}.

Probably the best value near the earth is 10^{-11} cm^2; then with $n_e^2 10^3$/cc, $\lambda_e = 10^8$ cm and the width of the shock front ~ 3 to 4×10^8 cm, compared to a sun-earth distance of 1.5×10^{13} cm.

REFERENCES

1. E. H. Vestine *et al.* Publications 578 and 580, Dept. Terr. Mag., Carnegie Inst., Washington, D.C., 1947.
2. E. C. Bullard *et al.*, "The Westward Drift of the Earth's Magnetic Field," *Phil. Trans. Roy. Soc. London, A, 243:* 67–92 (1950).
3. W. M. Elsasser, "Induction Effects in Terrestrial Magnetism. Part I. Theory," *Phys. Rev., 69:* 202, *70:* 106 (1946); "The Earth's Interior and Geomagnetism," *Rev. Mod. Physics, 22:* 1–35 (1950).
4. F. S. Jory, "Influence of Geomagnetic Quadrupole Fields upon Cosmic-Ray Intensity," *Phys. Rev., 102:* 1167 (1956).
5. R. Gall and J. Lifshitz, "Albedo of Cosmic Rays in Earth's Dipole and Quadrupole Magnetic Field," *Phys. Rev., 101:* 1821 (1956).
6. E. H. Vestine. Tech. Memo., Appl. Physics Lab., Johns Hopkins Univ., 1947.
7. S. Chapman. In *Rocket Exploration of the Upper Atmosphere.* London: Pergamon Press, 1954, p. 292.
8. S. F. Singer *et al.*, "Measurement of the Earth's Magnetic Field at High Altitudes at White Sands, New Mexico," *J. Geophys. Res., 55:* 115–126 (1950); *Phys. Rev., 77:* 398 (1950).
9. S. F. Singer *et al.*, "Evidence for Ionosphere Currents from Rocket Experiments near the Geomagnetic Equator," *J. Geophys. Res., 56:* 265–281 (1951); *Phys. Rev., 82:* 957 (1951).
10. S. F. Singer. In *Rocket Exploration of the Upper Atmosphere.* London: Pergamon Press, 1954, p. 256.
11. S. F. Singer, "Research in the Upper Atmosphere with Sounding Rockets and Earth Satellite Vehicles," *J. Brit. Interplan. Soc., 11:* 61–73 (1952); "A Minimum Orbital Instrumented Satellite—Now," *ibid., 13:* 74–79 (1954).
12. S. F. Singer. In *Rocket Exploration of the Upper Atmosphere.* London: Pergamon Press, 1954, p. 369. "Studies of a Minimum

Orbital Unmanned Satellite of the Earth (MOUSE). Part I. Geophysical and Astrophysical Applications," *Astronautica Acta, 1:* 171–184 (1955).

13. D. F. Martyn, "The Morphology of the Ionospheric Variations Associated with Magnetic Disturbance. I. Variations at Moderately Low Latitudes," *Proc. Roy. Soc. London, A, 218:* 1–18 (1953).

14. S. F. Singer, "A New Model of Magnetic Storms and Aurorae," *Trans. Amer. Geophys. Union* (in press).

15. S. F. Singer. In *Progress in Cosmic Ray Physics,* Vol. 4, edited by J. G. Wilson. Amsterdam: No. Holland Publ. Co., 1952.

16. H. W. Newton, "Solar Flares and Magnetic Storms," *Mon. Not. Roy. Astron. Soc., 104:* 4–12 (1944).

17. S. E. Forbush and E. H. Vestine, "Daytime Enhancement of Size of Sudden Commencements and Initial Phase of Magnetic Storms at Huancayo," *J. Geophys. Res., 60:* 299–316 (1955).

18. E. H. Vestine, "Note on Geomagnetic Disturbance as an Atmospheric Phenomenon," *J. Geophys. Res., 58:* 539–541 (1953); "The Immediate Source of the Field of Magnetic Storms," *ibid.,* pp. 560–562.

19. M. Sugiura, "The Solar Diurnal Variation in the Amplitude of Sudden Commencements of Magnetic Storms at the Geomagnetic Equator," *J. Geophys. Res., 58:* 558–559 (1953).

20. C. Chree. *Studies in Terrestrial Magnetism.* London: The Macmillan Co., 1912.

21. N. Fukushima, "Some Characteristics of Magnetic Storms. I. Magnetic Storm on August 3, 1949," *Rept. Ionosph. Res. Japan, 5:* 85–97 (1951).

22. Y. Kato and S. Utashiro, *Rept. Ionosph. Res. Japan, 4:* 118 (1950).

23. H. W. Newton, " 'Sudden Commencements' in the Greenwich Magnetic Records (1879–1944) and Related Sunspot Data," *Mon. Not. Roy. Astron. Soc.* (Geophys. Suppl.), *5:* 159–185 (1948).

24. T. Nagata, "Distribution of SC* of Magnetic Storms," *Rept. Ionosph. Res. Japan, 6:* 13–30 (1952).

25. N. Fukushima, *Rept. Ionosph. Res. Japan, 6:* 185 (1952).

26. J. P. Heppner, "Time Sequences and Spatial Relations in Auroral Activity During Magnetic Bays at College, Alaska," *J. Geophys. Res., 59:* 329–338 (1954).

27. V. C. A. Ferraro, "On the Theory of the First Phase of a Geomagnetic Storm: A New Illustrative Calculation Based on an Idealised (Plane not Cylindrical) Model Field Distribution," *J. Geophys. Res., 57:* 15–49 (1952); and references therein.

28. T. Gold. In *Rocket Exploration of the Upper Atmosphere.* London: Pergamon Press, 1954, p. 366.

29. W. H. Bennett and E. O. Hulburt, "Theory of the Aurora Based on Magnetic Self-Focusing of Solar Ion Streams," *Phys. Rev., 95:* 315–319

(1954) ; "Magnetic Self-Focused Solar Ion Streams as the Cause of Aurorae," *J. Atm. Terr. Phys.*, 5: 211 (1954).

30. J. P. Wild. Reported in *J. Geophys. Res.*, *59:* 163 (1954).
31. J. Burgers, private communication.
32. A. A. Ashour and A. T. Price, "The Induction of Electric Currents in a Nonuniform Ionosphere," *Proc. Roy. Soc. London, A, 195:* 198–204 (1948).
33. S. F. Singer. *Geophysical Research with Artificial Earth Satellites,* in Advances in Geophysics, Vol. III, edited by H. Landsberg. New York: Academic Press, 1956.
34. F. Bloch *et al.*, "Nuclear Induction," *Phys. Rev., 69:* 127 (1946).
35. J. M. Knight and S. F. Singer, *Astronautica Acta,* 1956 (in press).
36. Atkinson and Halden, "Ionized Gas Flow in Electrically Energized Shock Tubes," Univ. of Oklahoma Res. Inst. Tech. Report, Aug., 1954; Shao-Chi Lin *et al.*, "Electrical Conductivity of Highly Ionized Argon Produced by Shock Waves," *J. Appl. Phys., 26:* 95–109 (1955).

```
┌─────────┐
│         │
│   25    │
│         │
└─────────┘
```

Satellite Geomagnetic Measurements

---

by J. P. Heppner

U.S. NAVAL RESEARCH LABORATORY,
WASHINGTON, D.C.

ABSTRACT

Measurements of the total scalar magnetic field from a satellite above the densely ionized regions of the upper atmosphere could, in theory, answer or help answer a number of important questions concerning geomagnetic storms and other disturbances. Here, the practical requirements and techniques for obtaining useful data are examined.

Introduction

Magnetic measurements taken from a satellite above the highly ionized regions of the upper atmosphere could, in theory, determine whether or not the reduction in the earth's field during magnetic storms is due to electric currents at altitudes greater than that of the satellite, such as the extraterrestrial ring currents proposed by Störmer, Chapman, and others, or due to ionospheric currents. Theoretically, satellite magnetic measurements could also improve our knowledge of the altitude and latitude distributions of the equatorial and auroral zone "linear" currents. They could also check the concept of "sheet" currents over middle-latitude and polar-cap regions during magnetic disturbances. Many upper-air scientists would perhaps not be surprised

234

to see new ideas evolve from such measurements rather than merely an improvement of present concepts.

The first objective is to take a practical look at the theoretical possibilities to see what orbital, surface-station, tracking, and instrumental requirements must be satisfied to give definite data on magnetic-disturbance fields.   Second, the most promising satellite geomagnetic experiment, the determination of the existence or nonexistence of an extraterrestrial ring current, will be treated in more detail.   Third, the merits of getting accurate measurements of the earth's main field at satellite altitudes will be outlined.   Fourth, a nuclear magnetic-resonance magnetometer suitable for satellite measurements will be briefly described.

Throughout the discussion it is assumed that the total scalar magnetic field is to be measured.   The possibility of measuring components or a total vector field from the initial weight-restricted satellites appears remote as these measurements would require extremely accurate aspect information.

Magnetic Disturbance Fields

Orbit and Surface-Station Requirements

As the disturbance field is found by subtracting the undisturbed field from the measured intensity, the determination of disturbance intensities depends greatly on knowing the magnitude of the main field at the point of measurement.   Values calculated for satellite altitudes from surface measurements are by themselves not sufficiently accurate for this purpose.   It will thus be necessary to derive the main field at satellite altitudes from the satellite measurements.   To do this, a number of satellite measurements must be received at each surface station. Consequently, the orbit requirements depend principally on the number and distribution of surface stations for a given orbit.

With the exception of world-wide reductions in the geomagnetic field during magnetic storms, magnetic disturbances are distributed in magnetic latitude zones.   This suggests that the ideal orbit would be polar; however, even a quick practical look reveals the need for a very large number of surface stations equipped with telemetering receivers and tracking equipment capable of pinpointing (see tracking requirements) the satellite's location at the time of each measurement.   As each satellite measurement must be correlated with nearby magnetic measurements at the surface, a similar number of magnetic stations would be required.   An alternative of telemetering data only at the poles and providing a memory system in the satellite is ruled out from the standpoint of needing to know the satellite location very accurately at each instant and with reference to a surface station, to say nothing of the complexity and weight of an adequate system.

The simplicity of an equatorial orbit is advantageous for studying the equatorial electrojet and the ring-current question. The advantages are: a minimum number of surface stations is required, tracking requirements are less severe than for other orbits, and the simplicity of the main field at the equator would make data analysis easier and more reliable. A surface station located close to both the geographic and geomagnetic equators would be ideal.

From an orbit inclined to the equator, but not extending to the auroral zones, the same disturbance currents could be measured as in the case of an equatorial orbit, with the possible inclusion of middle-latitude currents, provided there is an adequate number of surface stations. Assuming any practical number of stations, the number of data on the equatorial electrojet would be considerably less than for an equatorial orbit with only one station. However, for an inclined orbit the number of stations required may not be prohibitively large for measurements pertaining to the ring-current question. A string of stations located roughly along a meridian over the latitude range of the satellite could receive about one measurement per satellite revolution, the same as one station in the case of an equatorial orbit. For example, for a 30° N. to 30° S. inclined orbit and a latitudinal coverage of 10° per station, six stations ideally spaced would be adequate. Altering these figures by reasonable factors may not increase the number of stations beyond what seems feasible.

The limitations imposed by the choice of orbit can be summarized as follows: (a) a polar orbit is not suitable for geomagnetic-disturbance measurements unless a very large number of fully equipped surface stations is provided, (b) an equatorial orbit is ideal for measurements pertaining to the ring-current question and the equatorial electrojet, and (c) an inclined orbit is suitable for determining the existence or nonexistence of a ring current if a reasonable number (e.g., 6 to 12) of surface stations is provided.

Tracking and Instrumental Requirements

Compared to the magnitude of the earth's main magnetic field, the disturbance fields are small; they are also small when compared to the change in the main field over an appreciable north-south or vertical distance. Thus, inability to locate a satellite accurately would completely mask magnetic disturbances at the satellite; conversely, an unnoticed error in locating the satellite could be incorrectly interpreted as a magnetic disturbance.

TABLE 1

	Typical ΔH & ΔF disturbance values at the earth's surface (gammas)	Satellite Altitude = 200 miles			Satellite Altitude = 800 miles		
		Estimated simultaneous total field disturbance (ΔF) at 200 miles (gammas)	Altitude inaccuracy giving an equivalent field change (miles)	Altitude inaccuracy giving ±20% data (miles)	Estimated simultaneous total field disturbance (ΔF) at 800 miles (gammas)	Altitude inaccuracy giving an equivalent field change (miles)	Altitude inaccuracy giving 20% data (miles)
Magnetic Equator (Equatorial electrojet) Typical midday value	$\Delta H = \Delta F = +100$	-54	2.8	0.6	-10	0.9	0.2
30° Magnetic Latitude Moderate disturbance exclusive of ring current or equivalent contribution	$\Delta H = \pm 30$ $\Delta F = \pm 20$	∓ 20	0.8	0.2	∓ 20	1.3	0.3
67° Magnetic Latitude (Auroral zone current) Post midnight during moderate disturbance	$\Delta H = -600$ $\Delta F = -127$	$+70$	1.9	0.4	$+12$	0.6	0.1
90° Magnetic Latitude (Polar cap current) During moderate disturbance	$\Delta H = \pm 100$ $\Delta F = <1$	<1	<0.1		<1	<0.1	
Ring Current (?) Moderate magnetic storm At the equator:	$\Delta H = \Delta F = -100$	-100	5.1	1.0	-100	8.8	1.8
At 30° latitude:	$\Delta H = -100$ $\Delta F = -65$	-65	2.5	0.5	-65	4.3	0.9
Ionosphere sheet current having an effect at the surface equivalent to a ring current At the equator:	$\Delta H = \Delta F = -100$	$+100$	5.1	1.0	$+100$	8.8	1.8
At 30° latitude:	$\Delta H = -100$ $\Delta F = -65$	$+65$	2.5	0.5	$+65$	4.3	0.9

Note: Estimates do not include the effects of earth induction.

In Table I some typical disturbance intensities observed at the earth's surface are listed; actual intensities may be considerably larger for short periods. For each of these an estimate is made of the simultaneous total field disturbance at two satellite altitudes. The change in altitude or altitude inaccuracy which would give a difference from the main field value equivalent to the disturbance value at the satellite is then calculated. The altitude inaccuracy which would subject the disturbance values to a 20% uncertainty is also listed. Errors in latitude are less critical but nevertheless important; the ratios of horizontal to vertical gradients are about 2:3 at the equator, 1:3 at latitude 45°, and 1:6 at the poles.

A number of simplifying assumptions are made in constructing Table I. The earth's main field is assumed to be a dipole field with F (total intensity) = H (horizontal component) = 0.312 gauss at the magnetic equator. The equatorial electrojet and the auroral zone currents are assumed to be infinite line currents whose magnetic fields can be expressed as $\Delta F = 0.2I/R$ gammas (1 gamma = 10^{-5} gauss) with I in amperes and R in kilometers. The line currents are also assumed to be at an altitude of 70 miles, perpendicular to the local magnetic meridian, and directly over the surface station such that $\Delta Z = 0$ (Z = vertical component). The 30° magnetic latitude current, the polar-cap current, and the ionospheric sheet current equivalent to a ring current are assumed to be infinite sheet currents, below 200 miles, whose magnetic fields can be expressed as $\Delta F = \Delta H = 0.2\pi I$ (gammas) with I in amperes per kilometer; the field is thus independent of distance with $\Delta Z = 0$. The ring current is assumed to be sufficiently distant (at least several earth radii) to have a relatively constant field throughout the earth's atmosphere. To avoid introducing a questionable correction factor, the effects of currents induced in the solid earth have not been included. Induced currents would, in most cases, decrease the magnitude of the disturbance at the satellite.

The estimated disturbances of Table I roughly indicate the minimum accuracies which could be tolerated in a satellite magnetometer. For useful disturbance data greater accuracy is obviously needed. Considering the large errors that could arise from tracking uncertainties, corrections for induced currents, etc., it will be advantageous to use a magnetometer whose errors will be negligibly small or will not add appreciably to the other uncertainties. For example, if altitude tracking is good to one-half mile at the equator where the vertical gradient is about 19 γ/mile at 200 miles and 11 γ/mile at 800 miles, one would desire a magnetometer readable to less than 5 to 9 gammas. The magnetometer described in a following section is capable of this accuracy.

The Ring-Current Question

For both practical and scientific reasons measurements to determine the existence or nonexistence of an extraterrestrial ring current should take priority over other magnetic-disturbance measurements from a satellite. Considering the surface-station requirements imposed by a polar orbit, it seems advisable to concentrate attention on equatorial and inclined orbits. For these orbits the tracking requirements indicate that measurements of the equatorial electrojet would be more sensitive to errors than ring-current measurements. From the scientific standpoint, an answer to the ring-current question would be more important at this time than the study of other magnetic-disturbance problems. In fact, the auroral-zone and polar-cap disturbances are in many theories related to the ring-current hypothesis; thus proof or disproof of the ring current's existence could be more important to the understanding of these disturbances than measurements in their regions of occurrence.

It is instructive to look at the surface evidence for a ring current. Individual magnetograms taken during magnetic storms (simultaneous disturbances over the entire earth) are often similar in general appearance but dissimilar in detail for a given station and for different stations during a given storm. However, when the horizontal component (H) of a number of storms is averaged relative to the commencement times, a smooth curve results in which ΔH, the change relative to undisturbed days, is positive for from 2 to 5 hours and then decreases to a much larger negative value. After reaching the maximum $(-\Delta H)$ 8 to 20 hours after commencement, ΔH slowly goes to zero over a period of several days. The total field disturbance, ΔF, behaves similarly but decreases with increasing latitude or, more exactly, with increasing magnetic inclination (dip angle $= I$) as it is approximately $\Delta H \cos I$. The most generally quoted explanation for the negative ΔH disturbance has been that it is caused by electric currents flowing in a ring about the earth at a distance of several earth radii. However, many sound objections to this ring current have been put forth. Theoretically, it is not possible to establish the existence or nonexistence of this ring current solely from surface observations; a properly distributed current in the ionosphere would have the same effect at the earth's surface.

If it is assumed that all the current producing the disturbance is located either in the ionosphere or in a ring current at a large distance from the earth, the experiment is greatly simplified. Only the sign $(+ \text{ or } -)$ of the disturbance at the satellite is then needed and small errors become unimportant. The possibility that a fraction of the current is located in each of the regions should not, however, be disregarded. Recognizing this, the results would state that $x \pm n\%$ of the effect is the ionospheric current contribution and $(100 - x) \pm n\%$ is the ring-current contribution. Either (x) or $(100 - x)$ could be zero and $n\%$ would represent the possible error. This manner of stating results, although an improvement over a bland assumption with a yes or no answer, is still not scientifically rigorous. Other current configurations at different altitudes could likewise cause the $(-\Delta H)$ storm disturbance at the earth's surface. Thus, in stating that the experiment would decide whether the magnetic-storm current is an extraterrestrial ring current or an ionospheric sheet current, one is really stating that a decision can be made between two current configurations that appear probable from previous studies.

The $n\%$ possible error will depend principally on tracking uncertainties, the ability to derive the earth's undisturbed field at satellite altitudes, and magnetometer errors. The magnetometer errors are treated later; for the purpose here they can be considered small relative to other likely errors. The maximum allowable tracking uncertainty can be roughly estimated for a particular disturbance intensity. For the $\Delta F's$ of Table I and the case where only the sign of the disturbance at the satellite is required, the altitude uncertainty is given by the values under "altitude inaccuracy giving an equivalent field change." The column "altitude inaccuracy giving $\pm 20\%$ data" similarly gives the uncertainty for $n\%$ (tracking only) = 20%.

The determination of the earth's undisturbed field at the point where a satellite measurement is taken during disturbance is not a simple problem for the accuracies required here. Neglecting temporarily the influence of tracking and measurement errors, the determination depends on the uniformity of the earth's main field and the density of measurements taken during periods of magnetic quiet. The required density of measurements will of course depend on the uniformity of the field. As this factor is not known prior to analysis of the received data, the required density cannot be determined beforehand. The density of measurements which can be achieved depends on the orbital life, path, and altitude range. Several hypothetical situations and assumptions regarding the undisturbed field can be used for making rough estimates.

1) Take an equatorial orbit, one surface station located on both the geomagnetic and geographic equators, and assume that all measurements are taken at the exact instant the satellite crosses the zenith. If the orbit is a perfect circle, only one measurement during a period of no disturbance is necessary. For the more general elliptical orbit an expression is needed for F $(= H)$ along the zenith line connecting measured points. In the analysis of the earth's main field by Vestine et al.,[1] the agreement with observed field intensities was of the order of 1%; the analysis also indicated that magnetic sources external to the earth contributed less than 1% to the main field. If it can be assumed that all the main field has an internal origin, it appears that a much more accurate expression for F along a zenith line above 200 miles could

be found from the satellite measurements. As the effects of local and regional anomalies will be appreciably less, the coefficients determined by Vestine *et al.* could possibly give F to $<1\%$ error. If this is indicated by the measurements, the expression for F could probably be made considerably better by adjusting only the coefficient for the dipole term, which represents about 90% of the field, to give the best fit at measured points. As $F = f(r)$ only ($r =$ distance from the earth's center), a more exact equation should be obtainable from a least-squares determination of the coefficients, α_n, in

$$F = \sum_{n=1}^{N} \sum_{k=1}^{K} \alpha_n \left(\frac{a}{r_k}\right)^{n+2}$$

where a is the earth's radius, K is the total number of measurements, and the degree of the equation is such that $N \lessgtr K$. By comparison with the main-field analysis where harmonics up to $n = 6$ gave a 1% agreement, it seems probable that seven to nine measurements would give an adequate expression for F. The measurements should be distributed over the altitude range of the satellite. In practice, measurements would be taken over a finite east-west and vertical distance and the gradient of the field along the orbit as well as F would be obtained. For 20 sec of measurement and a 90-min orbit with altitude range from 200 to 800 miles, the altitude would change an average of about two miles. If it is found possible to get $\Delta F/\Delta r$ from the gradient along the orbit, an additional check on the expression for F is available. Gradients could also be used to find F at altitude $(r \pm s)$ from the undisturbed-field intensity at r if the error, e, in

$$\int_{r}^{r \pm s} \left(\frac{\partial F}{\partial r} \pm e\right) dr$$

is small such that

$$\int_{r}^{r \pm s} e\, dr \ll \Delta F,$$

the magnitude of the disturbance. $\partial F/\partial r$ should vary regularly, since irregularities observed near the earth's surface decrease rapidly with altitude. In brief, for an equatorial orbit it appears that the undisturbed field could be derived from a relatively small number of measurements, say <10. If there are small deviations from a true equatorial path, this number would have to be increased to account for changes with latitude.

2) Take an inclined orbit extending from 30° N. to 30° S. and a meridian string of surface stations; and assume accurate tracking and measurements along this meridian. Excluding special cases such as a circular orbit and times between meridian crossings which are exact fractions of a day, measurements will not occur twice at the same altitude or latitude. Instead, they will be distributed over the latitude and

altitude range of the satellite's meridian crossings. An approximate distribution is illustrated in Fig. 1 for an orbit with apogee at 800 miles, perigee at 200 miles, and an orbital period of 88 min. For this period the satellite crosses the meridian where measurements are being taken every 93.7 min. In Fig. 1 a meridian crossing at 200 miles at 30° N. is assumed for time, $t = 0$. If the orbit did not precess, all measurements at a given latitude would, to a first approximation, occur at the same altitude and a diagonal extending from 30° N., 200 miles, to 30° S.,

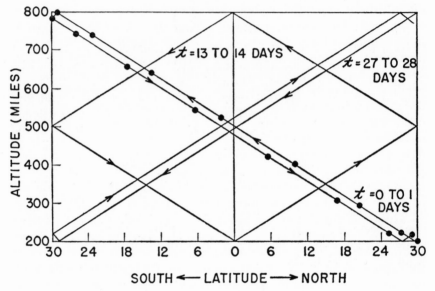

FIGURE 1.

800 miles, would illustrate the zone of measurement. However, the orbit assumed here should precess with a period of 54.8 days. In 27.4 days the altitude range, 200 to 800 miles, is traversed and in one day the altitude at a given latitude changes by about 22 miles. In Fig. 1 lines are drawn connecting meridian crossings, or measurement points, for the first day following $t = 0$. In this representation the lines form approximately a parallelogram. On successive days the parallelogram opens until both apogee and perigee occur at the equator at one-fourth the precessional period. Apogee and perigee then switch hemispheres and the parallelogram closes during the next quarter cycle. Although crude, this representation is helpful in estimating the density of measurements. As there are eight measurements between latitudes 20° and 30° for every seven between 20° N. and 20° S., dividing the meridian plane into three regions further simplifies the estimate: designate 20° N. to 30° N.—region A; 20° S. to 30° S.—region B; and 20° N. to 20° S.—region

C. In regions *A* (or *B*) and *C* the average measurement densities for less than 28 days operation are, respectively, 3780 and 8640 square miles of meridian plane per measurement. The distances between centers of squares with these areas are 87 and 131 miles, respectively.

It would be desirable prior to flight to know if one can hope to get an expression for *F* accurate to one to six parts in 3000 in this region from the satellite measurements. As $F = f(r, \theta)$, and more probably $f(r, \theta, \phi)$ as a perfect magnetic meridian cannot be expected, the problem is far more complicated than the equatorial case and estimates are difficult if not impossible without previous knowledge of the uniformity of the field. One can estimate that the number of coefficients required in an expression for $F = f(r, \theta, \phi)$ will be less than the number of measurements if measurements are taken over a number of days. The accuracy in a given region might be further improved by deriving independent expressions for *F* in each region such as the three regions designated for Fig. 1. If the orbital life is long and the total instrumental operating time is a limiting factor, it would then be best to take measurements only in the latitude range 20° to 30° N. (or S.). In 28 days, 112 measurements are possible in this range, and if half of these are taken during undisturbed conditions, there are still more useful measurements than the number of coefficients used to date in analyses of the main field over the entire earth. However, the ability to find an expression for *F* does not assure its accuracy and this can be determined only on analysis of the data received. As in the equatorial case, measurements of the gradient along the orbit will be a good check on the expression for *F*. They will also indicate the regularity of the gradients at satellite altitudes and this could be an important factor in analysis. For example, if a 1% error in *F* meant that gradients would also be accurate to 1%, it would be a relatively simple problem to find the undisturbed field at a desired point. In some direction *s* where $\partial F/\partial s$ is about 20 γ/mile and its rate of change can be calculated at all points to give an error $\gtrsim 0.2$ γ/mile, *F* at a distance of 87 miles (Fig. 1) would be obtained to ± 17 γ. At the earth's surface this method would be useless, as local anomalies lead to very large errors in gradients. However, local effects on gradients decrease rapidly with distance and much smoother variations are to be expected above 200 miles. If we also assume that *F* can be derived to an accuracy of $\ll 1\%$, the extrapolation of gradients could provide a simple means for determining the undisturbed field at points not too distant from points where the undisturbed field is measured. Again, accuracy is not assured without knowledge of the uniformity of the field. It is apparent that the density of measurements can be increased by narrowing the altitude range of the satellite; thus for magnetic-disturbance measurements it will be desirable to have an orbit as nearly circular as possible.

The Earth's Main Field

The difficulties encountered in trying to estimate whether or not the earth's undisturbed field can be derived accurately enough to permit disturbance measurements emphasizes the desirability of measuring the earth's main field at satellite altitudes. Principally, one would like to know the uniformity of the field and get a check on how well it can be predicted from surface observations. Used with simultaneous analysis of the earth's field at the surface, satellite measurements might also be helpful in deciding whether or not there is a permanent contribution to the main field which is external to the earth. In the spherical-harmonic analysis of the main field this contribution is proportional to $(r/a)^{n-1}$ and would become effective with increasing r and n. The practical applications of the magnetic field at great altitudes in ionospheric physics problems, in missile aspect measurements, etc., give additional reasons for making these measurements.

Nuclear Magnetic-Resonance Magnetometer

The characteristics desired in a satellite magnetometer are similar to those desired in a magnetometer for magnetic-disturbance measurements from high-altitude rockets. For the latter application the Naval Research Laboratory has been sponsoring development work at Varian Associates, Palo Alto, California, on a proton magnetic-resonance magnetometer. The magnetometer will be tested in an Aerobee rocket in June, 1956, and will be flown in at least five rockets during the International Geophysical Year. The advantages of this magnetometer over other possible magnetometers are basically its simplicity and freedom from errors.

In a magnetic field F the magnetic moments of protons precess about the field at an angular frequency ω given by $\omega = \gamma_p F$ where γ_p is the gyromagnetic ratio of the proton. The expression γ_p has been determined to be $2.67528\,(\pm 0.00006) \times 10^4$ sec^{-1} gauss^{-1}. A magnetometer is made by placing a coil around a sample of liquid, such as water, which contains a high proportion of protons. A current is first passed through the coil to produce a magnetic field (of the order of 100 gauss) polarizing the protons' magnetic moment. The polarizing field is then cut off sharply and the protons' moment precesses about the earth's field. The precessing moment induces a voltage of frequency $\omega = \gamma_p F$ in the coil, which has now been switched to the measuring circuit. This signal is amplified by an audio amplifier and fed to the telemetering transmitter. On the ground the output of the telemetering receiver is put through a narrow-band-pass amplifier and frequency-counting system. As the frequency count depends only on an atomic constant and the field strength and is independent of the orientation of the coil in the magnetic field, no calibration is required; it is necessary only to have a frequency standard at the ground station. Although the frequency is independent of orientation, the signal amplitude is proportional to the square of the sine of the angle between the coil axis and the magnetic field; when this angle is 45°, the amplitude is reduced to one-half its maximum value, and at 0° no signal is observed. If in a satellite all angles of orientation are to be expected, it will thus be necessary to have two perpendicular bottles and coils to assure measurements at all times. As the spin of the coil about any axis but its own will add or subtract from the proton spin, a third bottle and coil may be required at right angles to the other two if the spin axis of the satellite is not predictable and there are no other instruments in the satellite which determine the spin direction. With more than one coil, the coils would be read alternately if only one telemetering channel is available; with additional channels, they could be read simultaneously.

Based on the rocket units presently being constructed, the following specifications can be estimated:

Weight.—A satellite unit with one bottle and coil, including battery power for 240 measurement periods lasting 10 sec each, would be about 10 lb. Additional coils would add about 4 lb each. It seems probable that with miniaturization and special care this total weight could be reduced to 6, 8, or 10 lb for 1, 2, or 3 coils, respectively.

Time per Measurement.—The frequency would be read for periods of 0.1 to 0.3 sec; as a slightly longer polarizing time is required, about 2 to 4 independent measurements per second would be obtained.

Environment.—Measurements to ±2 gammas will be unaffected by temperature as long as the liquid sample does not boil or freeze. As there are no suspended elements, the instrument will not be damaged by acceleration forces. The effects of magnetic fields due to eddy-current induction and circuit currents can be made negligible by making the satellite of a nonconducting material and by proper wiring of circuit elements.

Telemetering.—The magnetometer requires a telemetering system that will transmit frequencies up to 1600 cps.

Accuracy.—The proton precessional magnetometer in satellite application would probably be accurate to ±2 gammas. This is well within the 5 to 9 gamma accuracy desired in reviewing the instrumental requirements.

It is possible that there are other magnetometers which could be used in a satellite. Several types are under study at NRL; one is a miniature electron-beam magnetometer; another is based on electron paramagnetic resonance.   However, to date these instruments do not have the combination of simplicity and accuracy under satellite conditions which is inherent in the proton precessional magnetometer.

REFERENCE

1. E. H. Vestine *et al.*   *The Geomagnetic Field, Its Description and Analysis.*   Carnegie Inst. of Washington, Publ. 580, 1947.

26

Geomagnetic Information Potentially Available from a Satellite

by Ludwig Katz
IONOSPHERIC PHYSICS LABORATORY,
GEOPHYSICS RESEARCH DIRECTORATE,
AIR FORCE CAMBRIDGE RESEARCH CENTER

ABSTRACT

The origin of the geomagnetic variations is believed to be in the high atmosphere. If one carries out a spherical-harmonic analysis on the remainder obtained by subtracting the average value of the geomagnetic field from observed data, one can obtain the ratio of the contributions of sources exterior and interior to the solid earth. The value thus obtained is about 2 to 3. This ratio is not inconsistent with the view that the internal portion is due only to induction. Calculations of this type do not yield the height at which the currents, which constitute the external source, flow; and assumptions must be made in this regard in order to continue the analysis.

Direct experimental evidence of current systems above 90 km height has been obtained by Maple, Bowen, and Singer. Ionospheric measurements indicate that the diurnal and other changes to which the ionosphere is subject vary not only the electron density but also the height and thickness of the layers. It is only the lumped effect of such changes which can be obtained from earth-bound geomagnetic observations. By utilizing systematic data from various altitudes, the current systems could be uniquely determined. In addition, spatial variations of the current systems, particularly latitudinal ones, could be studied more systematically from observation posts having different solar exposure than the terrestrial observatories. Possible magnetic variations due to current systems flowing at much greater heights (e.g., the Chapman-Ferraro ring current at about 5 earth radii) can be isolated from ionospheric ones by carrying out observations at altitudes beyond the ionopause.

It will also be possible to conduct valuable experiments regarding the relatively constant permanent portion of the field. A spherical-harmonic analysis of the terrestrial magnetic field permits us to break it up into its dipole, quadrupole, etc., components. The dipole field obtained from such an analysis has an axis tilted about 11.5° to the earth's rotational axis and intersecting the earth's surface near Thule, Greenland. However, recent cosmic-ray experiments give indications that yield a dipole equator considerably different from the one deduced from geomagnetic surface data. The mass-spectrometer action at the earth's field on charged cosmic-ray particles could be determined from a satellite and an effective dipole field as well as its eccentricity could be determined.

Geomagnetic Information Potentially Available from a Satellite

The magnetic field of the earth is a potential field and can therefore be described in terms of a potential V, such that $F = -\text{grad } V$, where V satisfies Laplace's equation $\nabla^2 V = 0$. The solution of this differential equation is a sum of spherical harmonics of the well-known form:

$$V = a \sum_{n=1}^{\infty} \sum_{m=0}^{n} \left[(c_n{}^m \cos m\lambda + s_n{}^m \sin m\lambda) P_n{}^m (\cos \theta) \left(\frac{a}{r}\right)^{n+1} \right.$$
$$\left. + (\gamma_n{}^m \cos m\lambda + \sigma_n{}^m \sin m\lambda) P_n{}^m (\cos \theta) \left(\frac{r}{a}\right)^n \right].$$

This type of analysis permits a determination of the relative contributions of external and internal sources. An analysis of the average field yields external portions of the same magnitude as the possible error introduced by the sparsity of the data. However, an analysis of the variation field, such as the diurnal, storm-time variation, etc., obtained from a systematic long-term study of observatory data, yields a predominantly external contribution. Thus, even though the sources of the permanent magnetic field reside within the solid earth, those associated with the variations the field undergoes must be explained in terms of sources outside the lithosphere, e.g., currents flowing in the high atmosphere.

The spherical-harmonic type of analysis, though capable of differentiating between sources inside and outside a spherical shell over whose surface the potential is known, cannot determine the position of the source in space. Thus, assuming the availability of ground data only, the external sources can be studied further only if additional as-

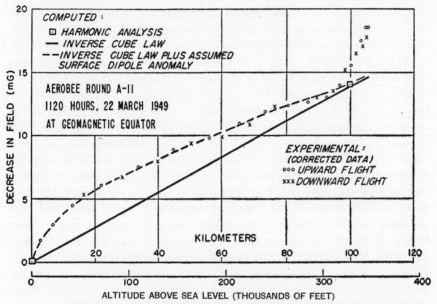

FIGURE 1. Decrease of earth's magnetic field (from actual field at sea level) vs altitude above sea level for Aerobee A-11 flight.

sumptions are made. From ionospheric considerations, it seems reasonable to presuppose current flow at a height near 100 km and most calculations of the current systems are based on assumed thin currents at this height. The currents arrived at in this way are in order of magnitude 10^5 to 10^6 amperes.

The presence of such current systems at altitudes exceeding 90 km has been demonstrated experimentally by Singer *et al.*,[1] who measured the magnetic field as a function of altitude, using magnetometers mounted in Aerobee rockets which attained an altitude of about 105 km. They observed a discontinuity in the magnetic field in the height range 93 to 105 km (see Fig. 1). This isolated experiment is of great value in giving credence to the so-called dynamo theory of magnetic variations which assumes currents due to tidal and thermal motions of the high atmosphere in the presence of the geomagnetic field. However, much more experimental work remains to be done to define the currents responsible for the geomagnetic variations observed. The altitude distribution of the current density will, of course, be interrelated with the electron density which can be determined from ionospheric measurements. However, since we are interested in currents it is not only the charge density which is of interest to us but also the transport velocity of these charges. In addition, it should be remembered that the diurnal and other changes to which the ionosphere is subject vary not only the number density of the charges but also the geometry of the layers. It is only the lumped effect of such changes which is reflected in the geomagnetic records at earthbound observatories. Systematic geomagnetic observations from a number of earth-centered spheres would make the solution to our problem unique and the exact locations of the currents could be determined. It is true that the number of measurements possible in the predictable future is not sufficient to permit the establishment of the magnetic potential for a sphere parallel to the earth's surface; however, it is that type of data which would be ideally suited for a complete analysis. Even the establishment of isolated values would be of considerable value. Thus, if the diurnal variations, for instance, were observed simultaneously both from the ground and from stations at known height intervals, our understanding of the ionospheric changes causing this variation could probably be improved. It is probably true that the exact orbits of early satellites cannot be predetermined and that we must content ourselves with measurements in more or less random orbits. This will, of course, make the analysis of data much more cumbersome. Even though such data will not give us the ultimate answer to all our problems, they will improve our knowledge of the location and strength of current sources, and the temporal changes which these undergo. It will, no doubt, also not be possible in the early stages of satellite flight to have orbits between the known ionospheric layers, so as to separate contributions from high layers from those due to currents in layers closer to the earth's surface.

Chapman and Ferraro, in their theory of magnetic storms, hypothesized a ring current at a distance of about 5 earth radii, the effect of which is held responsible for some of the features of magnetic storms, particularly the sudden commencements. These sharp increases in the horizontal component of the field, followed by a slower decrease to a value below normal and a subsequent slow recovery to normal, constitute the general behavior of magnetic storms and are very often worldwide in nature. If currents at such tremendous altitudes exist, their contribution can be isolated from those originating in the ionospheric layers by taking measurements at altitudes beyond the ionopause.

The foregoing has concerned itself with the variations in the geomagnetic field. However, it will also be possible to conduct valuable investigations regarding the main field from a satellite. A harmonic analysis of the permanent field enables us to break it up into its dipole, quadrupole, etc., components. The dipole field obtained from such an analysis has an axis tilted about 11.5° to the earth's rotational axis and intersecting the earth's surface near Thule, Greenland. It is this dipole field which has been used by cosmic-ray researchers to calculate the bending effects of the geomagnetic field on incoming charged particles,

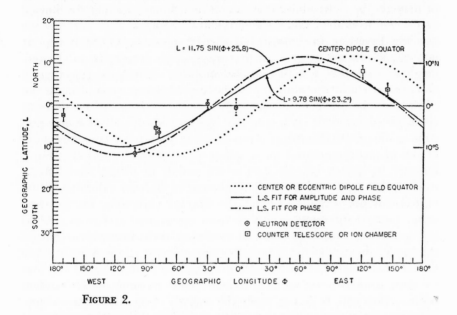

FIGURE 2.

permitting the calculation of expected energy cut-off's at given latitudes, magnetic rigidities of particles, etc. The U.S.S. "Atka" on its recent equator crossings both to and from the Antarctic carried a neutron monitoring pile.[2] The intensity minima obtained during these crossings do not correspond to the dipole equator obtained from magnetic observatory data. Simpson, Fenton, Katzman, and Rose[2] have consequently searched the literature for other cosmic-ray data relevant to the dipole equator and found that the equator indicated by available cosmic-ray data corresponds to a dipole inclined at approximately the same angle to the earth's rotation axis but intersecting the surface about 45° west of the accepted point (see Fig. 2). Cosmic-ray experiments performed from a satellite would make it possible to observe directly the incidence of the primary radiation which is essentially affected only by the dipole component as the higher-order terms decay rapidly with distance. Thus, the minima in counting rates observed during pole-to-pole orbits of the satellite could be utilized to determine the equator of the effective dipole field. More refined experimentation yielding not only the position of the minimum but the absolute value, for a specific altitude from the ground, could be used to determine the eccentricity of the dipole field, i.e., how far from the center of the earth the dipole corresponding to the best description of the earth's field is displaced from the center of the earth. If the dipole field so determined should turn out to be significantly different from that obtained from observatory data, this discrepancy must of course be resolved. In any case, if a more accurate dipole field can be obtained in this manner, the higher-order terms in turn might be determined more accurately by subtracting the known dipole field from the total field observed at the ground.

The practical feasibility of early satellite experiments may depend not only on the nature of the experiment and the feasibility of attaining the desired position in space, but also on the availability of light, rugged, and compact instrumentation. Although doubtless more suitable instrumentation will be developed with time, two types of magnetometers are presently available which might prove adequate for the purpose, namely, the total-field magnetometer used in the earlier described Aerobee experiment of Singer *et al.*, and a newly developed instrument utilizing the dependence of the Larmor precession frequency on magnetic field. Other types, depending on various principles such as the variation of magnetic permeability with field strength are currently under development. Wire loops could be utilized to measure the current induced by the rate of cutting magnetic flux lines, and this parameter might be utilized to determine the spin rate of the satellite if the knowledge of this parameter should be of interest.

In conclusion, the earth's magnetic field, being by its very nature space dependent, is of course ideally studied from a moving vehicle. It will, however, be a long time before satellite travel will be sufficiently predeterminable, accurate, and repeatable to permit ideal utilization of this tool. However, much use can be made even of isolated measurements for the studies of certain aspects of geomagnetism. Even a better knowledge of the vertical decay rate of the more local, anomalous features of the earth's field would constitute significant progress and would, no doubt, also be of interest to geologists, mining engineers, etc. In short, our experience in satellite experimentation and flight control will go hand in hand with our ability to perform more significant experiments and it is hoped that this potentiality of observing and studying this space-and-time-dependent vector field not only in the plane of the earth surface but in three dimensions will enable us to gather a better insight into some of the still unsolved problems of geomagnetism.

REFERENCES

1. S. F. Singer *et al.*, "Evidence for Ionosphere Currents from Rocket Experiments near the Geomagnetic Equator," *J. Geophys. Res., 56:* 265–281 (1951).
2. Reported at International Cosmic Ray Conference, Guanajuato, Mexico, September, 1955.

27

Ionospheric Structure as Determined by a Minimal Artificial Satellite

by *Warren W. Berning*
BALLISTIC RESEARCH LABORATORIES,
ABERDEEN PROVING GROUND, MARYLAND

ABSTRACT

A minimal artificial satellite is here defined as one of such small size that internal equipment can consist of no more than a small beacon used in the electronic tracking of the satellite. On the assumption that the beacon transmits a continuous wave, errors will be incurred in the tracking system data whose magnitudes depend on the electron density in the ionosphere and on the frequency of transmission.

The material contained herein briefly discusses the problems and develops the analytical methods necessary for determining ionospheric electron densities from trajectory measurements. It is shown that a fairly detailed knowledge of the orbit permits determination of equivalent electron density at the satellite as well as total electron content below the satellite altitude. A small ambiguity in the data may be largely removed by geometrical considerations or eliminated by the suitable placement of additional ground receivers.

Introduction

On the premise that the earlier attempts to establish an artificial satellite will be concentrated on minimal vehicles, the Ballistic Research

Laboratories have conducted a study[1] on the scientific aspects and tracking problems of such a minimal vehicle. In the study it was assumed that the satellite was limited in size (20 in.) and weight (5 lb). With these limitations in mind, the effort was concentrated on the scientific possibilities of the vehicle.

The principal results of the BRL study indicated that achievement of the maximum amount of information depended, to a large extent, on the nature and completeness of the tracking complex, and that, further, the employment of a small continuous-wave beacon in the satellite simplified considerably the ground equipment required for adequate electronic tracking. The details of the tracking system proposed as a result of the BRL study may be found in the above reference. It suffices here to mention in the most general terms the nature of the electronic tracking system and the manner in which it is related to the subject of this paper.

Over the past several years the BRL have developed and placed in use a so-called electronic theodolite. This device, in its most elemental unit, consists of two wide-angle fixed receivers at either end of a short baseline. The beacon radiation from the object being tracked is compared in phase by the two receivers and the resultant difference is a function of both the azimuth and elevation of the beacon relative to the center of the short baseline. Four receivers in a square array furnish both azimuth and elevation of the ray path from receivers to the beacon. Two square arrays at either end of a long baseline provide four angles, or an overdetermination of beacon position relative to the long fixed baseline. In the specific application of this tracking system to the satellite, two kinds of information may be derived. The phase data provide information on satellite position, but in addition the installation of a ground reference transmitter permits determination of closing speeds from the derived doppler data. With the expected angular speeds of the satellite and the proper choice of beacon frequency, it is possible to obtain position data in essentially real time, using very narrow band (less than 1 cps) postdetection filtering. This in turn allows employment of a very low power transmitter in the satellite with resulting long life and small weight. For the doppler data, however, fairly wide band filters are required and the signal-to-noise ratio is much too small for real-time doppler information. For the latter it is necessary to employ correlation techniques to extract the signal, thus trading reduction time for beacon power.

In the following sections are discussed the effects of the ionosphere upon such a tracking system—specifically the doppler information—and the method of extracting information on the ionosphere from the data records.

The Problem

As the satellite beacon radiation passes through the ionosphere, the presence of free charges, principally electrons, changes the phase propagation velocity so that the doppler frequency derived at a ground receiver differs from that obtained in the absence of the ionosphere.   The magnitude of the difference depends on the radial speed, the electron concentration at the satellite, the electron distribution, and the radiation frequency.   The difference is further complicated by the geometry of the satellite passage.

If the true radial speed of the satellite, relative to the ground receiver, is known with sufficient accuracy from some other data source unaffected by the ionosphere, it will be possible to obtain information on the ionospheric structure from the derived doppler data.   Fortunately, the dynamics of the satellite orbit are sufficiently well known so that even crude orbital measurements, if of considerable number, will yield very good information on radial speeds relative to earth-fixed receivers, which is independent of the ionospheric characteristics.   It is possible in principle, and has been possible in practice in the firings of high-altitude sounding rockets at White Sands Proving Ground, to derive ionospheric data from a fairly precise knowledge of the orbit and proven techniques for the reduction of doppler data.   The introduction of a ground reference signal for obtaining doppler data complicates the problem since this signal will undoubtedly differ in frequency from the beacon signal.   This difference arises from frequency drift in the beacon; but this difference may be measured, as the true radial speed goes to zero during satellite passage.

In the following section the simple theory is derived which relates doppler-data errors to the ionospheric structure.

Simplified Theory

In the discussion which follows it is assumed that the satellite in a circular orbit passes directly over the ground receiver station.   This assumption greatly simplifies the treatment but does not affect the validity of the argument.

Consider, first, a plane wave arriving at the ground receiving station from a transmitting beacon in the satellite.   The equation for the amplitude is given by

$$y = y_0 \sin\left[\omega_1 (t' - t_1) - \omega \int_0^{r_1} dr/c + \varphi_0 \right] \tag{1}$$

where
$$\omega_1 = \omega \left[1 \mp \frac{\dot{r}}{c_1} + \frac{1}{2} \frac{\dot{r}^2}{c_1^2} \mp \cdots \right]$$

$\omega = 2\pi f_0 =$ angular frequency of beacon radiation
$\dot{r} =$ radial speed of satellite relative to ground receiver
$c_1 =$ propagation speed of radio waves at satellite
$c =$ propagation speed along radiation path
$t' =$ time as measured in receiver frame of reference

$(t' - t_1)$ = time interval over which ω_1 can be determined
(i.e., $\dot{r}$ is assumed constant)

r_1 = radial distance from satellite to ground receiver
at time t_1

φ_0 = arbitrary phase constant.

If attention is directed to the time interval $(t' - t_1)$, and this time interval is sufficiently small, the latter two bracketed terms in equation (1) appear as constant phase angles and need not be considered in the doppler frequency determination.

Equation (1) was derived by a Lorentz transformation from the satellite frame of reference to a frame of reference very close to the satellite but stationary with respect to the ground receiver. This intermediate frame is stationary only in the limited sense that no radial motion takes place between its origin and the origin of the earth-fixed frame of reference. Rotations about the origin are permissible in either of the so-called stationary frames of reference, as is rotation of one origin about the other. Thus, through ω_1, the first bracketed term considers localized ionospheric effects arising from radial motion of the satellite relative to the ground (or intermediate) frame of reference, whereas the second bracketed term considers principally the phase variations arising from transverse motion of the satellite relative to the receiver-satellite radius vector and is concerned with the integrated ionospheric effects along the radial path. This simplified treatment assumes, then, that linear superposition of radial and transverse satellite motions is permissible in obtaining net ionospheric effects in the problem treated here.

Assume now that there exists at the receiver a reference signal equal in frequency to the beacon-transmitted signal. Mixing these signals and considering only the difference term gives rise to a doppler frequency

$$f_D = \frac{(\omega_1 - \omega)}{2\pi} \doteq \mp f_0 \frac{\dot{r}}{c_1} \qquad (2)$$

where terms of order two and greater in $\dot{r}/c_1$ have been neglected. In standard doppler-data reductions it is assumed that $c_1 = c_0$, the vacuum velocity of light. Accordingly, an error doppler frequency arises because of the fact that $c_1 \neq c_0$ in the ionosphere. This error in doppler frequency may be written

$$\epsilon_1 f_D = \mp \frac{f_0 \dot{r}}{c_0}\left(1 - \frac{c_0}{c_1}\right) = \mp \frac{f_0 \dot{r}}{c_0}(1 - n_1) \qquad (3)$$

where n_1 = index of refraction at the satellite.

At sufficiently high radio wave frequencies, such as the 74-mc/sec radiation considered here, the index of refraction, n_1, is given very accurately by the Eccles-Larmor theory. In this, the effects of electron (or ion) collisions and the earth's magnetic field are neglected. Thus,

$$n_1 = \left[1 - \frac{4\pi N_1 e^2}{m\omega^2} \right]^{1/2} \tag{4}$$

where N_1 = number density of ions or electrons

e = electronic charge

m = mass of ion or electron

$\omega = 2\pi f_0$ = radio wave frequency.

If e and m are taken as the charge and mass of the electron, respectively, equation (4) becomes

$$n_1 = \left[1 - \frac{80.5 N_{e_1}}{f_0^2} \right]^{1/2} \tag{5}$$

where N_{e_1} = equivalent electron density in electrons/meter^3.

With a frequency of 74 mc/sec, the second bracketed term in equation (5) is much smaller than 1. Expanding equation (5) binomially,

$$n_1 \doteq 1 - \frac{40.25 N_{e_1}}{f_0^2} \tag{6}$$

to a very good approximation. Substituting equation (6) into equation (3) gives

$$\epsilon_1 f_D = \mp \frac{\dot{r}}{c_0 f_0} \cdot 40.25 N_{e_1}. \tag{7}$$

In actual data reduction, the quantity $\epsilon_1 f_D$ is not observed. Rather, $\dot{r}$ is obtained from the doppler data and compared to $\dot{r}$ obtained from other sources (here a rather complete knowledge of the orbit), and the difference is related to the equivalent electron density by the expression

$$\frac{\Delta \dot{r}}{\dot{r}} = \frac{40.25 N_{e_1}}{f_0^2}. \tag{7a}$$

Referring to equation (1) and Fig. 1, it is seen that even if $\dot{r}$ is zero (i.e., $\epsilon_1 f_D = 0$), the phase angle $\int_0^{r_1} dr/c$ changes with time because of variation in the intervening ionosphere between satellite and receiver. This changing phase angle gives rise to a second false doppler frequency. One can write

$$\Phi = \omega \int_0^{r_1} \frac{dr}{c}. \tag{8}$$

From Fig. 1 we note that for that portion of the radiation path lying within the ionosphere,

$$\int_r^{r_1} \frac{dr}{c} \doteq \frac{1}{\sin B} \int_{h_1}^{h_s} \frac{dh}{c}$$

where h_1 = height of ionosphere base above the earth
h_s = height of satellite above earth's surface.

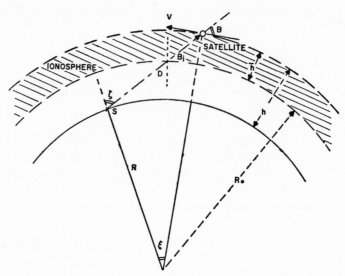

FIGURE 1.   Geometry of a satellite passing directly over an observing station, S.

Along the whole radiation path then,

$$\int_0^{r_1} \frac{dr}{c} = \frac{1}{c_0} \left(r_1 - \frac{1}{\sin B} \int_{h_1}^{h_s} dh \right) + \frac{1}{\sin B} \int_{h_1}^{h_s} \frac{dh}{c}$$

whence

$$\Phi = \frac{\omega}{c_0} \left\{ r_1 + \frac{1}{\sin B} \int_{h_1}^{h_s} (n-1) \, dh \right\} . \qquad (9)$$

Using equation (6), differentiating equation (9) with respect to time, and noting that we are concerned here with the ionospheric effects due to transverse motion alone (i.e., $\dot{r}_1 = 0$), the following equation is obtained:

$$\dot{\Phi} = - \frac{2\pi(40.25)}{c_0 f_0} \left\{ \int_{h_1}^{h_s} N_e \, dh \right\} \frac{d \csc B}{dt} . \qquad (10)$$

Noting now that $\int_{h_1}^{h_s} N_e \, dh$ represents the total equivalent electron content in a vertical column of one-square-meter cross section between the satellite and the earth, and designating this integral by $\bar{N}_e$, equation (10) becomes

$$\epsilon_2 f_D = \frac{\dot{\Phi}}{2\pi} = -\frac{40.25}{c_0 f_0}\left[\left(\frac{R}{r_1}\right)^2\left\{1-\left(\frac{R}{r_1}\right)^2\sin^2\xi\right\}^{-1/2}\cdot\sin\xi\cos\xi\,\xi_0\right]\bar{N}_e \quad \textbf{(11)}$$

where the geometry of Fig. 1 has been used and $\xi_0 = 2\pi/\tau$, τ being the orbital period. From equation (11) it is seen that the second doppler frequency error, $\epsilon_2 f_D$, depends on the total equivalent electron content in the ionosphere.

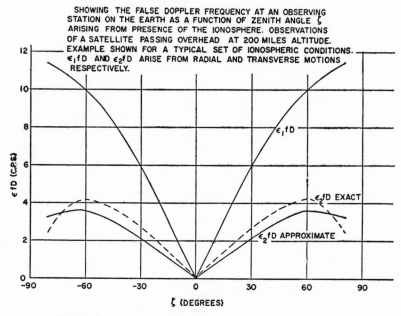

SHOWING THE FALSE DOPPLER FREQUENCY AT AN OBSERVING STATION ON THE EARTH AS A FUNCTION OF ZENITH ANGLE ζ ARISING FROM PRESENCE OF THE IONOSPHERE. OBSERVATIONS OF A SATELLITE PASSING OVERHEAD AT 200 MILES ALTITUDE. EXAMPLE SHOWN FOR A TYPICAL SET OF IONOSPHERIC CONDITIONS. $\epsilon_1 fD$ AND $\epsilon_2 fD$ ARISE FROM RADIAL AND TRANSVERSE MOTIONS RESPECTIVELY.

FIGURE 2.

In actuality, equation (11) represents only an approximation since in its derivation it was assumed that

$$\int_r^{r_1}\frac{dr}{c} = \frac{1}{\sin B}\int_{h_1}^{h_s}\frac{dh}{c}.$$

Referring to Fig. 1 it is seen that the validity of this assumption depends on the vertical distribution of the ionosphere below the satellite. Only if the principal electron content occurs in a stratified layer close to the satellite altitude will the approximation be a good one. Such a condition occurs at night with the satellite traveling in the $F2$-layer. The proper equation can easily be derived, however. Writing

$$\int_r^{r_1}\frac{dr}{c} = \int_{h_1}^{h_s} dh/c\sin B(h)$$

and from Fig. 1

$$\sin B(h) = \left[1 - \frac{R^2 \sin^2 \zeta}{\left(R_0 + \int_{h_1} dh \right)^2} \right]^{1/2}$$

then equation (9) should be written

$$\Phi = \frac{\omega}{c_0} \left\{ r_1 - \frac{40.25}{f_0{}^2} \int_{h_1}^{h_s} \frac{(b+h) N_e(h) \, dh}{[h^2 + 2bh + (b^2 - a^2)]^{1/2}} \right\}. \tag{12}$$

Taking the time derivative of equation (12),

$$\epsilon_2 f_D = \frac{\dot{\Phi}}{2\pi} = -\frac{40.25 R^2 \sin \zeta \cos \zeta \, \dot{\zeta}}{c_0 f_0} \int_{h_1}^{h_s} \frac{(b+h) N_e(h) \, dh}{[h^2 + 2bh + (b^2 - a^2)]^{3/2}} \tag{13}$$

where
$$\left. \begin{array}{l} a = R \sin \zeta \\ b = R_0 \end{array} \right\} \text{ see Fig. 1}$$

$N_e(h) = $ vertical distribution of electrons

and the integration is carried out from the base of the ionosphere to the satellite position. It is seen that solution of equation (13) requires a knowledge of the electron distribution $N_e(h)$. If, now, one assumes the ionosphere to be constituted of a series of stratified layers in which the electron density is constant, equation (13) assumes the more convenient computational form

$$\epsilon_2 f_D = -\frac{40.25 R^2 \sin \zeta \cos \zeta \, \dot{\zeta}}{c_0 f_0} \cdot \sum_{i=0}^{S} N_{e_i} \frac{1}{[h^2 + 2bh + (b^2 - a^2)]^{1/2}} \bigg|_{h_i}^{h_{(i+1)}} . \tag{13a}$$

As an example of the magnitudes of the error frequencies $\epsilon_1 f_D$ and $\epsilon_2 f_D$ expected in a typical orbital passage, the following were assumed:
1) Satellite passage directly over receiver.
2) Satellite in circular orbit at 200 miles altitude.
3) Ionosphere composed of two layers:
   a) $N_e = 0$; $0 < h < 86$ miles
   b) $N_e = 10^{11}$ elec/m^3; $86 < h < 124$ miles
   c) $N_e = 10^{12}$ elec/m^3; $124 < h < 200$ miles
4) Transmitter frequency $f_0 = 74$ mc/sec.

With these assumed conditions, equations (7), (11), and (13a) are shown in Fig. 2, where $\epsilon_1 f_D$ [equation (7)], $\epsilon_2 f_D$ approximate [equation (11)], and $\epsilon_2 f_D$ exact [equation (13a)] are plotted as a function of zenith angle ζ. It is seen that at large zenith angles the principal error doppler frequency arises from satellite radial motion. With a single doppler receiving station no method exists for separating $\epsilon_1 f_D$ and $\epsilon_2 f_D$, so neither the electron density nor the total electron content can be determined uniquely. Thus a good approximation to electron density at the satellite is obtained from the doppler data only at large zenith angles. By locating a second doppler receiving station not too distant from the first, it is possible to separate $\epsilon_1 f_D$ and $\epsilon_2 f_D$, provided locations are such that radial speeds relative to the two receivers are different, whereas both receivers observe the satellite through the same ionospheric structure. The geometrical argument for this is shown in Fig. 3. The accuracy with which these two error components can be separated is

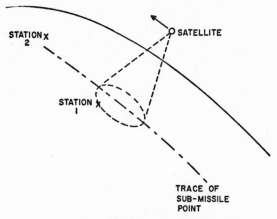

FIGURE 3. Neglecting large lateral variations in the ionosphere, any two stations lying at the intersection of the dashed cone and earth's surface will "see" the satellite through essentially the same ionospheric structure. This is approximately true even when the cone passes over the two stations at different times, if their separation is not too great.

quite low. A more satisfactory separation of components can probably be obtained from simple inspection of the total error-doppler frequency curve and the knowledge (analytical) of how the components vary with zenith angle.

Conclusions

In the preceding section a simplified theory of ionospheric exploration utilizing a satellite beacon and suitable ground instrumentation has been presented. In practice, of course, the treatment is more difficult because of geometrical considerations and observing-system accuracy degradation (as a function of geometry). However, even neglecting these practical considerations, the exploration proposed here is subject to a variety of errors. For example, it is necessary to know the radial speed, $\dot{r}$, to a high degree of accuracy—preferably with an error no greater than 0.05%—in order to obtain reasonably accurate data on the ionospheric structure. Such accuracies in the radial speed require a reasonably sophisticated observation and data-reduction system. Certainly, the observation system, and the orbit flown, should be such that the loss in satellite energy in an orbital period is small compared to the probable errors in energy determination; and further, that there be numerous observations during an interval in which the actual energy loss is approximately equal to the probable errors in the energy determination.

With the tracking systems proposed in the BRL Study Report it is estimated that the probable error in true radial speed, $\dot{r}$, would be approximately 5 fps. Referring to Fig. 2, and remembering that the wavelength at 74 mc/sec is approximately 13 ft, it is seen that the ionospheric error in radial speed determined from doppler data is roughly 145 fps at large zenith angles. Thus, the experiment proposed in this paper offers a reasonably good measure of the equivalent electron density at the satellite.

REFERENCE

1. L. G. deBey *et al.*   *Scientific Objectives and Observing Methods for a Minimum Artificial Earth Satellite*, BRL Report 956, 1955.

28

Temperature and Electron-Density Measurements in the Ionosphere by a Langmuir Probe

by Gunnar Hok, H. S. Sicinski, and N. W. Spencer
DEPARTMENT OF ELECTRICAL ENGINEERING,
UNIVERSITY OF MICHIGAN

ABSTRACT

Langmuir probe techniques offer interesting possibilities for obtaining important data by measurements from an ionospheric satellite. The feasibility of such measurements has been demonstrated in a preliminary manner on rockets in the lower E-layer of the ionosphere.

The most straightforward data calculated from probe records are for temperature. Approximate thermal equilibrium is assumed in each stratum of the ionosphere. During part of each voltage sweep predominantly electrons are collected; this electron current yields both temperature and electron density. The collection of positive ions appears difficult to translate into useful information.

The purpose of this paper is to direct attention to the Langmuir probe technique as a means for collecting important data from a satellite in the ionosphere. The rates at which electrons and ions are collected at the surface of such a probe give information about the ambient temperature and about the density of electrons and ions in the gas surrounding the probe. The feasibility of mounting a probe on a satellite and of extracting temperature and density data from continuously recorded volt-ampere curves for the probe will be briefly discussed below.

The probe method was developed in the 1920's by Irving Langmuir and his associates[1] for the study of electric discharges through gases. The potential of a small cylindrical probe immersed in the "plasma"

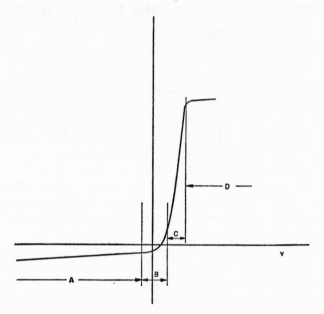

FIGURE 1.   Typical probe characteristic.

under study is swept periodically over a suitable range, and the current collected is observed as a function of the potential (Fig. 1). When the negative particles are primarily electrons and consequently have a charge-to-mass ratio three or four orders of magnitude larger than any positive ions, the collected currents at positive and negative probe potentials differ greatly. In the range *A* (Fig. 1) a negligible fraction of the electrons approaching the probe have enough energy to reach it; the current collected is pure positive-ion current. In the ranges *C* and *D*, on the other hand, the current is primarily formed by electrons, even if negative ions are present in the gas.

When the probe is carried by a missile floating in an ionized atmosphere, no fixed reference potential is available. If the total surface of the missile itself is conducting, it also collects ions and electrons and constitutes in a sense a larger probe. As long as the area of the missile is several orders of magnitude larger than the area of the small probe, the potential of the former is stable enough to serve with a negligible error as a reference potential for the latter. The quantitative theory relating the probe characteristic to temperature and densities of ions and electrons is consequently essentially the same as for a single probe connected through a voltage source to a fixed reference potential, with some reservations considered later in this paper. The most straightforward data calculated from probe measurements are for temperature. If each stratum of the ionosphere can be considered to be in approximate thermal equilibrium, all particles have Maxwell-Boltzmann energy distributions. This assumption is satisfactory if the lifetimes of all the particles present are very long compared to the mean free time, so that at any moment nearly all the particles have a long history of elastic collisions. The equilibrium temperature is obtained from the slope of a plot of the logarithm of the current in range *C* of the probe curve, where electrons reach the collector through a retarding field and contributions from other types of particles are negligible. The probe geometry is not critical for these measurements, as long as no potential minima or saddle points exist in the vicinity of the probe. A constant reference potential is important, but its value with respect to the plasma potential does not have to be known. The voltage resolution required is reduced at higher temperatures, which makes this method of measurement particularly attractive for use in the F-layer, where temperatures of a few thousand degrees are anticipated.

The break in the probe curve that marks the transition between ranges *C* and *D* occurs when the probe potential equals the plasma potential, so that no field exists which turns back a fraction of the electrons; all the random electron current directed toward the probe is actually collected. When the temperature is known, the electron density can be simply calculated from the current measured at this point. For this measurement the probe geometry again is not critical, as long as no potential minima or saddle points occur. Since no use is made of the voltage scale, it is not for this purpose necessary that the reference potential be completely independent of the collected current, but it is essential to know that the saturation in range *D* is due to limited electron current to the small probe rather than to limited positive-ion current to the total satellite surface. In this range of potential the drain of electrons due to the presence of the probe is appreciable, and it may be necessary to study the diffusion of electrons in the vicinity of the probe in order to determine whether or not the electron density at the probe will differ appreciably from the electron density in the undisturbed ionosphere.

In range *A* of the probe characteristic the current collected is practically pure positive-ion current. The conventional probe theory relates the observed current in this range (or the slope of a plot of some function of the current) to the geometry of the probe, to the temperature, and to the density and mass of the positive ions. However, it appears somewhat questionable that data derived from this range of the satellite probe curves may yield any appreciable quantity of useful and reliable information. A number of errors and uncertainties are difficult to eliminate in the reduction of the data, and even if this were not the case, the data cannot stand on their own feet as far as giving both ion mass and number density, or either one without previous knowledge of the other. The primary errors are connected with the high-velocity air flow and with the fact that the accelerated ion flow in range A is critically geometry-dependent. Nonetheless, the possibility is not excluded that collateral information may be derived from these data, which may be useful to confirm or extend the results of other experiments, for instance, of a mass-spectrometer nature.

A satellite velocity of 18,000 mph means that in the satellite frame of reference the electrons will have a drift velocity corresponding to about two-tenths of a millivolt, which is less than 1% of any reasonable thermal energy. The corresponding "drift energy" of an ion of mass number 16, on the other hand, exceeds 5 electron volts, which is two or three orders of magnitude above thermal energy. Consequently, the ion current to any probe will vary considerably with the aspect of the satellite, while the electron current can be assumed to be practically unaffected. A favorable consequence of the high drift energy of the ions is a much increased collection of positive ions on the satellite surface, leading to improved stability of the satellite potential.

Since it appears impractical to stabilize the aspect of the satellite, a random orientation and a slow spin about an arbitrary axis are to be anticipated. For this reason it is suggested that four independent probes would be advisable, distributed over the surface of the sphere as the corners of an inscribed tetrahedron. Whatever the spin axis of the satellite, one of the probes would be reasonably close to the equator of the satellite, and the four probes would provide good samples of the probe characteristic as a function of position relative to the sun and to the direction of motion. It is hoped that the period of the spin will be considerably larger than the period of the voltage sweep, so that the spin period can be recognized on the records and possible anomalies produced by the aerodynamics or by the radiation from the sun can be isolated and studied separately.

Lacking sufficient information about transmitter power, antenna configuration, etc., the authors have not yet made any attempt to estimate the modification of the probe characteristics produced by the electromagnetic field from the satellite's own radio transmitter.

The projection of a Langmuir probe into the ionosphere is not without precedent. In 1947 one successful flight of a V-2 rocket carried such a probe of a somewhat rough-and-ready design into the lower E-layer and proved the feasibility of the method by recording probe characteristics of the typical appearance, although the reduction of the data was made difficult by an unfavorable geometry, enforced by the circumstances, and unknown surface conditions of the missile as a whole.[2-4]

In conclusion we may express the conviction that a satellite with a clean, conducting surface and carrying small, well-designed probes is capable of giving consistent, reliable data about temperature and electron concentration in the ionosphere.

REFERENCES

1. H. H. Mott-Smith and I. Langmuir, "The Theory of Collectors in Gaseous Discharges," *Phys. Rev., 28:* 727–763 (1936).
2. G. Hok *et al. Dynamic Probe Measurements in the Ionosphere.* Upper Air Research Program Report No. 3, University of Michigan, February, 1951.
3. G. Hok *et al.,* "Dynamic Probe Measurements in the Ionosphere," *J. Geophys. Res., 58:* 235–242 (1953).
4. G. Hok and W. G. Dow, "Exploration of the Ionosphere by Means of a Langmuir-Probe Technique," in *Rocket Exploration of the Upper Atmosphere.* London: Pergamon Press, 1954.

29

A Satellite Propagation Experiment

by *L. M. Hartman and R. P. Haviland*
SPECIAL DEFENSE PROJECTS DEPARTMENT,
GENERAL ELECTRIC COMPANY

ABSTRACT

A satellite ionosphere and propagation experiment is proposed. Satellite equipment consists of a low-power c-w transmitter operating on a frequency near the ionosphere cut-off frequency corresponding to maximum geometric line-of-sight distances from the satellite. Statistical data on coverage are sought by enlisting aid of operators in the Radio Amateur Service. Particular measurements to be made at specially equipped stations are reviewed.

The prospect of an earth satellite presents an opportunity for scientific investigation on a worldwide scale never before attempted. It is the purpose of this paper to suggest a way in which one of these investigations can be practically and meaningfully carried out. This experiment has been suggested by the irregular and largely unexplained losses of signal strength experienced in the several moon echo measurements that have been reported. As is well known, these signals have varied from the theoretically expected reception at VHF frequencies to values as much as 10 to 30 or more db below this figure. It is generally felt that the explanation of this phenomenon lies in the ionosphere, perhaps in the almost unexplored region above the maximum of the

268

F2-layer. Since the orbits of the early satellites may lie in the region from about 200 to 800 miles above the earth, or from a point well within to one well above the F2-layer, an opportunity exists for propagation experiments which could contribute greatly to our knowledge of this region. It is our intention in this paper to outline broadly one of these experiments.

Two types of data would be sought from this experiment. One type would include specific and accurate measurements to be made at selected and planned locations. The other would consist of statistical data to be obtained by enlisting the aid of operators in the amateur service all over the world.

The wide distribution of amateur stations can be appreciated by reference to the listing by countries given at the end of this paper. It will be noted, however, that these stations tend to be clustered along several definite meridians. The largest number are in the Americas, with the principal concentration along 75° W. longitude and including stations from Greenland to the Falkland Islands. Another large group are located along 10° E. longitude, from Norway to South Africa. A third but smaller group lie along 140° E. longitude, from Japan to Australia. These are essentially the meridians selected for major investigation during IGY. In addition, there are a number of stations around 140° W., including Alaska and Hawaii, and possibly other concentrations along 50° and 80° E. longitudes.

Frequencies assigned to the amateur service which appear useful in this experiment include 14, 21, 28, and 50 mc/sec, plus several higher bands such as 220 mc/sec. Receiving equipment is available for all of these, but is more generally available for the bands below 50 mc/sec. The lower frequencies have two further advantages. Both the transmitting and the receiving equipment are generally simpler and transmitter power is lower than at higher frequencies to achieve the same received power. The proposed experiment therefore is based on the selection of one of these frequencies (14, 21, or 28 mc/sec) for the transmitter frequency to be used in the satellite.

It is clear that the frequency selected must lie above the lowest and preferably above the highest critical frequency to be encountered for the several ionospheric layers. At the time of the launching, assumed to be early 1958, the sunspot number will be approximately at its cyclical high. On the basis of experience during past cycles it is believed that the critical frequencies of the F2-layer will correspond approximately to those in this array:

	Winter	*Summer*
Noon	13	8
Midnight	4	7

The critical frequencies of the E- and F1-layers may be disregarded since they lie in the region of 4 mc/sec.

At any of the amateur frequencies, therefore, reception could be expected at points vertically below the satellite. The experiment, however, is essentially a compromise between minimum transmitter power on the one hand and maximum statistical coverage on the other. The latter is supported by the far greater theoretical interest associated with oblique incidence. Hence, the widest possible "cone of reception" should be sought, consistent with reasonable transmitter power. Such a cone is defined approximately by the maximum line-of-sight distance from the satellite without regard for deviation or displacement of the propagation path. For satellite positions well above the F2-layer maximum, this maximum line-of-sight path also corresponds to the maximum usable frequency (MUF) for maximum "one-skip" transmission between points on the earth's surface, assuming of course a symmetrical electron-density distribution about the F2 maximum, an assumption which is probably unwarranted. Assuming an MUF factor of about 3 for such a maximum line-of-sight path, therefore, the following array indicates the approximate maximum usable frequencies which can be expected at the time of the experiment.

	Winter	Summer
Noon	39	24
Midnight	12	21

Again the E- and F1-layers are disregarded since, although the corresponding MUF factors are higher than for the F2-layer, the resulting expected maximum usable frequencies do not exceed about 20 mc/sec.

It is now apparent that 14 mc/sec lies below the F2 MUF most of the time and 21 mc/sec, although to a lesser extent, still lies below the MUF, especially during daylight hours. It is concluded, therefore, that a frequency of approximately 28 mc/sec should be adopted for this experiment. This frequency would insure maximum amateur coverage and yet is sufficiently close to F2 MUF values (lying below these values only around noon in the winter months) to provide ample opportunity for the observation of anomalous propagation.

For a satellite orbit between altitudes of 200 and 800 miles the maximum line-of-sight distances are about 1250 and 2500 miles. These distances correspond to free space path gains between isotropic antennas of -130 db and -136 db, respectively. Good amateur equipment typically includes a receiver with a noise figure of 6 db, a bandwidth of 8 kc, and a Yagi antenna with an effective gain of 8 db above a dipole. Therefore, the power required at the antenna to provide a 10:1 signal-to-noise ratio is -151 dbW. Assuming an isotropic antenna at the satellite, the required transmitter powers are then -25 and -21 dbW. A transmitter of 10-milliwatt output will thus provide nearly full theoretical coverage at 28 mc/sec in the absence of absorption.

Due to the large orbital velocity of the satellite it would probably be desirable to use as nondirective a receiving antenna as possible, that is, a dipole with gain of 3 db. This would reduce the range for a 10:1 S./N. to 750 and 1200 miles, respectively. This antenna would be useful for about 8 min if the satellite passed directly over the receiver.

Special stations could obtain greater S./N. than 10:1. Antenna gains of 14 db should be readily obtainable. Additional gains of about 10 db are possible by reducing receiver bandwidth. Detectable signals should therefore be possible with attenuations of as much as 26 to 30 db below free space transmission.

In principle, the generation of a high-frequency signal of the level required here is simple. Practically, however, the severe limitations on weight imposed by minimum satellite operation will require careful transmitter design. It appears that the transmitter should be crystal controlled to provide stability. Both vacuum-tube and transistor oscillators and amplifiers should be considered in design, since the power required by the tube filament may be offset by the higher efficiency as compared with a transistor.

For an experiment of moderate duration, perhaps one week, it appears that batteries are the best power source and that the total weight of the experiment may be held to about 1 lb. Solar power absorption alone does not appear to provide a desirable power source, since it is available somewhat less than half of the time. However, for long-life experiments it may be possible to use solar energy to charge batteries. A number of complications are introduced by this, but it seems possible to design equipment having an operating life of several months for a weight of about 3 lb.

The satellite antenna pattern should be reasonably nondirective. Considering simplicity, it appears that the best compromise would be a quarter-wave antenna, working against the satellite body as a ground plane. The antenna may be very thin, since bandwidth is no problem. This suggests the use of a silver-plated piano-wire whip, which could be coiled during ascent and released as the satellite body separates from its carrying rocket. It would appear desirable for the satellite release mechanism to impart angular momentum to the satellite at separation to insure that the antenna nulls do not yield false data. An alternate method would be to use three independent transmitters with separate antennas mounted parallel to rectangular co-ordinate axes. If these three transmitters were tuned to different frequencies, this arrangement would yield data concerning satellite attitude.

If battery voltages are expected to vary appreciably, it may be desirable to include a simple voltage-sensitive tone modulator, to furnish a calibration. Other types of telemetry may be added; however, it appears desirable to maintain a narrow-band signal. This suggests that telemetry be confined to slowly varying quantities, such as solar ultraviolet intensity.

The minimum receiving station would require simply a receiver, an antenna, and a clock. The noise figure of the receiver should be around 6 db, which is attained in modern types or which can be obtained by a simple preamplifier. Usable data can be obtained with a dipole antenna, but a rotary beam would of course be superior.

The data recorded would be:

1) The time
2) The relative strength of signal in normal amateur units
3) The antenna orientation
4) The equipment used
5) Notes on the sound of the signal.

It is believed that a number of advanced amateurs or club groups would set up a number of intermediate-type stations to conduct controlled measurements of the following types:

1) Continuous recording of signal strength
2) Vertical angle of arrival of signal
3) Degree of polarization
4) Phase comparison of signals received by separated antennas
5) Local ionospheric conditions
6) Recording of telemetry imposed on the signal.

A complete installation, amateur or not, would of course conduct measurements in all of these areas.

To secure this assistance, it is suggested that the International Amateur Radio Union and its member societies be invited to give full publicity to the program in their publications. This should include the concept of the experiments, notes on construction and calibration of equipment, methods of reporting data, the principles of satellite operation, orbital data, and so on.

It is of course evident that an experiment as outlined here cannot furnish direct data concerning propagation conditions above the F2-layer maximum. Other experiments, therefore, also need to be conceived and planned to accomplish direct scientific objectives. Such experiments may well include a second satellite or, more simply, a high-altitude rocket, such as an Aerobee-Hi, containing a receiver and launched to reach peak altitude near the time of satellite passage. In the latter case optimum timing would appear to be daylight hours in the winter, when the normal layers are depressed in height and ionization levels are near maximum. It is not our purpose here, however, to explore these additional possibilities.

TABLE I

Location and approximate number of amateur stations

Prefix	Country or Place	No. of Stations	Prefix	Country or Place	No. of Stations
AC3	Sikkim	2	FL8	Somaliland	1
AC4	Tibet	1	FM7	Martinique	7
AB	Pakistan	4	FO8	Tahiti	11
C	China	1	FP8	St. Pierre &	
CE	Chile	945		Miquelon Is.	15
CO-CM	Cuba	1100	FQ8	Fr. Equatorial	
CN2	Tangier Zone	23		Africa	20
CN8	Fr. Morocco	280	FR7	Reunion Is.	1
CP	Bolivia	87	FU8	New Hebrides	3
CR4	Cape Verde Is.	16	FW8	Wallis Is.	1
CR5	Portuguese Guinea	6	FY7	Fr. Guiana	5
CR6	Angola	50	G	Great Britain	7790
CR7	Mozambique	52	GC	Channel Islands	30
CR8	Goa (Port India)	1	GD	Isle of Man	28
CR9	Macao	4	GI	Northern Ireland	197
CS3	Azores Islands	1	GM	Scotland	476
CT1	Portugal	240	GW	Wales	304
CT2	Azores Islands	4	HA	Hungary	N.A.
CT3	Madeira Is.	10	HB	Switzerland	420
CX	Uruguay	1420	HC	Ecuador	78
DJ, DL-			HC8	Galapagos Islands	2
DM2	Germany	4747	HE9L	Liechtenstein	1
DU	Philippines	58	HH	Haiti	30
EA	Spain	710	HI	Dominican Republic	20
EA6	Balearic Islands	10	HK	Colombia	188
EA8	Canary Islands	31	HL1	Korea	1
EA9	Sp. Morocco	20	HP	Rep. of Panama	48
EA9	Rio de Oro	3	HR	Honduras	42
EA	Spanish Guinea	3	HS	Thailand (Siam)	5
EI	Ireland	168	HZ	Saudi Arabia	8
EL	Liberia	10	I	Italy	179
ET2	Eritrea	27	I	Trieste	6
ET3	Ethiopia	7	IS	Sardinia	4
F	France	1960	IT	Sicily	5
FA	Algeria	130	I5	Somalia	12
FB8	Madagascar	20	JA	Japan	2027
FO8	Fr. Togoland		JY	Transjordan	2
FE8	Fr. Cameroons	5	KA	Japan (U.S.	
FF8	Fr. West Africa	30		Citizens)	173
FG7	Guadeloupe	2	KA	Iwo Jima	1
FI8	Fr. Indochina	9	KB6	Canton Islands	4
FK8	New Caledonia	11	KC6	Caroline Islands	18

TABLE I (Continued)

Location and approximate number of amateur stations

Prefix	Country or Place	No. of Stations	Prefix	Country or Place	No. of Stations
KG4	Guantanamo Bay, Cuba	19	PZ	Surinam	4
KG6	Marianas Islands	91	SM	Sweden	2300
KG6I	Bonin Islands	1	SP	Poland	N.A.
KG6S	Saipan	1	ST	Sudan	12
KH6	Hawaiian Islands	977	SU	Egypt	2
KJ6	Johnston Island	10	SV	Greece	13
KL7	Alaska	788	TA	Turkey	3
KM6	Midway Island	3	TF	Iceland	35
KP4	Puerto Rico	382	TG	Guatemala	74
KP6	Palmyra Islands	1	TI	Costa Rica	550
KR6	Okinawa	74	TI9	Cocos Island	6
KS4	Swan Island	1	U	Soviet Union	N.A.
KS6	Samoa	2	VE	Canada	7787
KT1	Tangier Zone	12	VK	Australia	3461
KV	Virgin Islands	20	VO	Newfoundland	120
KW6	Wake Island	15	VO6	Labrador	40
KX6	Marshall Islands	8	VP1	British Honduras	12
KZ5	Canal Zone	172	VP2	Leeward Islands	12
LA	Norway	1190	VP2	Windward Islands	18
LU	Argentina	6275	VP3	Br. Guiana	4
LX	Luxembourg	30	VP4	Trinidad & Tobago	40
LZ	Bulgaria	N.A.	VP5	Jamaica	21
MI	San Marino	1	VP7	Bahama Islands	27
MP4	Bahrain Islands	14	VP8	Falkland Islands	16
MP4	Kuwait	10	VP9	Bermuda Islands	35
MP4	Qatar	9	UQ2	N. Rhodesia	65
OA	Peru	229	UQ3	Tanganyika	30
OD5	Lebanon	25	VQ4	Kenya	123
OE	Austria	204	VQ5	Uganda	17
OH	Finland	1044	VQ6	Br. Somaliland	2
OK	Czechoslovakia	N.A.	VQ8	Mauritius	7
ON	Belgium	513	VQ8	Chagos Islands	1
OQ5	Belgium Congo	172	VR1	Gilbert Islands	8
OX	Greenland	32	VR2	Fiji Islands	29
OY	Faeroe Islands	15	VR3	Fanning Is.	1
OZ	Denmark	1874	VR4	Solomon Is.	2
PA-PI	Netherlands	957	VR6	Pitcairn Is.	2
PJ	Netherlands, W. Indies	38	VS1	Singapore	42
			VS2	Malaya	56
PX1	Andorra	1	VS4	Sarawak	2
PY	Brazil	7003	VS5	Brunei	1
			VS6	Hong Kong	37

TABLE I (Continued)

Location and approximate number of amateur stations

Prefix	Country or Place	No. of Stations	Prefix	Country or Place	No. of Stations
VS9	Aden	5	ZD8	Ascension Is.	1
VU	India	135	ZD9	Tristan da Cunha	2
WI	United States	141,082	ZE	S. Rhodesia	120
XE	Mexico	423	ZK1	Cook Islands	5
XZ	Burma	32	ZK2	Niue	3
YJ	New Hebrides	3	ZL	New Zealand	2309
YI	Iraq	3	ZM	Samoa, Western	8
YK	Syria	9	ZP	Paraguay	343
YN	Nicaragua	25	ZS	Union of S. Africa	2094
YO	Romania	1	ZS3	Southwest Africa	26
YS	El Salvador	38	ZS7	Swaziland	5
YU	Yugoslavia	356	ZS8	Basutoland	9
YV	Venezuela	429	ZS9	Bechuanaland	8
ZB1	Malta	38	3A2	Monaco	25
ZB2	Gibraltar	5	3V8	Tunisia	26
ZC3	Christmas Island	2	4S7	Ceylon	65
ZC4	Cyprus	14	4X4	Israel	101
ZC5	N. Borneo	4	5A	Libya	59
ZD1	Sierra Leone	10	9S4	Saarland	49
ZD2	Nigeria	10			
ZD3	Gambia	1		Total Except	
ZD4	Gold Coast	16		U.S.	70,446
ZD6	Nyasaland	9		Grand Total	211,528

Source: Radio Amateur Call Book Magazine, V32 N2, Summer, 1955.

In conclusion we wish to emphasize the unusual opportunity provided by the first earth satellite to achieve much more than bare scientific data. There is here a genuine basis for a co-operative undertaking involving thousands of persons in many countries, working together toward mutual goals and generating an invaluable mass of data which would be of interest and use to all. Certainly this is the spirit of the International Geophysical Year.

30

Electromagnetic Propagation Studies with a Satellite Vehicle

by *Fred B. Daniels*
SIGNAL CORPS ENGINEERING LABORATORIES,
FORT MONMOUTH, NEW JERSEY

ABSTRACT

A parameter of considerable importance in connection with ionospheric theory is the integrated ion density in a vertical column. The value of this parameter may be obtained by measuring the rotation of the plane of polarization of a radio wave which has traveled through the ionosphere. It is proposed that such a measurement be made, using radio signals transmitted from a satellite vehicle. The transmitters normally used for tracking and telemetering can be utilized for this experiment if the frequencies and power output are suitably chosen.

Introduction

Very little is known about the ion density of the earth's upper atmosphere at levels above the F2-layer. The usual method of measuring ion densities is to determine the upper limit, or penetration frequency, of radio waves reflected from the ionosphere. This is accomplished by means of a specially designed radio transmitter known as a sweep-frequency, vertical-incidence ionosphere recorder. Inasmuch as total reflection occurs for all frequencies up to that frequency which corresponds to the maximum ion density, it would not be possible to detect a layer higher than the F2-layer, having a lower maximum ion density than the latter. Occasional observations made at times when the F2-layer ion densities were very low have given some evidence of the existence of a so-called G-layer at a height of 500–600 km.[1] Alternative explanations of the observed reflections are, however, possible. The existence of the G-layer is therefore still problematic. There is an experiment that could be performed in connection with the satellite program that would solve this problem, and that would also yield information regarding the distribution of ion density above the F2-layer maximum. (Heretofore, this distribution has been computed only from the observed value of the F2-layer penetration frequency, together with certain assumptions as to the temperature and the form of the ionic distribution function.)

The proposed experiment is a determination of the integrated value of the ionization from the earth's surface to the satellite, by measuring the rotation of the plane of polarization of a radio wave transmitted from the satellite. By making such a measurement for a range of satellite altitudes from perigee to apogee, and by combining the data with information obtained from moon radar and ionosphere recorders, information regarding the ion density as a function of height may also be obtained. The integrated value of the ion density assumes considerable importance in the light of recent work done by Ratcliffe,[2] who computed this quantity up to the F2-layer maximum from vertical-incidence ionosphere records. He found that it behaved in a quite regular manner with respect to the sun's zenith angle, and did not exhibit the eccentricities evidenced by the values of the F2-layer maximum density. Ratcliffe's results, however, were based on data obtained at only three stations (College, Alaska; Watheroo, Australia; Huancayo, Peru). Furthermore, the data from Huancayo did not give consistent results during sunspot minima, apparently because of the existence at that time of a subsidiary layer above the F2-layer maximum. It would therefore seem to be quite desirable to make direct measurements of the total ion density at as many locations as possible in order to check Ratcliffe's conclusions and thus to settle the question of dependence of total ionization on the sun's zenith angle.

Theory

The theory of the experiment is quite simple. In its passage through the ionosphere, a linearly polarized wave of sufficiently high frequency, the direction of propagation of which is not too nearly normal to the magnetic field, will be resolved into two waves that are circularly polarized in opposite senses and that travel with different velocities. Two such waves are the equivalent of a slowly rotating linearly polarized wave. It has been shown by Hatanaka[3] that the plane of polarization of such a wave undergoes a rotation which is directly proportional to the integrated ion density along the propagation path. The amount of rotation is given by the expression

$$\theta = 2.97 \times 10^{-2} H f^{-2} \cos \phi \int N \, dr$$

where N = ion density

dr = element of path length

ϕ = angle between the direction of propagation and the earth's magnetic field

H = the earth's magnetic field

θ = angle of rotation of the plane of polarization

f = frequency of the transmitted wave.

(A simplified derivation of the above expression is given in the Appendix.)

Using a value of $2 \times 10^{17} \, m^{-2}$ for $\int N dr$ and assuming a frequency of 200 mc/sec, Hatanaka found that θ would be 6 radians, a value so large that some ambiguity would be involved in its exact determination. (The reason for this is that any measurement of the direction of the electric vector of the wave could give only the true value plus or minus an integral multiple of 180°.) By making use of two or more appropriately chosen frequencies, however, this ambiguity could be resolved. If, for example, frequencies of 400 and 800 mc/sec were used, the amount of rotation would be 86° and 21.5°, respectively, for the assumed value of ion density. The higher frequency could therefore be used to determine the quadrant in which θ lies, and the lower frequency would serve as a "vernier" to give a more accurate value of θ. The use of two well-separated frequencies transmitted from a rocket was suggested by Hatanaka as a method of measuring the electron density of the ionosphere. An alternative method, which may have some practical advantages, would be to use two closely spaced frequencies near 100 mc/sec. If, for example, frequencies of 100 and 105 mc/sec were adopted, the angle between the planes of polarization of the two waves would be 138°, for the previously assumed value of ion density. This angle could be measured without ambiguity.

An experimental confirmation of the rotation of the plane of polarization has been reported by Murray and Hargreaves,[4] who observed long-period deep fading of 120-mc/sec signals that had been reflected from the moon. The maximum effect was found to occur within a few hours of sunrise, when the ion density would be changing rapidly. By switching back and forth between two orthogonally polarized receiving antennas, it was found that signals were strong in one plane when they had completely disappeared in the plane at right angles. The existence of long-period fading has also been observed at the Signal Corps Engineering Laboratories, where a moon radar is currently being operated on 151 mc/sec.

Instrumentation

To perform this experiment, two additional transmitters will be required on the satellite if frequencies of 400 and 800 mc/sec are used. (It is assumed that the tracking and telemetering transmitters will be operated on frequencies in the neighborhood of 100 mc/sec.) If, however, the alternative method is adopted, and frequencies of the order of 100 and 105 mc/sec are used, only one additional transmitter will be needed, as the transmitter used for tracking can serve as the second. If the modulation of the telemetering system is cut off while the polarization measurement is made, the telemetering transmitter may be used for the second frequency, and the entire experiment can then be carried out without any additional equipment on the vehicle. The transmitted power levels which would be used for tracking and telemetering would also suffice for the polarization measurements. If the assumption is made that the limiting noise is that due to cosmic radiation,[5] the power output of each transmitter must be about one-half watt at 100 mc/sec for a predetection signal-to-noise ratio of 10 db, for a receiver bandwidth of 100 kc/sec, and half-wave dipole transmitting and receiving antennas. These figures do not allow for antenna circuit losses, nor for losses due to unfavorable antenna aspect.

The orientation of the plane of polarization of the received signal could be determined with two circularly polarized receiving antennas and a continuously variable phase-shifting network that varies the relative phase of the signals from the antennas. The detector output would be impressed on the vertical plates of an oscilloscope, and the horizontal sweep would be activated by the phase-shifting device. This would result in a continuous presentation which could be recorded photographically.

General Comments

The desirability of using signals from a satellite for the polarization experiment may be questioned, inasmuch as reflections from the moon could be used to achieve the same result. One answer to this objection is that other effects are also present in the case of reflections from the moon, such as rapid fading with periods as short as 1 sec. This fading has been assumed to be due to the librations of the moon, but this cannot definitely be established until all other possibilities are eliminated. Performing the experiment with a transmitter just above the ionosphere should localize the source of the fading. Furthermore, data from both the satellite experiment and moon radar are needed in order to get information about the dependence of ion density on height. The satellite experiment would therefore supplement the moon experiment, and each would be of value in interpreting the results of the other.

The experiment described is quite uncomplicated in that there is a very simple relationship between the quantity measured and the parameter that is to be computed. No involved corrections need be applied—no questionable approximations have been made. Furthermore, a single observation gives the value of the integrated ion density corresponding to a given time and place. Most important of all, it is quite possible that the experiment can be performed with no additional equipment on the satellite vehicle, other than that normally required for tracking and telemetering. Even if it is not feasible to provide two transmitters in the satellite, valuable information can be obtained from measurements made on one frequency only, if the data are supplemented by measurements made with moon radar and conventional ionosphere recorders.

Acknowledgment

The author wishes to acknowledge his indebtedness to Dr. H. G. Booker for calling his attention to the paper by Hatanaka and for pointing out the possible application to the satellite.

APPENDIX
Rotation of the Plane of Polarization by the Ionosphere

From magneto-ionic theory,[6] it is known that a linearly polarized wave incident on an ionized medium in the presence of a magnetic field is split into two components that are elliptically polarized with oppositely directed rotations. If the wave frequency is much higher than the collision, plasma, and gyromagnetic frequencies, and if the direction of propagation is not too nearly normal to the magnetic field, the polarization ellipses become circles. The first three conditions are approximately satisfied in the ionosphere for frequencies of 100 mc/sec or greater, and the fourth condition can be satisfied by a suitable choice of the propagation path. The medium has different indices of refraction for the two wave components, and the vectors representing the two states of polarization therefore rotate with different velocities. If λ_1 and λ_2 are the wavelengths corresponding to the two propagation

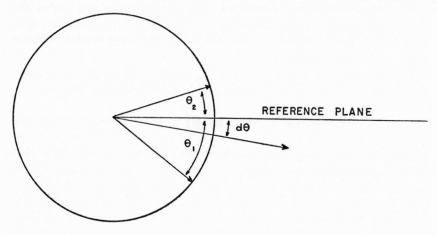

REFERENCE PLANE

FIGURE 1.

velocities, and dr is an increment of path length, the rotations of the two components will be given by

$$\theta_1 = 2\pi \frac{dr}{\lambda_1} \qquad \text{and} \qquad \theta_2 = 2\pi \frac{dr}{\lambda_2}.$$

The accompanying figure shows the relation between θ_1, θ_2, and $d\theta$, the angle through which the plane of polarization rotates as the wave travels the distance dr. From the figure,

$$\theta_2 + d\theta = \theta_1 - d\theta$$

or
$$d\theta = (\theta_1 - \theta_2)/2.$$

Substituting for θ_1 and θ_2 and expressing λ in terms of the index of refraction η, angular frequency ω, and free-space velocity C_0, we have

$$d\theta = \omega\, dr\, (\eta_1 - \eta_2)/2C_0. \qquad (1)$$

Under the assumptions given in the first paragraph, the Appleton-Hartree expression for the index of refraction can be written

$$\eta = [1 - X/(1 \pm Y_L)]^{1/2} \cong 1 - X/2(1 \pm Y_L) \qquad (2)$$

where $X = (\omega_N/\omega)^2 = [e^2/(\epsilon_0 m \omega^2)]N$

ω_N = angular plasma frequency

e = electronic charge

ϵ_0 = permittivity of free space

m = electronic mass
N = electron density
$\omega_L = \omega_M \cos \phi$
$\omega_M = (e/m)\mu_0 H$ = angular gyromagnetic frequency
$Y_L = \omega_L/\omega$
μ_0 = permeability of free space
H = earth's magnetic field
ϕ = angle between the direction of phase propagation and the magnetic field.

Substituting the two values of η given by equation (2) into equation (1), putting in numerical values of the constants, and integrating, gives

$$\theta = 2.97 \times 10^{-2} H f^{-2} \cos \phi \int N \, dr \quad \text{(radians)}$$

where H is to be expressed in ampere turns/meter, f in cps, N in electrons/m^3, and dr in meters.

REFERENCES

1. S. K. Mitra. *The Upper Atmosphere,* 2nd ed. Calcutta: The Asiatic Soc., 1952, p. 236.
2. J. A. Ratcliffe, "Some Irregularities in the F2 Region of the Ionosphere," *J. Geophys. Res., 56:* 487–507 (1951).
3. T. Hatanaka, Scientific Report No. 5, Contract No. AF 19 (604)–73, Air Force Cambridge Res. Center, 30 August 1955.
4. W. A. S. Murray and J. K. Hargreaves, "Lunar Radio Echoes and the Faraday Effect in the Ionosphere," *Nature, 173:* 944–945 (1954).
5. H. V. Cottony and J. R. Johler, "Cosmic Radio Noise Intensities in the VHF Band," *Proc. IRE, 40:* 1053–1060 (1952).
6. S. K. Mitra. *Op. cit.,* Chapter VI.

Study of Fine Structure and Irregularities of the Ionosphere with Rockets and Satellites

by *Wolfgang Pfister*
IONOSPHERIC PHYSICS LABORATORY,
GEOPHYSICS RESEARCH DIRECTORATE,
AIR FORCE CAMBRIDGE RESEARCH CENTER

ABSTRACT:

Almost all experiments using the ionosphere as a propagation medium reveal the presence of irregular or blobby structure in the electron distribution, and, consequently, a variety of methods is in use to determine something about the blobby structure, either by propagation through the ionosphere as in the radioastronomic technique or by reflection within the layers. Only limited information is available from rocket experiments, but due to the fact that a rocket or satellite travels in the midst of the ionosphere, experiments using transmissions between the vehicle and the ground will be able to add a new and very valuable type of information. Up to now, the contribution of the irregularities has been looked at more as a nasty by-product which must be smoothed out in the data analysis. However, from the data available, an analysis in terms of irregular structure appears to be quite promising. Based on experience with known techniques, a set of experiments for a satellite is being proposed. It is a combination of the pulse-delay experiment similar to the Air Force electron-density rocket experiment with a kind of drift-type experiment measuring the signal amplitude fluctuations at three closely spaced receivers. The real advantage of the fine-structure experiment with satellites or rockets will be that the changing aspect allows us to gain a three-dimensional picture of the configuration of the blob, while so far we are used to looking only at the two-dimensional diffraction pattern at the ground.

Introduction

A systematic study of fine structure and irregular structure in the ionosphere is a fairly recent branch of ionospheric research. It is important for a better understanding of the physics of the ionized layers, especially of the dynamical processes, and it has a direct relation to practical applications like back-scatter and forward-scatter techniques.

Almost all experimental studies in this field have been based on the propagation of electromagnetic waves in the ionosphere. Most commonly used are the techniques which are based on the reflection of radio waves in the ionosphere. They may differ in instrumentation and may use vertical or oblique incidence, pulse or c-w, fixed or sweep frequency, phase, amplitude, or time-delay indicators. Another technique utilizes one-way transmission through the whole ionosphere. It is the application of radioastronomy to the study of ionospheric properties. Both types of techniques have their advantages and disadvantages. The radioastronomy technique avoids the difficulties of interpretation due to the reflection process; on the other hand, it gives only an integrated effect over the entire region and it is difficult to measure height dependence of the ionospheric structure.

One can see easily that a propagation path with one endpoint in the midst of the ionosphere has many advantages, especially if this endpoint can be moved around as desired. Such a path can be obtained with a rocket or a satellite. So far, hardly any effort has been spent to obtain information about local irregularities by a rocket experiment. Nevertheless, in view of the importance of these studies from the standpoint of theoretical ionospheric physics, as well as from the standpoint of practical communication systems, it is very worthwhile to plan these experiments for rockets and satellites.

Experience from Past Rocket Experiments

The idea to use rocket experiments for a study of the irregular structure of the ionosphere was suggested by the analysis of another rocket experiment, one which was designed to measure the electron-density distribution in a stratified ionosphere by using the time delay of a pulse transmitted between rocket and ground. The earliest experiments of this type have been made with V-2 rockets. Eric Beth analyzed one set of these data and found that as soon as the rocket had entered the ionosphere the time-delay data were scattered to such a degree that it was almost hopeless to deduce reasonable information about the dependence of electron density on height. He concluded that the scatter of the delay data was due to heavy turbulence in the lower part of the ionosphere.

Later on, Aerobee rockets have been used, the technique has been improved, and the pulses are transmitted successively on seven frequencies between 4 and 5 mc/sec. The pulse delay should decrease continuously from the 4-mc/sec pulse to the 5-mc/sec pulse. However, the data consistently showed considerable jumps in delay between groups of pulses which again have been interpreted as due to turbulent structure of the ionosphere. By selecting the pulses of the shortest time delay for a particular frequency and by some smoothing, it was possible to derive a time-delay curve for the "smooth" ionosphere. These results have been reported by Lien *et al.* at the Oxford Rocket Meeting, 1953.

Recently, another experiment with an Aerobee has been analyzed. This time we are concerned with the data from a transmission downward to the ground on 6 mc/sec. This type of experiment has the advantage that the qualities of the received pulse can be seen on the film, together with the time delay. Pulses were transmitted with a repetition rate of 300/sec. Fig. 1 shows the readings of the delay time of the leading edge plotted every tenth of a second vs time of flight and altitude whenever data were available for the upward trajectory, each dot being the average of from one to three readings. The scatter of the delay data is considerable, but a closer inspection reveals that the scatter is not random around a mean value and that it has a large periodic component of about 2 sec; this periodicity is obviously a direct effect of the rotation of the rocket. The amplitude range of these delay fluctuations is about 1.5 to 2 microseconds. The easiest way to eliminate the effect of the rocket roll is to integrate the delay data over the period of the roll. Of course, this procedure will eliminate also any effect due to small-scale irregularities in the electron concentration.

Fig. 2 shows the delay vs altitude curves for the upward and downward trajectories. The x's and o's are 0.5-km mean readings to eliminate any fluctuations in the order of the rocket roll and faster. It will be noticed that these mean readings do not produce a curve with a monotonically increasing delay with respect to altitude. Under the assumption of a smooth, horizontally stratified ionosphere a decrease in the delay curve can occur only under very limited conditions of rocket

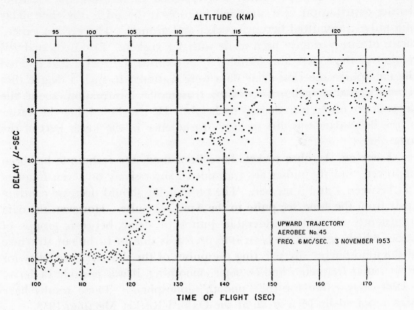

FIGURE 1.

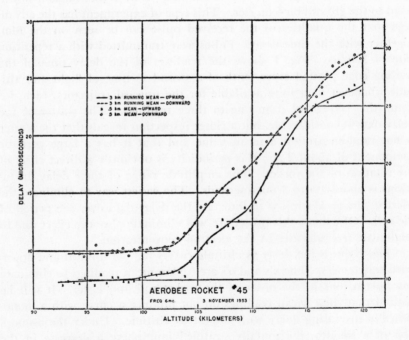

FIGURE 2.

position and configuration of the magnetic field, conditions not given in the present case. We therefore conclude that there are considerable deviations from the smooth, horizontally stratified ionosphere toward a more blobby structure. From the delay data presented in the slide, the blobs appear to have a dimension of roughly 3 km. Without going into a detailed analysis of blob intensity, the ratio of the electron concentration between blob maximum and blob minimum might be stated as one to two in the present case.

The further analysis of the data was done for the horizontally stratified ionosphere. Therefore, running means over height intervals of the size of the blob structures have been taken.

Possible Rocket Experiments

The setup of the Air Force electron-density experiment at Holloman Air Force Base as it has been developed in recent years seems to be very useful not only to measure the smooth ionosphere but also to study blobby structures in the order of 1 km or somewhat more. The measurements are made at five receiving sites on the ground. One of them gives essentially vertical transmissions through the ionosphere. The other four stations measure at considerable angles off the vertical. By combining the delay data from different aspects, one should be able to obtain a fairly good three-dimensional picture of the blob structure.

A complete analysis would have to go more or less through the following steps of procedure. Suppose data are available from one rocket experiment. This would mean ten different delay curves—five from the upward trajectory and five from the downward trajectory. Each curve would be smoothed and a corresponding electron-density vs altitude curve would be computed. The average of the ten electron-density curves would be considered as a first approximation to the horizontally stratified ionosphere. Now the ten delay curves from this idealized ionosphere would be computed and compared with the experimental delay curves. One probably will find that in the smoothing process some of the details of the horizontally stratified ionosphere have been lost. These details could be restored and a final approximation to the horizontally stratified ionosphere would be obtained. One could then study the deviations in the delay curves due to the blobby structure. Obviously it is not possible to obtain the blobs individually, since the network of stations at the ground is not sufficiently complete. However, it certainly will be possible to distinguish between randomly distributed isotropic blobs and blobs which are more nearly oblong and orientated in the direction of the magnetic field. In any case, average dimension and intensity of the blobs would be available.

So far, we have considered only pulse-delay data. In our experiment the pulse amplitude is measured also. This means that we have a kind of scintillation experiment. An evaluation of the amplitude data should provide a check for the time-delay data. However, they probably are more useful for the study of the finer structure of the ionosphere, a purpose for which the pulse-delay data might not have enough accuracy.

The interpretation of the scintillation experiment in the rocket is very similar to that of the radio-star scintillations or the fading experiment with a vertical sounder. The received signal is not due to a ray coming from a single direction, but rather to a superposition of a multiple number of waves arriving from a cone around a main direction. The interference of all these waves causes the scintillation. From the diffraction pattern on the ground, one can compute the so-called angular spread of the waves. The cause of the spread, of course, is the irregular structure of the propagating medium. Another quantity to be obtained from the scintillation experiment is the speed of fading. In the experiment with the vertical sounder the fading is entirely due to a motion of the propagation medium either in the form of drift or of turbulence. In the radio-star experiment the speed of fading can be influenced by the motion of the star across the sky. In the rocket experiment, however, the medium is almost stationary in the time to be considered and the fading is due to the motion of the rocket in a medium of local irregularities.

The scintillation experiment can be improved considerably if three closely spaced receivers are used in the ground, an arrangement which is familiar for drift measurements. But drift velocity and direction are only two of the parameters which can be obtained from this experiment. There are four more independent parameters which describe the diffraction pattern observed at the ground and which can be obtained from a first-order correlation analysis. They are the characteristic or turbulent velocity, the length of the major axis of the correlation ellipse, the ratio of the major to the minor axis, and the direction of the major axis. The last three parameters can be expressed also as corresponding parameters of the angular spread. Additionally, it is possible to determine the horizontal scale of the irregularities themselves, provided the relative-amplitude fluctuations on the ground are small enough. In case of the rocket experiment where the velocity of the vehicle is much higher than any other velocity, it probably is not possible to measure drift and turbulent velocity. But there should be no problem in measuring at least four parameters, provided the irregular structure changes slowly enough with the height.

We are planning to supplement our present rocket experiment with a three-receiver technique à la drift experiment. It is not necessary to go into further details, since at the present moment we are especially interested in experiments for a satellite and we have learned enough from the rocket experiment to be reasonably sure about what can be done with a satellite with respect to ionospheric irregularities.

Satellite Experiments

First of all, a principal disadvantage of the satellite in comparison with the rocket might be pointed out. In an experiment like ours, in which the effect of the medium on the propagation over a long path is observed, only the integrated effect can be measured unless (as in the rocket experiment) the path length changes in the direction of the propagation. The satellite stays essentially at the same height, and if measurements are made at a number of single locations only, it is not possible to determine the height of a layer of irregularities. On the other hand, it is obvious that a satellite can give us changes in irregularities in horizontal dimensions like the sizes of sporadic E clouds or the change of the character of the fine structure with latitude. The satellite also may pass over a certain area at different times of the day, thus allowing us to study diurnal variations of the irregular structure. The difficulty of the height determination can be overcome to a certain extent by observing the signal from the satellite simultaneously at widely spaced receiving stations on the ground; the more stations, the more complete and reliable the height information.

Let us consider now some details of a possible useful experiment for a satellite. Although any orbit would be suitable for this type of experiment, we will assume that the orbit goes over the poles and the subsolar point at a height slightly above the F2-layer height, that is, about 300 km. We choose a frequency for the transmitter in the satellite which is about the MUF 3000 for the ionosphere at the location of our observing point. Then we will "see" the transmitter at this frequency up to a distance of 1500 km, while the distance of ray optical visibility is 1900 km. This will give us a measurement of the maximum electron density of the ionosphere and the best possible accuracy in the delay-time data in the range of receptivity.

As in the rocket experiment, the delay time is measured between the pulse transmitted on the low frequency in the order of 20 mc/sec and a reference pulse transmitted on a much higher frequency. As the satellite passes by, the delay decreases from a high value to a minimum at the point of closest distance, and then increases again. The delay can be computed for a smooth ionosphere and deviations due to structure irregularities can be detected.

The best antenna for the satellite would be an arrangement of crossed dipoles so that the radiation in the direction of the receiving station is not a function of position and orientation of the satellite. A good antenna on the ground is also a crossed dipole which favors the ordinary of magneto-ionic components, since for vertical reception the two components would not be separated enough in time.

In order to obtain the desired height resolution of the irregular structure, at least a second receiving station is recommended. This station would be located best in the direction of the orbit; in our case, north-south. The distance between the two stations should be comparable with the height of the orbit, or about 300 km. Depending on the result of the first experiments, more receiving stations might be considered.

Supplementary to this pulse-delay experiment, a fading or scintillation experiment with three closely spaced receivers is recommended. This arrangement requires a recording of the received pulse amplitudes. In view of the high speed of the vehicle and of the resulting high speed of fading, it might be necessary to increase the pulse-repetition rate somewhat over the 600/sec rate, which is used presently in the beacon of the rocket experiment. It also is conceivable to perform an independent fading experiment with c-w or to combine this with a radio-star scintillation experiment. In any case, it is very desirable to supplement the measurement from the satellite at the same location with any of the familiar ground experiments for drift measurement. The time between transits of the satellite gives a good opportunity for having this done and a comparison between the different types of measurements is very valuable.

In all experiments of the three-receiver technique, the information obtained is a statistical description of the diffraction pattern on the ground. The diffraction pattern varies in character with the depth of penetration of the wave in the vertical-incidence experiment. The radio-star experiment could be considered as a limiting case of complete penetration. Now the diffraction pattern changes also with the angle of incidence against the vertical. In the satellite experiment, this angle of incidence changes rapidly within a few minutes and this fact opens the possibility of extending the two-dimensional correlation ellipse of the horizontal diffraction pattern into the third dimension. The inhomogeneities or scattering centers in the ionosphere are not isotropic, as can be demonstrated by the frequently observed elliptical shape of the correlation pattern on the ground. There is no reason to assume that the pattern in the vertical plane should be circular; on the contrary, a preferred direction along the lines of the magnetic field is expected.

A short outline of the general idea of the analysis might be of interest. The experiment consists of a variation of the angle of incidence on an irregular diffracting ionosphere. With variation of this angle the angular spread and the size of the correlation ellipse on the diffraction pattern on the ground are changed. If the frequency is high and the relative-amplitude fluctuations are small, the horizontal pattern of the irregularities themselves can be recognized in the diffraction pattern on the ground. This observation is independent of the angle of incidence. However, the amplitude fluctuations vary with the angle of incidence. The deepest fluctuations are observed if the wave is transmitted parallel to the major axis of the scattering blobs. The axis ratio can be found by comparing the maximum and minimum deepnesses of fluctuation. Of course, the assumption is made in the analysis that the blobs are statistically alike over the whole visible path of the satellite. Otherwise, more receiving stations along the path must be used.

Let me review briefly. The whole measuring system, as proposed, consists of a satellite with pulse transmitter at about 20 mc/sec and reference high-frequency beacon transmitter, a number of pairs of receiving stations spaced a few hundred kilometers apart in the north-south direction, each station being equipped for the pulse-delay and the fading experiments. To obtain good geographical coverage, one pair of receiving stations might be placed in the auroral zone, one at midlatitude, and one near the magnetic equator. Of course, the effort on the ground is considerable, but the information to be gained is not obtainable otherwise.

The most serious difficulties of the suggested experiments are, at present, the weight limitations in the satellite, and it is worthwhile looking into the possibility of using the existing telemetering transmitter in the satellite. If the frequency of this transmitter is sufficiently low, say perhaps 75 mc/sec, it should be possible to measure the effects of ionospheric irregularities in an experiment which observes amplitude or phase fluctuation at the ground. For planning purposes one might figure on a scale of 2 km for the ionospheric irregularities and on an average electron-density increase in the blobs of $10^4/cm^3$, values suggested by a preliminary analysis of rocket data. The standard deviation in angle of incidence caused by these blobs at 75 mc/sec is, according to a semi-empirical formula based on homogeneous spheres, $\sigma = (\Delta f_N{}^2/2f^2)^{0.84}$ radians or $\sigma = 19$ mils. The angular spread determined from fading experiments between 1 and 5 mc/sec can be expressed by a similar formula, $\sigma = 0.2f^{-1.68}$, where f is measured in mc/sec and σ in radians. If this formula is applied to 75 mc/sec, the result would be $\sigma = 7$ mils.

It is hoped that these data give the necessary information for equipment designers with respect to accuracy requirements and time constants.

32

Meteoric Bombardment

---

by Maurice Dubin
IONOSPHERIC PHYSICS LABORATORY,
GEOPHYSICS RESEARCH DIRECTORATE,
AIR FORCE CAMBRIDGE RESEARCH CENTER

ABSTRACT

An experiment for the detection of meteoric particles entering the earth's atmosphere is proposed for a projected earth satellite. A brief review of the research on meteors is made to point out the advantages of measurements made from a satellite. Such measurements would be of scientific importance in determining the role of interplanetary particles as related to the geophysics of the atmosphere, the structure of the ionosphere, sporadic E, noctilucent clouds, airglow, etc. Meteoric particles colliding with the satellite may also constitute a hazard affecting the reliability of other scientific experiments.

A method for measuring the influx of meteoric particles into the earth's atmosphere, based on the detection of the acoustical energy generated upon impacts, is described. This technique is reviewed with respect to feasibility, reliability, and sensitivity. Results from V-2 and Aerobee rocket firings using this approach are also presented. The acoustical method for the detection of meteoric particles seems promising as a means of extending our knowledge of the mass and density of interplanetary matter, and is therefore recommended as a satellite experiment.

292

Background

Interplanetary matter in collision with the atmosphere of the earth transfers the kinetic energy of motion relative to the earth into heat, light, and ionization.   These reactions are often detectable from the earth's surface and thereby measurements concerning the influx of meteors may be made.   The streaks of light from meteors may be observed visually and photographically, and in this manner the number, size, velocity, and radiants of meteors have been measured.   Radio methods for the measurement of reflections from the ionization trails of meteors have afforded a means of detecting and classifying meteors which are invisible during the daylight hours and are too small to be detected visually.   From visual and radio observations of meteors, a fundamental understanding of meteor physics has been achieved; numerous books and articles which review the state of knowledge on meteors are available.[1-5]

An idea of the dynamics of the interaction of meteors in the earth's atmosphere, the physical reactions occurring, the velocity distribution of particles, the daily accretion of meteoric material by the earth, and the size distribution and composition of the meteors is available and is briefly reviewed.

The composition of meteors varies considerably; some of the chief constituents as deduced from meteor spectra are calcium, nickel, iron, magnesium, manganese, chromium, and sodium.   Meteorites falling on the earth are classified in two contrasting types, the iron meteorites and the stony meteorites, based on their iron content.   Meteors may also be broadly classified as shower meteors and nonshower or sporadic meteors.   Shower meteors, it is believed, originated from disintegrated comets; hence, whenever the earth crosses such an orbit a shower, characterized by a particular radiant and meteor velocity, occurs.   Although visible effects from showers are rather spectacular, the total influx of meteoric material from sporadic meteors is far greater than that from shower meteors.   The mass density of the individual meteoroids is somewhat in doubt.   One may consider that from meteorite samples the density of the particles is about 3 or 4 gm/cm^3.   However, the theory of cometary origin of meteoric material from ices in comet tails and recent measurements at Harvard using the Baker Super-Schmidt cameras allow the possibility that the meteoric material has a density as small as one-twentieth gm/cm^3 and consists of a sponge-like, porous composite which may disintegrate upon entering the atmosphere.

It seems that all sporadic and nonsporadic meteors whose orbits have been measured belong to the solar system.   A meteoroid at the sun-earth distance has a heliocentric velocity of about 42 km/sec.   The velocity of approach of a meteor is its velocity relative to the earth. Since the earth has a velocity of 29 km/sec in its orbit around the sun, a meteor traveling with a velocity v with reference to the same system may appear to have a velocity within the range of $v \pm 29$ km/sec. Also, the gravitational potential of the earth sets the lower limit of velocity with which a particle may enter the upper atmosphere at about 11 km/sec. A particle belonging to the solar system and striking the earth head-on may have a velocity as great as 73 km/sec. Thus, the range of velocities of meteoric particles striking the earth is from 11 km/sec to 73 km/sec.

F. G. Watson[1] has integrated the estimated masses of all meteoric material falling upon the earth. He concluded that approximately a ton of extraterrestrial material per day is accumulated by the earth. These estimates were based on visual and radio measurements; an extrapolation down to very small particles was made on the assumption that the mass of material in each visual magnitude is a constant. The visual-magnitude system is based on luminosity step ratios of $(100)^{1/5}$ or 2.514, and relates to the fact that the luminous intensity of a meteor is proportional to the mass of the meteor.

Visual and radio methods of detection of meteors become insensitive for meteors of visual magnitude 10 or greater (less than 10^{-4} gm). For still smaller particles the term micrometeorite has been suggested by F. L. Whipple[6] because the large surface-to-mass ratio of these particles permits sufficiently rapid radiation of the interaction energy of the atmosphere so that the particle is stopped without serious physical changes. Particles of the size predicted by theory have been found on the earth. Evidence for a large influx of micrometeoritic material into the earth's atmosphere has been collected from measurements of zodiacal light, air pollution, and deep-sea sediments, and from rocket measurements. A daily accretion by the earth of about 1000 tons of material is indicated from these measurements. This accretion rate is not consistent with the extrapolation used by Watson, a problem requiring much further study and research.

Very small particles (visual magnitudes greater than 30) are probably removed from the solar system by the Poynting-Robertson effect. Order-of-magnitude estimates of the relationships between particle number, particle mass, visual magnitude, particle size, and line density of ionization produced are listed in Table I.[7]

Purpose of Experiment

Scientific information relative to meteoric bombardment is of importance to the fields of geophysics and astronautics, as well as astronomy. The influx of meteoric dust has been considered as a possible

TABLE I

Sporadic Meteors: Order-of-magnitude estimates of their mass, brightness, size, number, and the electron line density in their trails

	Mass (grams)	Visual Magnitude	Radius	Number of This Mass Swept up by the Earth Each Day	Electron Line Density (Electrons per Meter of Trail Length)
Particles reaching the ground	10^4	-12.5	8 cm	10	—
Particles totally disintegrated in the upper atmosphere	10^3	-10.0	4 cm	10^2	—
	10^2	-7.5	2 cm	10^3	—
	10	-5.0	0.8 cm	10^4	10^{18}
	1	-2.5	0.4 cm	10^5	10^{17}
	10^{-1}	0.0	0.2 cm	10^6	10^{16}
Approximate limit of radar measurements	10^{-2}	2.5	0.08 cm	10^7	10^{15}
	10^{-3}	5.0	0.04 cm	10^8	10^{14}
	10^{-4}	7.5	0.02 cm	10^9	10^{13}
	10^{-5}	10.0	0.008 cm	10^{10}	10^{12}
?	10^{-6}	12.5	40 μ	?	?
	10^{-7}	15.0	20 μ		
	10^{-8}	17.5	8 μ		
Micrometeorites	10^{-9}	20.0	4 μ	?	?
	10^{-10}	22.5	2 μ		
	10^{-11}	25.0	0.8 μ		
	10^{-12}	27.5	0.4 μ		
Particles removed from the solar system by radiation pressure	10^{-13}	30.0	0.2 μ		
	—	—	—		
	—	—	—		

cause of the nighttime layer and various forms[8] of sporadic E. Meteoric material may also effect the formation of noctilucent clouds observed at high latitudes. Evidence relating meteor shower activity to rainfall has been presented by Bowen.[9] Other effects associated with sodium emission, the airglow, the aurora, and forward-scattering radio propagation may also be related to the influx of meteoric material.

To predict, understand, and explain these phenomena, and to determine the possible hazard to a vehicle traveling above the protective barrier of the earth's atmosphere,[10] measurements of the density and size distribution of meteoric material in interplanetary space would be of value. Measurements of meteoric particles from a satellite vehicle are particularly desired because of the several advantages of utilizing a platform in space. Visual measurements are restricted to observing relatively large particles during the night; radio measurements are restricted to slightly smaller particles and are greatly limited by ionospheric disturbances. Both techniques require that a significant interaction with the atmosphere occur prior to detection on the ground. Neither ground-based method permits satisfactory measurements at various latitudes; a latitude effect is a distinct possibility.

In contrast, a meteoric-particle detector on a vehicle in a satellite orbit may measure the spatial distribution of meteoric material as well as latitude variations; measurement of the size distribution of meteoric material is also possible since a detector that is sensitive to the momentum of the impacts would yield an approximation of the mass distribution if a heliocentric velocity for the particles were assumed. Moreover, by comparison of the impact momentum with penetration and surface-impact data measured by laboratory methods, an idea of the possible hazards to vehicles at very high altitudes may be determined.

Experimental Approach

Methods of detection of interplanetary particles from an unmanned satellite are restricted. Visual observations, detection by electromagnetic induction from charges on the particles, and collection methods requiring recovery are hardly very practical. Impacts of meteoric material, however, result in a perturbing effect that affords a method of detection either by acceleration of the entire vehicle or by the generation of acoustical energy in the metallic skin of the vehicle. The detection of particles by impulses transmitted to an accelerometer located on the vehicle is recommended for large particles; however, the probability of collisions with large particles is so small that such measurements would be restricted to obtaining a figure for the probability of collision damage of the entire vehicle during a relatively long time, i.e., weeks or months. The acoustical method for the detection of particles down to very small sizes should be capable of detecting a fairly good sample of meteoric particles in a reasonable time, and is described as a possible initial experiment for a satellite vehicle.

The first measurements utilizing the acoustical technique were carried out under J. L. Bohn.[11] Ultrasonic acoustic energy detected by a crystal microphone and an amplifier in the region from 30 to 60 kc/sec could be associated with meteoric impacts upon the skin of a V-2 rocket for two separate flights. The acoustical apparatus had been installed in the V-2's to measure acoustical noise generated in the rocket during powered and free flight. In the cases where microphones were mounted flush with the skin of the rocket, impulses of a random and transient nature were detected during the Air Force V-2 flights of 8 December 1949 and 31 August 1950. These pulses were probably caused by meteoric impacts. Fig. 1 shows the altitude and time after take-off of the 66 pulses which occurred on V-2 No. 31 of 8 December 1949.

Equipment for detecting meteoric impacts was flown on an Aerobee rocket on 14 September 1955. The equipment consisted of an ADP crystal microphone mounted against a stainless-steel diaphragm 0.017 in.

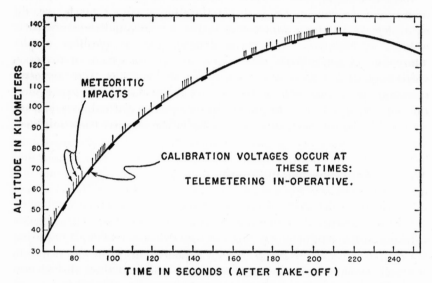

FIGURE 1. Possible meteoritic impacts. V-2 No. 31 8 Dec. 1949, U.S.A.F.

thick and approximately 25 in.^{2} in area. The microphone and amplifier had a peak at about 70 kc/sec, the latter had a 10-kc/sec band pass. The output to the amplifier was rectified by a circuit with a 1-millisecond time constant so that an impulse would be stored for telemetering. The amplifier output was limited to 5 volts into telemetering. In addition to the regular beacon telemetering system, a Bendix FM-FM telemetering transmitter with an output of 2 watts at 225 mc/sec was used. The Bendix unit was modulated by a 70-kc/sec sub-carrier oscillator. The amplifier telemetering unit, antenna, and power pack had a total weight of approximately 15 lb, since the design was intended for use with the small Deacon-Nike type rockets of limited payload. The microphone and associated amplifier, independent of the telemetering system, have a combined weight of about 5 lb. A transistorized version of the amplifier would reduce this weight considerably; the microphone itself weighs about 5 oz.

A sensitivity calibration of the equipment was carried out in an elementary manner. Sand was graded according to size, using a set of sieves. The diameter of the sand samples used for testing ranged from about 4000 microns to less than 100 microns. The graded sand was dropped upon the rocket skin diaphragm from a height of about 2 cm, and the relative over-all response of the system was recorded. The sensitivity of the system was such that sand particles of about 200 microns diameter falling from a height of 2 cm would produce a signal of about 2 volts at the amplifier output. Since the impulse to the system is momentum dependent, for a rocket traveling at about Mach one, the equivalent sensitivity would be such that a 2-micron-diameter particle would give approximately a 2-volt deflection at the amplifier output. Thus, for micrometeorites decelerated in the atmosphere, particles of visual magnitude +15 would produce a 2-volt deflection. For the rocket traveling above the atmosphere, the relative velocity of impact is of the order of 20 km/sec. At these velocities particles of visual magnitude +20 to +25 would produce a 2-volt pulse at the output of the amplifier. Since the amplifier and telemeter transmitter will detect down to noise level, an amplifier output pulse as low as 0.1 volt is still measurable. Accordingly, it seems that the acoustical method for detection of meteoric particles may be sensitive enough to reach the Poynting-Robertson limit in the detection of interplanetary particles.

A test of the acoustical system was also carried out for collisions with the rocket skin at points remote from the center of the diaphragm. For a fixed impulse the signal falls off exponentially with distance from the microphone. However, signals may be obtained from the tip and base of the rocket cone. The acoustical energy is transmitted through the rocket skin to the diaphragm, which seems to act as a sounding-board. Thus, as a satellite experiment, the entire surface of the satellite would be sensitive to the detection of meteoric impacts.

The equipment flown on 14 September 1955 operated satisfactorily during the entire flight. Although recovery was poor, the telemetered signal was received during the entire flight up to tail separation. The rocket failed to reach predicted altitude; peak altitude was 100 km, which is too low an altitude to permit the detection of small meteoric particles that have not been slowed down by the atmosphere. A sample section of the telemetering record has been included (Figs. 2 and 3).

Of interest also is the understanding of the physics of high-velocity impacts of particles with surfaces. Experimental information on impact effects at the velocities of meteoric particles is practically nonexistent; yet it is fundamental to the determination of the hazard to satellite vehicles from meteoric particles. Whereas large particles may penetrate the outer skin of the vehicles, small particles may produce a sputtering action which may adversely affect optical and solar battery surfaces.

Information about the number and strength of impacts, as well as the physical effect of the impacts, is necessary to evaluate the problem satis-

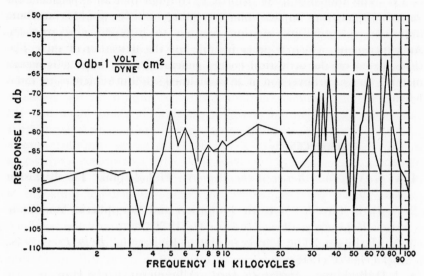

FIGURE 2.   Free-field calibration of ADP crystal microphone.

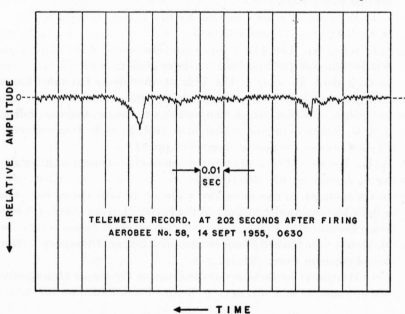

FIGURE 3.   Meteoritic-impact record.

factorily. Grimminger[10] and Whipple[12] have reviewed the probability of collision and penetration by meteorites. Their values for the penetrating probabilities from meteoroids remain a good approximation until additional experimental data are forthcoming.

It seems therefore quite realistic to consider that an experiment for detecting meteoric impacts on a satellite vehicle would contribute important scientific information relating to interplanetary particles. An experiment, which appears feasible for the detection of these particles, based on the acoustical energy generated upon impact, is recommended for an early version of an unmanned satellite vehicle using radio telemetry.

REFERENCES

1. F. G. Watson. *Between the Planets.* Philadelphia: The Blakiston Co., 1941.
2. A. C. B. Lovell, "Meteoric Ionization and Ionospheric Abnormalities," *Rept. Prog. Phys., 11:* 415–444 (1948).
3. N. Herlofson, "The Theory of Meteor Ionization," *Rept. Prog. Phys., 11:* 444–454 (1948).
4. J. D. Buddhue. *Meteoritic Dust.* Albuquerque: The Univ. of New Mexico Press, 1950.
5. F. L. Whipple, "Meteors and the Earth's Upper Atmosphere," *Rev. of Mod. Physics, 15:* 246–264 (1943).
6. F. L. Whipple, "The Theory of Micro-Meteorites," *Proc. Natl. Acad. Sci., 36:* 687–695 (1950); *ibid., 37:* 19–30 (1951).
7. O. G. Villard, Jr., *et al.,* "The Role of Meteors in Extended-Range VHF Propagation," *Proc. IRE, 43:* 1473 (1955).
8. M. Dubin. In *Meteors, A Symposium on Meteor Physics.* Edited by J. R. Kaiser as Special Supplement (vol. 2) to *J. Atm. and Terr. Phys.* London: Pergamon Press, 1955, pp. 111–118.
9. E. G. Bowen, "The Influence of Meteoritic Dust on Rainfall," *Austr. J. Phys., 6:* 490–497 (1953).
10. G. Grimminger, "Probability that a Meteorite Will Hit or Penetrate a Body Situated in the Vicinity of the Earth," *J. Appl. Phys., 19:* 947–956 (1948).
11. M. Dubin. In *Rocket Exploration of the Upper Atmosphere.* London: Pergamon Press, 1954, p. 26.
12. F. L. Whipple. In *Physics and Medicine of the Upper Atmosphere.* Albuquerque: The Univ. of New Mexico Press, 1952, pp.. 137–170.

33

Measurements of Interplanetary Dust

by S. F. Singer
UNIVERSITY OF MARYLAND

ABSTRACT

A simple theory is developed for the motion of charged interplanetary dust particles in the vicinity of the earth. We take up:
1) The average charge of dust particles
2) Day-night effect
3) Solar-flare effects
4) The resultant rigidity spectrum
5) Motion in the geomagnetic and gravitational field;
   Liouville's theorem
6) Trapped orbits and storage of particles
7) Streams and impact zones
8) Magnetic-storm effects.
These considerations are then applied to possible experimental tests in rockets or satellites:
1) Dependence of dust-particle flux on geomagnetic latitude
2) Geophysical implications of latitude dependence
3) Diurnal variation of intensity
4) Electromagnetic conditions in the vicinity of the earth;
variation of particle flux and anisotropy.
Some suggestions are made for resolving the discrepancy
between meteor data and optical measurements of interplanetary
dust-particle densities. The problem of dust-particle accretion is
briefly considered.

301

Introduction

The purpose of this paper is to develop some aspects of the hypothesis that particles of interplanetary* dust carry an electric charge and are therefore affected by electric and magnetic fields as well as by gravity and radiation pressure. If this hypothesis is true, study of interplanetary dust can give us a great deal of new information on the electromagnetic conditions of IP space. We will be particularly interested in developing those consequences which are capable of direct observations by means of rocket or satellite vehicles above the earth's atmosphere, including such phenomena as a possible variation of intensity with geomagnetic latitude, anisotropies and diurnal variations, and the effects of solar flares and magnetic storms, seasonal variation, etc.

The present paper was written at this time mainly to provide a stimulus to observations. It gives only a very *preliminary* account of a simple charged-dust theory. In particular, owing to lack of time, it has not been possible to explore the extensive literature on interplanetary dust. I am aware only of the discussion on charged dust in Alfvén's book *On the Origin of the Solar System*[1] and the brief statement in a paper by Spitzer and Savedoff.[2]

Physical Ideas about Dust Particles

We wish to say something about the size, density, and other physical properties of dust particles and about their distribution in the solar system. Not much is known. From optical observations of the F-corona and the zodiacal light van de Hulst,[3] Allen,[4] Blackwell,[5] Behr and Siedentopf,[6] and Elsässer[7] derived some ideas of the size distribution and of the spatial distribution of dust. The accretion of dust by the sun due to the Poynting-Robertson effect has been discussed by Whipple.[8] De Jager[9] has discussed accretion by the earth. Neither author considers the charge of the dust particle and electromagnetic forces.

In all cases there appears a discrepancy of a factor 10^3–10^4 (first noted by van de Hulst) between the dust density from optical data and the density as derived from an extrapolation of visual and radio meteor observations. Whipple[10] has reviewed various lines of evidence, including rocket observations by Bohn and Nadig[11] and by Burnight, leading to a space density of 1 particle in about 10^7 cm^3.

Little is known about the mass density of the particles. It may be as high as 8 gm/cm^3 if their origin is due to the pulverization of meteorites as has been suggested by Piotrowski.[12] On the other hand, Whipple[8] in particular has discussed a cometary origin for dust particles, mainly to ac-

---

*Abbreviated as IP in the following text.

count for their rapid removal by the Poynting-Robertson effect. His icy conglomerate model or Öpik's[13] dust-ball model would lead to much lower densities. We may estimate ρ_D as low as 0.1 gm/cm³, or even 0.01.

We also need some information on the shape of the dust particles. The charge distribution and capacity depend on it. It may be possible to determine some more about the shape from refined optical measurements,[14] but for the present we will assume the particles to be spherical.

The dielectric properties are important inasmuch as they affect the charge distribution. It is safe to regard the surface of the particle as an equipotential. We will neglect structure and assume the capacity given by the radius. The mechanical strength of the dust particle sets an upper limit to its charge. In the Appendix we show that we are well below the point where Coulomb forces would break up the particle.

It would be desirable to know more about the optical properties of the dust, its albedo for example, as well as its photoelectric properties, including work function W and quantum yield γ. We will have to make somewhat crude assumptions, e.g., $\gamma \sim 1$ in the far ultraviolet.

Sample Calculation of Magnetic Rigidity (*Momentum/Charge*)

We will determine $R \equiv M_D v / Q_D$ for an average dust particle having the following properties:

$$a = 10^{-4} \text{ cm}, \ \rho_D = 0.1 \text{ gm/cm}^3$$

$$M_D = \tfrac{4}{3}\pi a^3 \rho = \tfrac{4}{3}\pi (10^{-4})^3 \ 0.1 \sim 4 \times 10^{-13} \text{ gm}$$

$$C_D = 10^{-4} \text{ cm (esu)}.$$

We will assume a potential V_D of 120 volts = 0.4 statvolt; then

$$Q_D = 10^{-4} \times 0.4 = 4 \times 10^{-5} \text{ statcoul},$$

or

$$\frac{4 \times 10^{-5}}{4.8 \times 10^{-10}} e \sim 8 \times 10^4 e.$$

We will assume a velocity of 10 km/sec, which is about escape velocity. Then $Mv = 4 \times 10^{-13} \times 10^6 = 4 \times 10^{-7}$ gm-cm/sec, and we have:

$$M = \frac{4 \times 10^{-13}}{1.67 \times 10^{-24}} = 2.5 \times 10^{11} \text{ proton masses} = 2.3 \times 10^{20} \text{ ev}$$

$$p = m\beta c = 2.3 \times 10^{20} \times \left(\frac{10^6}{c}\right) \sim 8 \times 10^{15} \text{ ev}/c$$

$$\text{K.E.} = \tfrac{1}{2}m\beta^2 c^2 = \tfrac{1}{2} \times (2.3 \times 10^{20}) \left(\frac{10^6}{c}\right)^2 = 1.3 \times 10^{11} \text{ ev}$$

$$R = \frac{pc}{Ze} = \frac{8 \times 10^{15}}{8 \times 10^4} = 10^{11} \text{ volts}.$$

The latter is a rigidity which is comparable to 5.96×10^{10} volts, below which geomagnetic effects occur.

Calculation of Charge

We will consider two processes: (1) photoelectric emission of electrons and (2) electron accretion from the interplanetary gas.

1) *Photoelectric Emission*

Solar ultraviolet and X-ray photons will liberate photoelectrons; assume the particle has an equilibrium potential V_{eq}, and let N_v be the photon flux per cm^2 per sec with energy $eV \geq eV_{eq} + W$.

The rate of liberation of photoelectric charge is

$$\frac{dQ_{ph}}{dt} = N_v \pi a^2 \gamma e. \tag{1}$$

If we assume N_v of the form* $fV^{-\nu}$,

$$\frac{dQ_{ph}}{dt} = \gamma f \pi a^2 e V^{-\nu}. \tag{1'}$$

2) *Electron Accretion*

This is a complicated problem since the rate of electron accretion depends on n_e, V_D, T_e, and v_{DG} (the velocity of the dust particle relative to the IP gas). We will discuss two extreme cases first:

(a) v_{DG} *very large.*—The particle will sweep up a volume $\pi a^2 v_{DG}$ per sec, so that

$$\left(-\frac{dQ}{dt}\right) = e n_e \pi a^2 v_{DG} \frac{1}{n} \quad \text{(contribution of some ions which stick).} \tag{2}$$

As we shall see later that v_{DG} cannot remain large for very long.

(b) $v_{DG} \sim 0.$—The particle will now collect electrons from a sphere of radius d. The precise calculation of d would involve us in the problems of Coulomb field cut-off treated by Cowling and by Spitzer for the conductivity problem; in view of other large uncertainties it will be sufficient to obtain d from the equality

$$eV_d = eV_D \frac{a}{d} = \frac{3}{2} kT_e. \tag{3}$$

$$\therefore d = \frac{2eV_D a}{3kT_e}. \tag{4}$$

---

*At the earth's orbit. At any other distance from the sun $f' = f$ (distance)$^{-2}$, where distance is measured in astronomical units.

We must treat the following situation: the electrons can have very appreciable thermal velocities and many will therefore describe hyperbolic orbits. For these we can calculate a capture cross section σ. However, electrons at the low-energy tail of the Maxwell distribution, whose kinetic energy is less than eV, will describe bound orbits. Some of these may also intersect the dust particle; this fraction can again be calculated from our

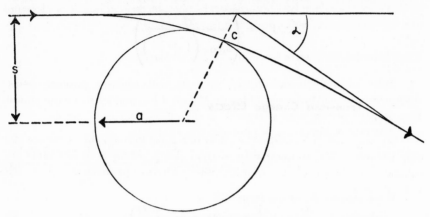

FIGURE 1. Diagram showing parameters entering into trajectory of an electron in the Coulomb field of a charged dust particle.

expression for σ. But a bound electron behaves unlike a captured one: it will screen the particle's external Coulomb field, but it will also present a space-charge repulsion field to a photoelectron from the particle.

To calculate σ, we consider the trajectory of a scattered electron. The Rutherford formula

$$\tan \frac{\alpha}{2} = \frac{1}{s} \frac{Qq}{4\pi\epsilon_0} \frac{1}{mv^2} \tag{5}$$

can be written as

$$\tan \frac{\alpha}{2} = \frac{C}{s}$$

where

$$C \equiv \frac{Qq}{4\pi\epsilon_0} \frac{1}{mv^2}.$$

The cross section*

$$\sigma = \pi a^2 \left(1 + \frac{2C}{a}\right). \tag{6}$$

(c) In general there will be a relative drift v_{DG} between particle and gas, or we may talk of a streaming of the gas. We will then consider that the rate of electron accretion is given by (2), but with σ replacing πa^2, i.e.,

$$\left(-\frac{dQ}{dt}\right)_a = en_e\sigma v_{DG} = en_e\pi a^2 v_{DG} \left(1 + \frac{2C}{a}\right). \tag{7}$$

In expression (7), C depends on V_D as well as T_e.

---

*I thank Dr. M. Galli for some important discussion and for deriving this expression.

Calculation of V_{eq}

To calculate V_{eq} for appreciable values of V_{DG}, we equate (1') and (7):

$$\gamma f \pi a^2 V_{eq}^{-\nu} = n_e \pi a^2 v_{DG} \left(1 + \frac{2C}{a}\right)$$

$$\therefore V_{eq} = \left(\frac{\gamma f}{n_e v_{DG} \left(1 + \dfrac{2C}{a}\right)}\right)^{1/\nu}. \tag{8}$$

Transient Charge Effects

We may wish to consider the effect of a solar flare on the charge of the dust particle. The simplest way to treat this problem is to introduce an enhancement factor η into the ultraviolet radiation to make it $\eta f V^{-\nu}$. In general, then,

$$\frac{dQ}{dt} = k \frac{dV}{dt} = \eta \gamma f V^{-\nu} \pi a^2 e - \left(\frac{dQ}{dt}\right)_a. \tag{9}$$

This equation not only describes the solar-flare effect, but also day-night effects. If, e.g., the particle goes into the earth's shadow, the first term on the right-hand side of (9) becomes zero.

Dynamics of Dust Particles

We will list and discuss the forces acting on the dust particle:
1) Gravitational
2) Radiation pressure
3) Friction with interplanetary gas
4) Electromagnetic.

We will be considering particles mainly in the vicinity of the earth's orbit and will neglect the Poynting-Robertson effect, and also changes in the physical condition of the particle, such as evaporation. With reasonable albedo values the temperature will be quite low.

1) *Gravitational Force Due to the Sun (at Earth's Orbit)*

$$\frac{GM.\,m}{r^2} = \frac{6.67 \times 10^{-11} \times 1.98 \times 10^{30} \text{ kg}}{(1.5 \times 10^{11} \text{ m})^2} \cdot \frac{4}{3} \pi a^3 \rho$$

$$= 7.8 \times 10^{-3} \pi a^3 \rho \text{ newtons.}$$

2) Radiation Force

We will give an order-of-magnitude estimate:

The incoming momentum/sec $= \int_0^\infty n_\nu \frac{h\nu}{c} d\nu \cdot \pi a^2.$ (10)

Some of the photons are absorbed, some diffusely reflected, some eject photoelectrons. The total force is ~ 1.5 times the integral, according to a rough estimate.

A numerical estimate: assume all photons at a given frequency, ν_0:

$$\text{Force} = 1.5 \frac{1400 \text{ watts/m}^2}{h\nu_0} \frac{h\nu_0}{c} \pi a^2$$

$$= 1.5 \times 4.6 \times 10^{-6} \pi a^2 \sim 7 \times 10^{-6} \pi a^2 \text{ newtons}.$$

In comparing (1) and (2) we can look at their ratio $(1)/(2) \sim a\rho 10^3$; with $a \sim 10^{-6}$ m, the density must be $\sim 10^3$ kg/m^3 (i.e., spec. grav. ~ 1) in order to make $(1) \sim (2)$.

3) Gas Friction

We can approach this problem from a continuum (plasma) theory, or we can consider individual particle interactions. We can neglect here the momentum transfers due to ions because of their higher mass; electrons are either captured or scattered. Thus the total momentum transferred per second is

$$F_{DG} = n_e v_{DG} \sigma \cdot m_e v_{DG} + \int_{s_0}^d 2\pi s ds \cdot n_e v_{DG} \cdot m_e v_{DG}(1 - \cos \alpha)$$

$$= n_e m_e v_{DG}^2 \left[\sigma + 2\pi \int_{s_0}^d (1 - \cos \alpha) s ds \right]. \quad (11)$$

Here $\pi s_0^2 = \sigma$.

Using equation (5), we find $(1 - \cos \alpha) = \dfrac{2}{(s/C)^2 + 1}$, and the integral I becomes

$$I = \int_{s_0}^d \frac{2s ds}{(s/C)^2 + 1} = C^2 \log \left[(s/C)^2 + 1 \right] \Big|_{s_0}^d.$$

Using equation (4),

$$I = C^2 \log \left[\frac{\dfrac{a^2}{C^2}\left(\dfrac{4e^2 V_D^2}{9k^2 T_e^2}\right) + 1}{\dfrac{a^2(1 + 2C/a)}{C^2} + 1} \right] \quad (12)$$

$$\therefore F_{DG} = n_e m_e v_{DG}^2 \{ \sigma + 2\pi C^2 \log [\quad] \}. \quad (13)$$

We can now give a semi-quantitative discussion of the motion between gas and dust, i.e., essentially v_{DG}. There is seen to exist a large frictional force mainly between the electrons of the plasma and the dust particle so that after a time τ the dust particle shares the motion of the gas, and $v_{DG} \sim 0$. To consider the matter in greater detail, one must calculate this "relaxation time" τ. The frictional force depends strongly on v_{DG}, but also on the charge of the dust particle; the charge in turn will change with a change in v_{DG}, since $(-dQ/dt)_a$ is a function of v_{DG}. We will see later that the value of τ depends very strongly on whether or not the plasma carries a magnetic field.

The value of the relaxation time is important in the following connection: the IP gas will in general be turbulent; the important scale of this turbulence depends probably on the sunspot cycle since emission of high-velocity gas from the sun will produce turbulence. If τ is very large, the dust particle will never catch up to the gas velocity, so that $\overline{v_{DG}^2}$ may be quite large with resultant effects on the average particle charge. On the whole, however, the particle will share the large-scale gas motion. We will later examine some observable consequences of this statement.

FIGURE 2.   The motion of a charged dust particle in a moving cloud of ionized gas which is polarized by a magnetic field frozen into the gas.

4) *Electromagnetic Forces*

We may consider the force

$$\vec{F}_{EM} = Q(\vec{E} + \vec{v} \times \vec{B}).$$

In MKS units; a magnetic flux density of 10^{-4} gauss $= 10^{-8}$ weber/m². If we take $v \sim 10^4$ m/sec and $Q \sim 8 \times 10^4 e \sim 1.3 \times 10^{-14}$ coul,

$$F_{EM} = 1.3 \times 10^{-14}(E + 10^4 \times 10^{-8}) \sim 10^{-18} \text{ newtons,}$$

assuming E to be zero. This may be compared with (1) and (2), which are seen to be quite larger. But if the particle moves with a velocity of 1000 km/sec and $B \sim 10^{-3}$ gauss, $F_{EM} \sim 10^{-15} nt$ and is quite comparable to (1) and (2).

We now consider what happens when a dust particle experiences a moving magnetic field, carried by an ionized streaming gas. It will then also experience the polarization field of the stream $E_{pol} = \vec{v} \times \vec{H}$. Under the influence of the combined electric and magnetic field the particle, independent of its charge, now drifts parallel to $\vec{v}$ until it reaches a velocity $\vec{v}$.

We see therefore that solar corpuscular streams are very efficient indeed in clearing the region around the sun of dust particles. This action will reduce the rate of accretion of dust by the sun. The dust can be pushed out quite far, depending on the energy density of the stream. The dust may then slowly return under the influence of the Poynting-Robertson effect.

It becomes then of some importance to estimate as accurately as possible the *"sweep-out effect."* We should also look experimentally, both optically and with rockets, for decreases in the dust-particle density following periods of strong solar activity.

The Rigidity Spectrum

Magnetic rigidity which determines the particle motion in a magnetic field is defined as momentum/total charge.

$$R = \frac{Mv}{Q} = \frac{4}{3} \pi a^3 \rho v \left(\frac{1}{C_D V} \right), \tag{14}$$

where V is the potential of the particle.

We will now assume that the particles have a unique velocity; due to the Poynting-Robertson effect they will travel in nearly circular orbits. (But this velocity may be different from the earth's orbital velocity.)

We will now assume a particle-size spectrum of the form

$$n(a) \, da = ga^{-\Gamma} \, da.$$

We also assume $C_D = \epsilon a$ and V independent of a. The rigidity as a function of a becomes

$$R = \frac{4}{3} \pi \frac{v}{V} \frac{\rho}{\epsilon} a^2$$

$$dR = \left(\frac{4}{3} \pi \frac{\rho}{\epsilon} \frac{v}{V} \right) 2a \, da;$$

therefore we rewrite $n(a)da = ga^{-(\Gamma+1)}a \, da$ and have

$$n(R) \, dR = g \left(\frac{R}{\frac{4}{3} \pi \frac{\rho}{\epsilon} \frac{v}{V}} \right)^{-(\Gamma+1)/2} \left(\frac{dR}{\frac{8}{3} \pi \frac{\rho}{\epsilon} \frac{v}{V}} \right)$$

$$n(R) \, dR = DR^{-\delta} \, dR \tag{15}$$

where

$$\delta \equiv \frac{\Gamma + 1}{2} \quad \text{and} \quad D \equiv \frac{3gV\epsilon}{8\pi\rho v}\left(\frac{4}{3}\pi\frac{\rho}{\epsilon}\frac{v}{V}\right)^{\delta}.$$

Latitude Dependence of Dust-Particle Flux

We must now discuss the motion of the particle in the earth's magnetic field. This is an exceedingly difficult point; only for the motion in a perfect dipole field, with the momentum as a constant of the motion, can we apply some of the results of the geomagnetic theory of Störmer. In our case, however, the momentum is not a constant of the motion (1) because of the effects of the earth's gravitational field, and (2) because of possibility of collisions with gas molecules, both elastic and inelastic, and scatterinig.

We can assume that (2) can be neglected beyond several hundred kilometers from sea level. Most deflections (at large impact parameter) will be small and reorient the particle trajectory by at most 1° or so of latitude. We neglect the effects of the magnetic field so near the earth, except for very complicated trajectories which occur near the cut-off rigidity.

Objection (1) may be serious, and may require us to carry through numerical orbit integrations.* Another possibility would be to introduce a geoelectric field in the model experiments of Brunberg and Rattner, and of Bennett,[15] to simulate the $1/r^2$ gravitational field.

It may be possible to neglect (1) to a rough approximation. We will assume that it is permissible, although it should be checked by numerically integrating trajectories. We recall that there may be an appreciable streaming velocity of the particles with respect to the earth, because of the gas motion. Hence, the additional influence of the earth would not change the momentum as severely as in the case of a particle falling in from rest. Another way of looking at the situation is to see at what distance the (1) magnetic acceleration exceeds the (2) gravitational acceleration.

$$(1) \quad \frac{Q \cdot (\vec{v} \times \vec{B})}{m} = \frac{Qv}{m} \frac{B_{\text{sea level}}}{r^3} R_E^3.$$

$$(2) \quad \frac{GM_E}{r^2} = \frac{g_{\text{sea level}}}{r^2} R_E^2.$$

The ratio

$$\frac{(1)}{(2)} = \frac{Qv}{m} \frac{B_{SL}}{g_{SL}}\left(\frac{R_E}{r}\right).$$

This is equal to 1 for

$$\frac{r}{R_E} = \frac{Qv}{m} \frac{B_{SL}}{g_{SL}}. \tag{16}$$

---

*C. Störmer has worked on the theory of this problem. See his recent book on *The Polar Aurora* (London and New York: Oxford University Press, 1955), p. 346.

Taking our numerical example again,

$$\frac{r}{R_E} = \frac{1.3 \times 10^{-14} \times 10^4 \text{ m/sec} \times 0.3 \times 10^{-4} \text{ w/m}^2}{4 \times 10^{-16} \text{ kg} \times 9.8 \text{ m/sec}^2}.$$

This happens to turn out to be exactly 1, so that in our numerical example the gravitational effects are important and must be carefully considered. At large distances ($\sim 10R_E$ or more) we may be able to neglect the magnetic forces.

We will now treat the case where the gravitational field can be neglected. A simple result is then obtained from the Störmer theory, giving the cut-off rigidity in the vertical direction as a function of latitude in terms of the value at $\lambda = 0°$.

$$R_c(\lambda) = R(0°) \cos^4 \lambda. \tag{17}$$

In the present discussion we will completely neglect the refinements important in cosmic-ray theory, such as the main cone, shadow cone, and penumbra. $R(0°)$ is

$$15 \times 10^9 \text{ volt} = 50 \, \frac{\text{kg m}}{\text{sec-coul}}.$$

The dependence of directional flux on latitude (in vertical direction) is

$$J_\lambda(0°) = \int_{R_c(\lambda)}^{\infty} n(R) \, dR = \int_{R_c(\lambda)}^{\infty} D R^{-\delta} \, dR$$

$$= \frac{D}{\delta+1} \, R^{-\delta+1} \Big|_{R_c(\lambda)}^{\infty} = \frac{D}{(\delta-1)} \, [R_c(\lambda)]^{-\delta+1}$$

$$= \frac{D}{(\delta-1)} \, [R(0°) \cos^4 \lambda]^{-(\delta-1)}. \tag{18}$$

Motion under Combined Magnetic and Gravitational Field; Liouville's Theorem

It is of importance to determine not only the trajectory of the dust particle in the combined fields, but also the intensity of particles. In general, the intensity near the earth will not be the same as at large distances. To determine the change, we apply Liouville's theorem from statistical mechanics. It states that along a trajectory the phase space density D of particles will remain constant, i.e., the number of points in the six-dimensional volume element is conserved.

$$D = \frac{\delta N}{\delta V},$$

where $\delta V = dx \, dy \, dz \, d\pi_x \, d\pi_y \, d\pi_z$, where $\vec{\pi} = \vec{p} + (e/c)\vec{A}$. We can use the ordinary momenta in spherical coordinates and express

$$\delta V = dx\, dy\, dz\; (d\Omega p^2 dp).$$

The differential directional intensity j is the number of particles in momentum interval dp at p, crossing area dA in a solid angle $d\Omega$ in a given direction per time dt

$$j = v\,\frac{dN}{dx\, dy\, dz\; dp\; d\Omega}.$$

Taking $(dx\, dy) = (dA)$ and $dz = v dt$, we have

$$j = \frac{p^3}{m}\, D. \tag{19}$$

In the gravitational field we have the following relation: let p_0 be the initial momentum (at $r = \infty$), then

$$\frac{p^2}{2m} = \frac{p_0^2}{2m} + \frac{GM_e m}{r} \tag{20}$$

$$\therefore j(r) = \frac{D}{m}\left[p_0^2 + \frac{2GM_e m^2}{r}\right]^{3/2}. \tag{21}$$

D is of course the phase space density which remains constant. It is proportional to the configuration space density in regions where p does not change.

Observable Latitude Dependence

It may turn out that at a particular latitude the minimum rigidity is not set by the geomagnetic field but by the sensitivity of the detector. We will therefore calculate the momentum and kinetic energy of a dust particle.

We have: $p = RQ$; at the equator $p_0 = 50Q$ kg-m-sec^{-1}.

If we again assume $Q \sim 80{,}000\, e = 1.3 \times 10^{-14}$ coul, then

$$p_{\min}(0°) = 6.4 \times 10^{-13} \text{ kg-m-sec}^{-1}$$

and

$$E_{\min} = \frac{p^2}{2m} = \frac{(6.4 \times 10^{-13})^2}{2 \times \frac{4}{3}\pi\rho a^3}.$$

Detection

Are they detectable? We will assume that we use a (highly idealized) condenser microphone to detect the impact of the dust particle.

We take the plate to be 0.02×0.02 m in area, and 10^{-4} m thick. Its density is 2000 kg/m^3. Therefore, its mass $= 8 \times 10^{-5}$ kg.

After impact, therefore, it acquires a velocity

$$\frac{6.4 \times 10^{-13}}{8 \times 10^{-5}} = 8 \times 10^{-9} \text{ m/sec.}$$

We consider that a detectable pulse is produced if the plate moves 1 micron (changing the capacity by perhaps $\frac{1}{2}\%$); this will require $\sim 10^{-3}$ sec and could be conveniently amplified using standard electronic techniques.

Geophysical Implications

We now develop various considerations in which dust particles either produce geophysical effects or act as indicators of electromagnetic fields in the environment of the earth. These considerations can often be treated using geomagnetic theory, and in some cases we find their analogy in the field of cosmic rays.

Dust Density and Total Influx

Some suggestions can now be made regarding the discrepancy between dust-particle densities deduced from optical measurement and from measurements of influx to the earth. A calculation of the influx must consider the possible effect of the earth's magnetic field. It is seen that there enters an accessibility factor which specifies, for each particle rigidity, the accessible fraction of the earth's surface. Measurement of a latitude dependence of J_λ will give the required data for such a calculation.

Auroral Effects

As a consequence of their interaction with the geomagnetic field and because of their general anisotropy (dust is concentrated in the plane of the ecliptic), low-rigidity (<5 kg-m-sec^{-1}-coul^{-1}) dust can arrive only in the auroral zones. Depending on their number, they may carry an appreciable amount of energy into the upper atmosphere and contribute to the various geophysical effects peculiar to the auroral zone.

Anisotropy, Diurnal Variation

We will now examine some immediate consequences of the fact that the dust particles may enter the region of the earth still carrying the velocity of the interplanetary gas.

1) If this gas is streaming with respect to the earth (and there is no reason

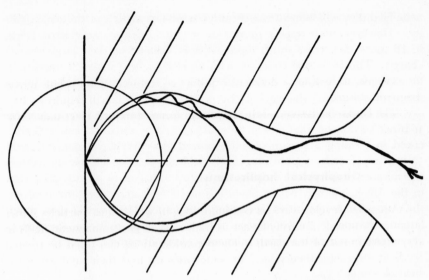

FIGURE 3. Schematic diagram showing the $Q\gamma$-space for $\gamma \lesssim -1$, for low rigidity dust particles; and the trajectory of a charged dust particle. The shaded regions are not allowed because of the dipole field of the earth.

to believe that the gas in the earth's orbit moves at 30 km/sec), we will observe an anisotropy (hence a diurnal intensity variation) of the dust although complicated by the geomagnetic field. (See discussion on motions above.)

2) During periods of emission of solar corpuscular streams, dust particles may achieve very high velocities directed approximately radially outward from the sun. This should lead to the incidence of a beam of high-rigidity particles which would be well defined and lead to observation of a more striking anisotropy.

Impact Zones

In general, a definite anisotropy such as produced by a parallel dust stream with respect to the earth will result in there being definite regions of precipitation. These can be investigated by calculating detailed trajectories; they will be prominent for low rigidities, of the order of 5–20 kg-m-sec^{-1}-coul^{-1}, and at intermediate latitudes and low latitudes.

Magnetic-Storm Effects

Dust particles have a peculiar advantage for investigating electromagnetic conditions in interplanetary space. With respect to a static magnetic field they will behave exactly as a cosmic-ray particle of the same rigidity. However, with respect to moving magnetic fields, i.e., electric fields, in IP space they react much more strongly because of their large electric charge. This increased coupling with an electric field makes it important, for example, to look for a different behavior of cosmic rays and dust during magnetic storms.

The cosmic radiation often exhibits large decreases, $\sim$ several percent. It is not certain to what extent these are caused by the deceleration experienced in crossing a stream of solar ionized gas carrying a magnetic field (à la Alfvén) or by a pure magnetic shielding effect which merely reduces the number of particles reaching the earth.[16] It can be readily seen that in the Alfvén picture, where potentials of 10^8 volt and more are involved, the dust-particle intensities [according to equation (19)] would show much larger variations.* It would seem then that dust particles can be used as very sensitive indicators of interplanetary electrodynamics.

APPENDIX
Maximum Charge of a Dust Particle

We will investigate the stability of a dust particle against breakup. We will assume that its charge Q is divided into two parts separated by one radius length a.

The Coulomb force

$$F = \frac{Q^2/4}{\epsilon_0 4\pi a^2} = \frac{Q^2}{\dfrac{10-9}{36\pi} \times 16\pi a^2} = \frac{Q^2 \times 10^9}{\frac{4}{9}a^2} \text{ newtons}$$

A numerical example: $Q = 20{,}000\,e$, $a = 10^{-6}$ m

$$F = \frac{(2 \times 10^4 \times 1.6 \times 10^{-19})^2 \times 10^9}{\frac{4}{9} \times 10^{-12}} = 2.3 \times 10^{-8} nt.$$

The ultimate tensile strength of materials is $\sim 1 - 500$ kg/mm² (from Chem. Rubber Publ. Handbook).

1 kg/mm² $= 9.8nt \times 10^6$/m², $\therefore$ Ult. tens. strength $\sim 5 \times 10^9 nt$/m²

Returning to our numerical example,

$$\text{Tensile stress} = \frac{2.3 \times 10^{-8} nt}{\pi \times 10^{-12}} \sim 10^4 nt/\text{m}^2.$$

We conclude, tentatively, that we could increase the charge (or potential) of the dust particle by a factor of 100. However, we cannot really be

---

*It should be possible also to measure a difference in behavior between primary protons and α-particles.

sure of this because of our imperfect knowledge of the structure and composition of the particles.

REFERENCES

1. H. Alfvén. *On the Origin of the Solar System.* Oxford: Clarendon Press, 1954, pp. 67–78.
2. L. Spitzer, Jr., and M. P. Savedoff, "The Temperature of Interstellar Matter. III," *Astrophys. J., 111*:593–608 (1950).
3. H. C. van de Hulst, "Zodiacal Light in the Solar Corona," *Astrophys. J., 105*:471–488 (1947).
4. C. W. Allen, "The Spectrum of the Corona at the Eclipse of 1940 October 1," *Mon. Not. Roy. Astron. Soc., 106*:137–150 (1946).
5. D. E. Blackwell, "A Comparison of the Intensities of Infrared and Violet Radiation From the Solar Corona at the Eclipse of 1952 February 25," *Mon. Not. Roy. Astron. Soc., 112*: 652–664 (1952).
6. A. Behr and H. Siedentopf, "An Examination of the Zodiacal Light and Gegenschein from Photoelectric Measurements at the Jungfraujoch," *Z. Astrophys., 32*:19–50 (1953) in German.
7. H. Elsässer, "The Space Distribution of Zodiacal-Light Material," *Z. Astrophys., 33*:274–285 (1954) in German.
8. F. L. Whipple, "A Comet Model. III. The Zodiacal Light," *Astrophys. J., 121*:750–770 (1955).
9. C. de Jager, "The Capture of Zodiacal Dust by the Earth," *Mém. Soc. Roy. Sci. Liège, 15*:174–182 (1955).
10. F. L. Whipple. In *Advances in Geophysics.* New York: Academic Press, 1952, p. 132.
11. M. Dubin. In *Rocket Exploration of the Upper Atmosphere.* London: Pergamon Press, 1954, p. 26.
12. S. Piotrowski, "The Collisions of Asteroids," *Acta Astronomica, A, 5*: 115–138 (1953).
13. E. J. Öpik, *Irish Astron. J., 2*:193 (1953).
14. S. F. Singer. In *Rocket Exploration of the Upper Atmosphere.* London: Pergamon Press, 1954, p. 371.
15. E. A. Brunberg and A. Rattner, "Experimental Determination of Electron Orbits in the Field of a Magnetic Dipole," *Tellus, 5*:135, 269 (1953). W. H. Bennett, private communication.
16. S. F. Singer. *Op. cit.,* p. 369.